ELECTRICAL ENGINEERING AND ECONOMICS AND ETHICS FOR PROFESSIONAL ENGINEERING EXAMINATIONS

hayden professional engineering examination series

LAWRENCE J. HOLLANDER
editor-in-chief

Professional Engineer
New York State

BASIC ENGINEERING SCIENCES AND STRUCTURAL ENGINEERING FOR ENGINEER-IN-TRAINING EXAMINATIONS
H. Apfelbaum and W. Ottesen

CIVIL ENGINEERING AND ECONOMICS AND ETHICS FOR PROFESSIONAL ENGINEERING EXAMINATIONS
M. Sanders and S. Dublin

ELECTRICAL ENGINEERING AND ECONOMICS AND ETHICS FOR PROFESSIONAL ENGINEERING EXAMINATIONS
J. Lyons and S. Dublin

MECHANICAL ENGINEERING AND ECONOMICS AND ETHICS FOR PROFESSIONAL ENGINEERING EXAMINATIONS
E. Stamper and S. Dublin

ELECTRICAL ENGINEERING AND ECONOMICS AND ETHICS FOR PROFESSIONAL ENGINEERING EXAMINATIONS

JOHN S. LYONS, P.E.
Texaco, Inc.

AND

STANLEY W. DUBLIN
Institute of Environmental Medicine,
New York University Medical Center

HAYDEN BOOK COMPANY, INC.
Rochelle Park, New Jersey

 Library of Congress Catalog Number 79-137584

Printed in the United States of America

3 4 5 6 7 8 9 PRINTING

75 76 77 78 YEAR

FOREWORD

In the 1970's the number of licensed professional engineers in the United States and its territories will surpass 500,000, and by the end of the decade may approach three quarters of a million. Licensure will be required in an ever-increasing array of new activities; registered engineers will be active in consumer protection, air pollution control, water pollution control, urban planning and renewal, not to mention the traditional projects of designing bridges, dams, office buildings, computers, power systems, etc. No discipline of engineering is exempted, for laws that regulate licensure in engineering are primarily for the protection of the public.

The Hayden series of preparatory books for engineering licensure is designed for both study and reference. These books present problems that occur over and over again on the preliminary and professional examinations for licensure in engineering. As the examinations among the states change in style and content over a span of years, the basic fundamentals of engineering found in these books will remain as important keystones in bridging the gap from student to licensed professional engineer.

The first volume in the series is devoted to the preliminary examinations (Engineer-in-Training). The remaining volumes, identified by major engineering disciplines (electrical, mechanical, civil, etc.), are designed for preparing the reader for the professional examinations, sometimes referred to as the second-day or final examinations. An important feature of these books is the terse development of each subject, beginning with an easily understood explanation and concluding with one or more sample problems with complete solutions. The engineering student will find himself completely at ease with these books, since the authors have acted on the premise that the reader is versed in engineering, that he has handled engineering problems, and that he is approaching the time when his State Board of Examiners will consider him qualified for taking the examinations.

The authors have been most careful not only in selecting the problems for inclusion in the books, but also in the preparation of the solutions to these problems; at all times the authors have considered the needs of the candidate who is preparing for the preliminary and professional examinations in engineering.

Although the problems and solutions in these books have been checked and rechecked for accuracy many times, candidates should understand that problems in engineering often are open to different interpretations or their solutions are affected by different municipal or national codes and other requirements. In all cases it is the State Board of Examiners of Professional Engineers in each state that determines what is acceptable to it.

LAWRENCE J. HOLLANDER

PREFACE

There are many well-qualified electrical engineers who have not taken the necessary steps to become licensed. They have probably thought that licensure would "go away." The usual argument has been that registration is for civil engineers and mechanical engineers and there is no need for electrical engineers to become registered! The sad fact, however, is that these same electrical engineers, mid-career, find that the next rung on the ladder of success is blocked to them because of their not being licensed. Missing an opportunity to become a department head or chief electrical engineer in their company, being by-passed for promotion, or affected by a "reduction-in-force," finally triggers the impulse to become licensed.

This book will be of invaluable help to those who have long since seen the inside of an engineering classroom. It will provide the practitioner with the material that he needs to make a thorough review of the topics found in licensing examinations in electrical engineering and the companion subject of economics. Equally, the book gives the student just completing his undergraduate studies insight into the type of problems he must become familiar with as he begins his internship in engineering. Licensing for electrical engineers is just as important as for other disciplines; no branch of engineering is exempt.

When this book was being planned it was recognized that the subject of electrical engineering is dynamic. The selection of the problems was done with care to reflect those subjects that form the foundation for electrical engineering and are fundamental to the ever-changing technology.

The reader is urged not only to study the problems, but to sit with paper and pencil and work and rework the problems until the methods of solution are well understood and come easily. A unique feature of the book is a complete descriptive listing of the problems with the table of contents. In those states having open-book examinations the candidate will find this listing of problems most helpful for rapid retrieval of information; precious time is saved.

The following objectives have guided the preparation of this review book:

(1) to present a wide range of tested and realistic problems in electrical engineering,

(2) to present the principles of electrical engineering in a well-planned arrangement, but without the many details that are found in a textbook; the emphasis is on problems and their solution,

(3) to present these materials in language that is easily understood.

"The presentation that follows is not intended to be a course in electrical engineering. Rather, it is a distillation of theory and basic formulas, with maximum emphasis on problems, their analyses and their solution." These are the words of John S. Lyons who in 1970 on the eve of publication of his book suddenly passed away. Mr. Lyons for more than a decade had been preparing the electrical engineering material presented here.

LAWRENCE J. HOLLANDER

The second section of this book provides a complete review of economics and ethics for Professional Engineering examinations. Avoiding the cookbook methods of many review texts which stress problem solutions at the expense of learning, the material here emphasizes basic principles in order to strengthen the reader's background and make unexpected exam questions easier to handle. The somewhat different approach of using summarized formulas, where basic formulas are adapted to many uses, makes this book even more helpful.

Major topics covered are the role interest plays in an engineering project, depreciation, annual cost analysis, break even analysis, income taxes, corporation finance, as well as legal and ethical considerations.

STANLEY W. DUBLIN

CONTENTS

Electrical Engineering

Economics and Ethics

PROBLEMS
Electrical Engineering

Linear Circuits

Transformers

The National Electrical Code

Machinery

Transients

The Electrical Circuit Analog

Miscellaneous Problems

Economics and Ethics

Engineering Economy

Interest Problems

Depreciation

Annual cost

Present Valuation and Return on Investment

Break-Even Analysis

Incremental Analysis and Replacement Economy

Minimum Cost and Risk

Income Taxes

ELECTRICAL ENGINEERING AND ECONOMICS AND ETHICS FOR PROFESSIONAL ENGINEERING EXAMINATIONS

chapter 1
LINEAR CIRCUITS

The solution of most engineering problems requires familiarity with the use of complex quantities and facility in the construction of equivalent circuits. The reader should review the elementary relationships and diagrams presented in this chapter before proceeding further.

1-1 COMPLEX NOTATION

Rectangular form: $Z = R \pm jX$

Polar form: $Z = |Z| \underline{/\pm\theta}$

where $\theta = \tan^{-1} X/R$

Exponential form: $Z = |Z|\ e^{\pm j\theta}$

where θ is expressed in radians

Trigonometric form: $Z = |Z|(\cos\theta \pm j\sin\theta)$

1-2 EQUIVALENT CIRCUITS

To construct circuit diagrams for active networks, concepts of a constant-voltage and a constant-current source are used. The following two theorems are applicable to two-terminal, linear active networks containing only bilateral elements:

Thevenin's Theorem: *An active network can be represented by a constant-voltage source whose magnitude is the actual open-circuit voltage across the terminals of the original network, in series with an impedance equal to the open-circuit voltage divided by the short-circuit current available at the terminals of the original network.*

Norton's Theorem: *An active network can be represented by a constant-current source whose magnitude is the actual short-circuit current available at the terminals of the original network, in parallel with an impedance equal to the open-circuit voltage divided by the short-circuit current. The equivalent Thevenin and Norton circuits are shown in Fig. 1-1.*

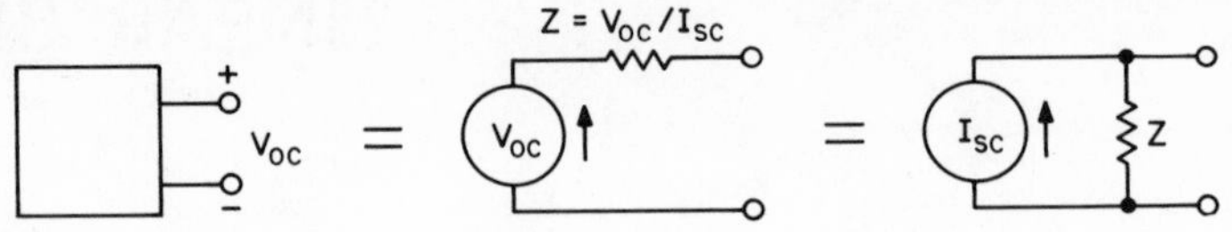

$Z = V_{OC}/I_{SC}$

Figure 1-1

Equivalent circuits of a coil, a capacitor, and finally a network containing energy sources are shown in Figs. 1-2 to 1-4. The reader should be familiar with elementary terms such as resistance, inductance, capacitance, impedance, reactance, susceptance, and admittance, and with their universal symbols.

Coils

For the left-hand (series) circuit of Fig. 1-2,

$$\begin{aligned} Z &= R_s + jX_s = 1/Y \\ &= R_s + j\omega L_s \\ &= G/|Y^2| + jB/|Y^2| \end{aligned}$$

$$R_s = \frac{R_p \omega^2 L_p{}^2}{R_p{}^2 + \omega^2 L_p{}^2}$$

$$L_s = \frac{R_p{}^2 L_p}{R_p{}^2 + \omega^2 L_p{}^2}$$

$$Q = \omega L_s/R_s$$

For the right-hand (parallel) circuit of Fig. 1-2,

$$\begin{aligned} Y &= G - jB \\ &= 1/R_p - j/\omega L_p \\ &= R_s/|Z^2| - j\omega L_s/|Z^2| \end{aligned}$$

$$R_p = \frac{R_s{}^2 + \omega^2 L_s{}^2}{R_s}$$

$$L_p = \frac{R_s{}^2 + \omega^2 L_s{}^2}{\omega^2 L_s}$$

$$Q = R_p/\omega L_p$$

$$R_p \cong Q^2 R_s$$

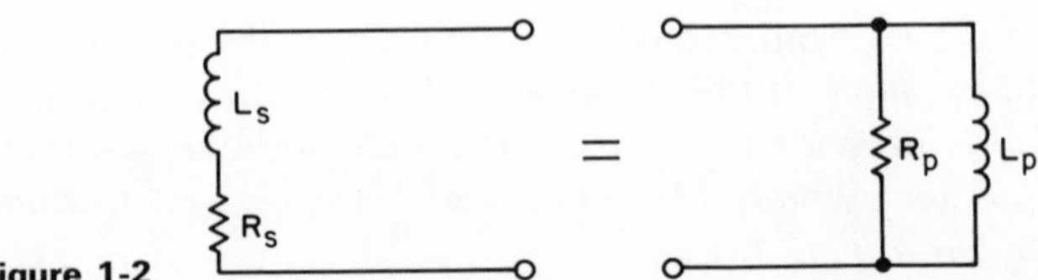

Figure 1-2

Capacitors

For the series circuit of Fig. 1-3,

$$Z = R - jX = 1/Y$$
$$= R - j/\omega C_s$$
$$= G/|Y^2| - jB/|Y^2|$$
$$R_s = \frac{R_p}{R_p{}^2\omega^2 C_p{}^2 + 1}$$
$$C_s = \frac{R_p{}^2\omega^2 C_p{}^2 + 1}{R_p{}^2\omega^2 C_p}$$
$$Q = 1/\omega C_s R_s$$

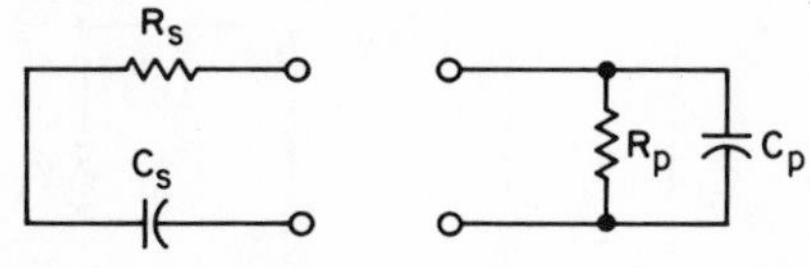

Figure 1-3

For the parallel circuit of Fig. 1-3,

$$Y = G + jB$$
$$= 1/R_p + j\omega C_p$$
$$= R/|Z^2| + jX/|Z^2|$$
$$R_p = R_s + \frac{1}{\omega^2 C_s{}^2 R_s}$$
$$C_p = \frac{C_s}{R_s{}^2\omega^2 C_s{}^2 + 1}$$
$$Q = \omega R_p C_p$$

Note: Frequently, approximations are made for simplicity. For example, at high frequencies, C_s and C_p can be considered equal.

Active Networks

For the circuits of Fig. 1-4,

$$I_1 = E_1/Z_1 \qquad Y_1 = 1/Z_1 \qquad \text{etc.}$$

1-3 MESH AND NODAL EQUATIONS

Rather than write the many voltage and current equations expressing Kirchhoff's laws, it is more convenient to write mesh current or nodal voltage equations, which are derivations of Kirchhoff's laws. After a little practice, one can, by observing the circuit diagram, eliminate the equations and directly write the matrix giving the desired unknown. Mesh and nodal equations are used not only in solving d-c and a-c (steady-state) networks, but also in obtaining instantaneous (transient) values, once the transform impedance network is drawn. The solution of this latter type of problem will be covered later.

A mesh current is a current that is conceived to be circulating, say clockwise, in a particular mesh. This concept is used when there is a predominance of series elements, or when the energy sources are in the constant-voltage form. A nodal voltage is the potential of a particular node with respect to a selected reference node, with current flowing away from the particular node. This concept is used when there is a predominance of parallel branches or when it is desired to consider the energy sources as constant-current sources. For an orderly solution, *all* energy sources should be shown as constant-voltage or constant-current sources, but not both.

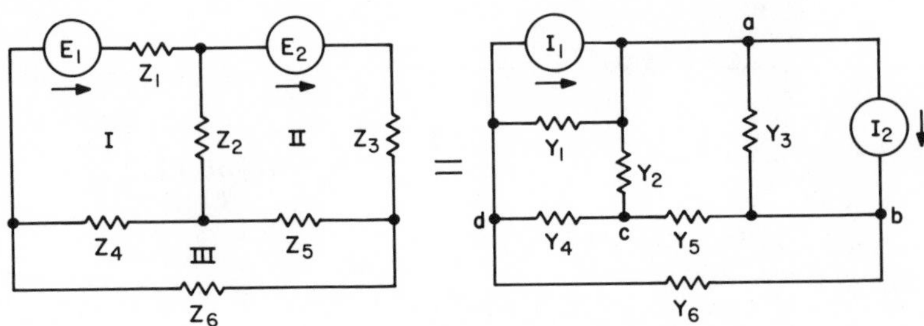

Figure 1-4

To illustrate the above concepts, mesh and nodal equations for the active networks shown in Fig. 1-4 are listed in Table 1-1. Note that the terms are arranged to facilitate writing of the matrices. For the mesh equations, all voltage sources are to the left of the equal sign and voltage drops are on the right, the clockwise direction being taken as positive. Each equation contains a basic term (for the particular mesh) and mutual terms (preceded by a negative sign) for each adjacent mesh. Impedance values are used as coefficients.* For the nodal equations, all current sources are to the left (currents *into* the node being taken as positive), and each equation contains a basic term (for the particular node) and mutual terms (preceded by a negative sign) for each principal node separated by a passive element from the particular node. Admittance values are used for the parameters.

1-4 FOUR-TERMINAL NETWORKS

Any linear, passive, four-terminal network containing only bilateral elements can be represented by what are known as equivalent T and equivalent pi networks. Open-circuit and short-circuit measurements are used to obtain the values of the parameters of the equivalent circuit. Obviously, if the frequency is changed, the

* By definition, mutual impedance is the impedance common to adjacent meshes. Transfer impedance is the ratio of voltage applied in the *j*th mesh to the current flowing in the *k*th mesh, with all other voltages removed.

Table 1-1 Mesh and Nodal Equations

Mesh Equations

Mesh I:	$E_1 =$	$(Z_1 + Z_2 + Z_4)I_I$	$-(Z_2)I_{II}$	$-(Z_4)I_{III}$
Mesh II:	$E_2 =$	$-(Z_2)I_I$	$+ (Z_2 + Z_3 + Z_5)I_{II}$	$-(Z_5)I_{III}$
Mesh III:	$O =$	$-(Z_4)I_I$	$-(Z_5)I_{II}$	$+ (Z_4 + Z_5 + Z_6)I_{III}$

Nodal Equations

Node a:	$I_1 - I_2 =$	$(Y_1 + Y_2 + Y_3)E_a$	$-(Y_2)E_c$	$-(Y_1)E_d$
Node c:	$O =$	$-(Y_2)E_a$	$+ (Y_2 + Y_4 + Y_5)E_c$	$-(Y_4)E_d$
Node d:	$-I_1 =$	$-(Y_1)E_a$	$-(Y_4)E_c$	$+ (Y_1 + Y_4 + Y_6)E_d$

Note: 1. No equation is written for Node b, since $E_b = 0$.

2. In the above routine, the sign of the parameter is included in the symbol. For example, if Z_2 were a capacitor, the entire second term on the right side of the first mesh equation would be $-(-j/\omega C_2)$ or $+j/\omega C_2$.

measurements would change and therefore the values of the parameters would change.

A common configuration is known as a lattice network. A symmetrical lattice used in phase-compensating networks is shown in Fig. 1-5. The open- and short-circuit equations are:

With terminals 2-2 open-circuited,

$$Z_{1\text{-}1} = Z_1 + Z_3 = \frac{Z_A(Z_B + Z_C)}{Z_A + Z_B + Z_C}$$

With terminals 1-1 open-circuited,

$$Z_{2\text{-}2} = Z_2 + Z_3 = \frac{Z_C(Z_A + Z_B)}{Z_A + Z_B + Z_C}$$

With terminals 2-2 short-circuited,

$$Z_{1\text{-}1} = Z_1 + \frac{Z_2Z_3}{Z_2 + Z_3} = \frac{Z_AZ_B}{Z_A + Z_B}$$

With terminals 1-1 short-circuited,

$$Z_{2\text{-}2} = Z_2 + \frac{Z_1Z_3}{Z_1 + Z_3} = \frac{Z_BZ_C}{Z_B + Z_C}$$

Conversions:

$$Z_A = \frac{Z_1Z_2 + Z_1Z_3 + Z_2Z_3}{Z_2} \qquad Z_1 = \frac{Z_AZ_B}{Z_A + Z_B + Z_C}$$

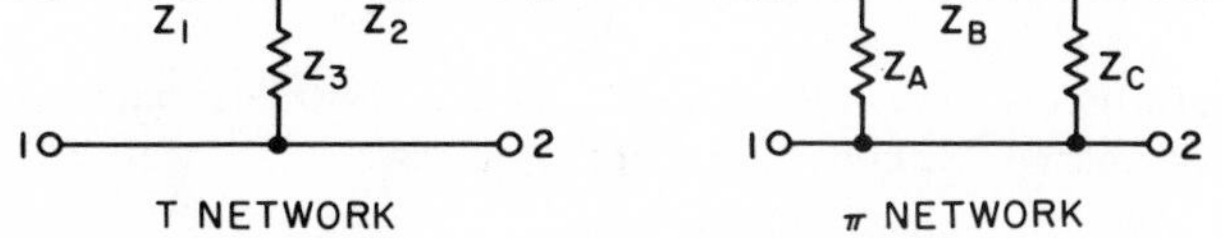

Figure 1-5

$$Z_B = \frac{Z_1Z_2 + Z_1Z_3 + Z_2Z_3}{Z_3} \qquad Z_2 = \frac{Z_BZ_C}{Z_A + Z_B + Z_C}$$

$$Z_C = \frac{Z_1Z_2 + Z_1Z_3 + Z_2Z_3}{Z_1} \qquad Z_3 = \frac{Z_AZ_C}{Z_A + Z_B + Z_C}$$

An equivalent symmetrical lattice can always be found for a four-terminal network, and the parameters will be physically realizable, even though the equivalent T or pi network may have negative resistance values. (See Fig. 1-6.)

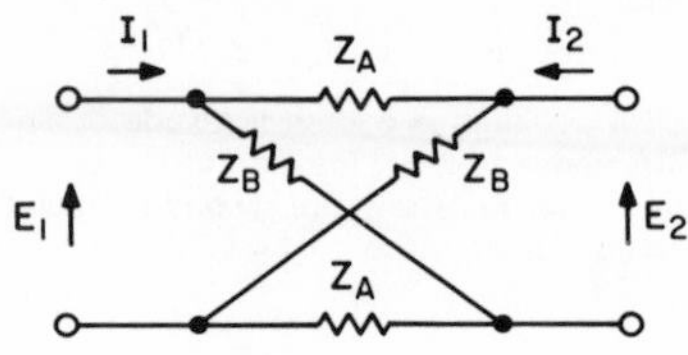

Figure 1-6. Symmetrical lattice network. The direction for I_2 is assumed positive.

For Fig. 1-6,

$$E_1 = \frac{Z_A + Z_B}{2} I_1 + \frac{Z_B - Z_A}{2} I_2$$

$$E_2 = \frac{Z_B - Z_A}{2} I_1 + \frac{Z_A + Z_B}{2} I_2$$

1-5 BASIC MEASUREMENTS

Although the variety of instruments used for electrical measurements is seemingly endless, the following is applicable to most instruments used today in electrical engineering.

The most common types of voltmeters and ammeters are:

(a) *Permanent-magnet moving-coil (PMMC), or d'Arsonval movement:* It has a shunt or series resistance, and is inherently a d-c milli- or microammeter. It is not used where any degree of accuracy is required.

(b) *Electrodynamometer:* It is inherently an rms sensitive milliammeter used with the necessary shunt or series elements to measure either ac or dc. It is frequently calibrated with known d-c currents or voltages.

(c) *Moving-iron movement:* It is an inexpensive, inherently rms sensitive device designed either on the repulsion or attraction principle. It can be used to measure either ac or dc, and it is simple in construction and rugged. For alternating currents above 5 amps and voltages above 600 volts, instrument transformers are used instead of electrodynamic or moving-iron meters.

Potentiometers, which are balancing circuits having a reference voltage cell, galvanometer, and calibrated resistances, are highly accurate to measure potentials. The null method of measurements eliminates variation in precision due to internal losses.

Resistance measurements are made by ohmmeters, voltmeter and ammeter combinations, loss of charge methods (using the time constant concept), and potentiometers.

Ohmmeters

For the series-type ohmmeter shown in Fig. 1-7,

$$s = \frac{R_h}{R_x + R_h}$$

$$R_h = \frac{R_1 R_m}{R_1 + R_m} + R_2$$

Half-scale indication occurs when $R_x = R_h$. The scale reads from infinity to zero.

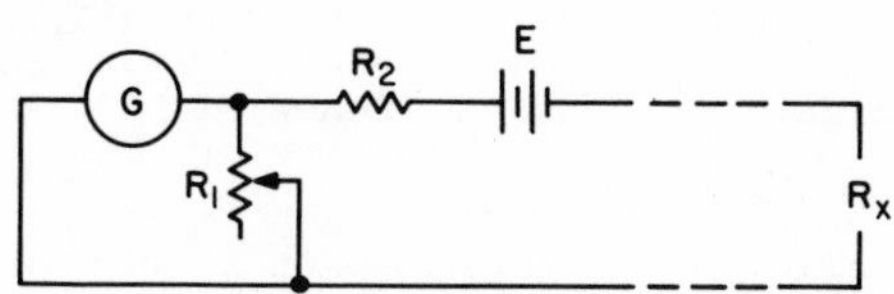

Figure 1-7

For the shunt-type ohmmeter shown in Fig. 1-8,

$$s = \frac{R_x}{R_x + R_p}$$

$$R_p = \frac{R_1 R_m}{R_1 + R_m}$$

Half-scale deflection indication occurs when $R_x = R_p$. The scale reads from zero to infinity.

For the ohmmeter equations,

s = decimal fraction of full-scale deflection
R_m = galvanometer circuit resistance
R_1 = compensating resistance for variation of battery voltage
R_2 = current limiting resistance
R_x = resistance being measured (unknown)

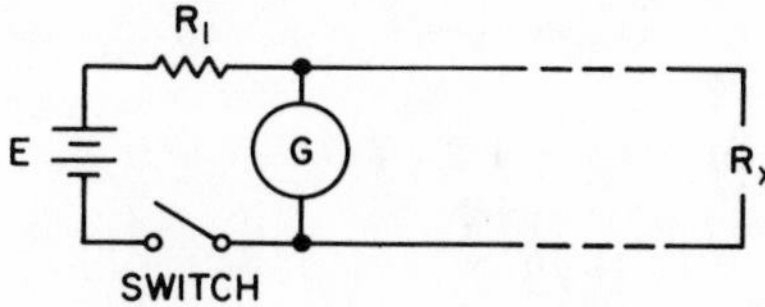

Figure 1-8

A third type of ohmmeter, and the most common portable instrument, is the crossed-coil ohmmeter (ratio meter). Its chief advantage is that it has an independent voltage source, a hand- or motor-operated d-c generator. The meter deflection is proportional to the ratio of the currents through R_x and a fixed resistor; the latter establishes the range of the instrument.

Wheatstone Bridge

See Fig. 1-9. For the balanced condition,

$$|Z_1|/|Z_3| = |Z_2|/|Z_4| \quad \text{and} \quad |Z_1|/|Z_2| = |Z_3|/|Z_4|$$
$$\theta_1 - \theta_3 = \theta_2 - \theta_4 \quad \text{and} \quad \theta_1 - \theta_2 = \theta_3 - \theta_4$$

For the unbalanced condition, the Thevenin equivalent voltage source E_0 is

$$E_0 = E\left(\frac{Z_1}{Z_1 + Z_2} - \frac{Z_3}{Z_3 + Z_4}\right)$$

Thevenin equivalent impedance Z_0 is

$$Z_0 = \frac{Z_1Z_2}{Z_1 + Z_2} + \frac{Z_3Z_4}{Z_3 + Z_4}$$

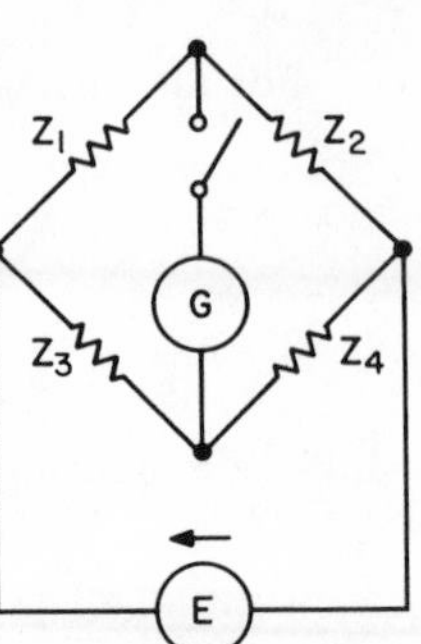

Figure 1-9

Given the sensitivity of the galvanometer, the deflection can be expressed in terms of any one of the unknown bridge arms. (The resistance of the voltage source circuit was ignored, for simplicity. For precise calculations and for variations of the Wheatstone Bridge, the reader is referred to the literature.)

1-6 POWER AND REACTIVE VOLT-AMPERES

Power can only be dissipated between two terminals when a component of the current flowing is in phase with the voltage between those terminals (i.e., $P = EI\cos\theta$). Since it is a scalar quantity, power cannot be represented with any significance on a phasor diagram showing voltage and current. As one component of a complex quantity, power, in watts, can be shown diagrammatically in quadrature with reactive volt-amperes. Arbitrarily, reactive volt-amperes is shown along the imaginary ordinate axis, above the abscissa (positive) for an inductive circuit and below the abscissa (negative) for a capacitive circuit. The phasor combination of watts and reactive volt-amperes, therefore, is usually shown as VI*, where I* is the conjugate of the current phasor. In any system, watts (generated or dissipated) is added algebraically and reactive volt-amperes is added algebraically. Basically,

Real power, P (watts) $= EI\cos\theta = I^2R$
Reactive power (vars) $= EI\sin\theta = I^2X$
Apparent power (VA) $= |E|\ |I|\ \underline{/\theta}$

where X = *net* reactance
θ = angle by which voltage leads current

In a-c circuits, a sinusoidal voltage of a given frequency and a sinusoidal current of a different frequency cannot result in any supply or dissipation of power. This is useful when calculating the power dissipated in a circuit having a nonsinusoidal voltage or current. All that is necessary is to calculate $EI\cos\theta$ for those voltage and current components having the same frequency.

1-7 POWER FACTOR CORRECTION

In power applications, the capacitor is the most widely used device to neutralize the reactive volt-amperes drawn by inductive lines and loads. Voltage drop is thereby minimized and the volt-ampere capabilities of generators, transformers, and lines are used to full advantage. In Fig. 1-10, total circuit current I_0 is appreciably smaller than the current I_L that would exist if the capacitor were not present.

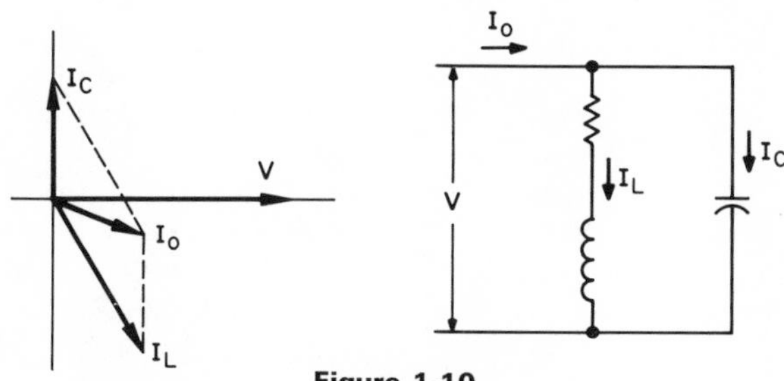

Figure 1-10

There are technical and economic limitations to the degree of power factor correction that should be applied. Since the parallel connection of capacitors is the more common mode, some of their limitations are discussed.

Leading power factor should be avoided, as this would result in increased receiving voltage; in those cases where the consumer generates part of his requirements, he would in effect be furnishing reactive power to the utility. Basically, capacitors should be associated with motors, so that as loads are disconnected, the corrective kvars are also disconnected. By connecting them to the load side of motor starters, the latter serve as switching devices for the capacitors. However, overload settings should be corrected to allow for the reduced current through the starter. Capacitors attached to buses should be used to supplement those connected to motors to obtain the desired overall power factor. Generally, large capacitors to be connected to the main high-voltage bus are more expensive (considering their associated switchgear) and do not reduce the current-carrying requirements for the feeders emanating from the bus. However, for small plants where the main reason for power factor correction is the reduction in power cost, the small amount of correction can be economically installed on the main bus.

With the exception of capacitors connected to motor starters, fused switches or circuit breakers should be used to isolate banks of capacitors for maintenance. Low-voltage capacitors should be specified to include internal fuses in all phases and a discharge resistor. The National Electrical Code requires that capacitors be discharged to a residual voltage of 50 volts or less in 1 minute for applications 600 volts and lower and in 5 minutes for applications above 600 volts. It is important that capacitors be adequately grounded. Most manufacturers specify the ratings of switching devices for capacitor applications; representative ratings are shown in Table 1-2.

At transformers, the kvar rating of the capacitors should not exceed two-thirds

Table 1-2 Recommended Minimum Ampere Rating

Standard Capacitor Equipment Rating, kvar	*Magnetic-Type Circuit Breakers*	*Contactors*	*Safety Switches*	*Molded-Case Circuit Breakers*
For 230-Volt Capacitors				
15	50	100	100	70
30	100	150	200	150
45	150	300	200	225
60	200	300	400	300
90	300	600	400	450
180	600	900	800	
270	1000	1350		
450	1600	2500		
630	3000	2500		
For 460-Volt Capacitors				
30	50	100	100	70
60	100	150	200	150
90	150	300	200	225
120	200	300	400	300
180	300	600	400	450
360	600	900	800	
540	1000	1350		
900	1600	2500		
1260	3000	2500		
For 575-Volt Capacitors				
30	50	50	60	70
60	90	100	100	125
90	125	150	200	175
120	175	300	200	225
180	250	300	440	350
360	500	600	600	
540	800	900		
900	1200	2500		
1260	2000	2500		

of the transformer kvar rating. This is to prevent harmful harmonics from appearing, and to limit the rise in secondary voltage at low loads. Manufacturers' recommended limits should be followed.

At motors, the kvar rating of the capacitors should not exceed the no-load magnetizing kvars of the motor. This is to avoid heavy torques and currents incident upon restoration of power, when the motor is still running following interruption of supply, since during this period the capacitors are furnishing excitation current. Large motors having heavy inertia loads should not be corrected above 0.95 power factor at full load. Representative values of capacitor ratings for motors are shown in Table 1-3.

Table 1-3 Typical (Maximum) KVAR Ratings of Capacitors

	NEMA Design B Motors						*NEMA Design C Motors*				
	rpm						*rpm*				
hp	*3600*	*1800*	*1200*	*900*	*720*	*600*	*1800*	*1200*	*900*	*720*	*600*
3	1.5	1.5	1.5	2	2.5	3.5	—	2	3	4	4.5
5	2	2	2	3	4	4.5	2	2.5	4	5	6.5
7.5	2.5	2.5	3	4	5.5	6	2.5	3.5	5	6.5	8
10	3	3	3.5	5	6.5	7.5	3.5	4	6	8	9.5
15	4	4	5	6.5	8	9.5	5	5.5	8	10	13
20	5	5	6.5	7.5	9	12	6	6.5	9.5	12	17
25	6	6	7.5	9	11	14	7.5	8	11	14	20
30	7	7	9	10	12	16	8.5	9	13	16	23
40	9	9	11	12	15	20	11	12	16	20	30
50	12	11	13	15	19	24	13	16	20	25	35
60	14	14	15	18	22	27	16	19	23	27.5	40
75	17	16	18	21	26	32.5	21	24	27.5	35	45
100	22	21	25	27	32.5	40	28	32.5	35	42.5	55
125	27	26	30	32.5	40	47.5	35	40	42.5	50	—
150	50	45	52.5	57.5	70	77.5	42.5	45	50	55	—
200	40	37.5	42.5	47.5	60	65	50	55	60	—	—
250	50	45	52.5	57.5	70	77.5					
300	57.5	52.5	60	65	80	87.5					
350	65	60	67.5	75	87.5	95					
400	70	65	75	85	95	105					
450	75	67.5	80	92	100	110					
500	77.5	72.5	82.5	97	107.5	115					

Note: Due to the continuing changes in motor design, current manufacturers' recommendations should be obtained if the selected capacitor ratings approach the above typical maximum values.

Economics of Power Factor Correction

Frequently, the desirability of power factor correction depends solely on the incentive in the power contract. A simple calculation is to compare the installed cost of the capacitors (including switchgear, if any) with the annual savings in electric power costs. The kvars required to improve the power factor to various values are determined (see Table 1-4) and that value selected for which the power savings exceed the net return otherwise available. For example:

Assume plant load: 5000 kVA
Load factor: 80%
Power factor: 85%
Installed costs of capacitors: $20/kvar
Purchased power cost (demand charge plus energy charge): $0.014/kW-hr
  (allowance of 0.4% discount for every 1% improvement in power factor above 80%)

Profit criterion: 30%
Annual kW-hr consumed: 29.8×10^6
Annual cost of power (before correction): $407,500

			Incremental		
kvar/kW (From Table 1-4)	*P.F.*	*Required kvar*	*Installed Cost*	*Power Savings*	*Return*
0.291	0.95	992	$19,840	$16,720	84%
0.079	0.97	269	5,380	3,340	62
0.048	0.98	164	3,280	1,670	51
0.060	0.99	204	4,080	1,670	41
0.143	1.00	485	9,700	1,670	17

It would be economically attractive, therefore, to correct to 99% power factor.

1-8 POLYPHASE CIRCUITS

A polyphase system is one in which lines and equipment are time-shared by two or more single-phase sources, equal in magnitude but separated in time by 1/nf seconds, where n is the number of phases and f is the system frequency in hertz. This time-sharing increases the occupancy of the lines and equipment, resulting in a greater economy than the single-phase system. If conductor sizes are based on current-carrying capacity, the weight of copper for the three-phase system is 86.7 percent of that required by a single-phase system delivering the same power at the same voltage. If percent voltage drop is the basis, the weight is 75 percent of that required by a single-phase system. Since the three-phase system is the most common polyphase system, the discussion and problems in this book are for the three-phase condition.

The ideal three-phase system is a balanced system such that the loads between the three pairs of wires are equal in magnitude and phase angle. Total power is three times the power per phase, or $\sqrt{3}\,\mathrm{EI}\cos\theta$, where E is the line-to-line voltage, I is the line current, and θ is the phase angle of each of the single-phase loads. One wattmeter is sufficient to measure the total power. The power factor is the cosine of the angle between the voltage across either of the single-phase loads and the current through each load.

In an unbalanced three-phase system, if there is a flow of current through the neutral conductor (earth return is considered to be a conductor), three wattmeters are required to measure power. If there is no neutral path, two wattmeters are adequate. (This is brought out in the problems at the end of the chapter.) The system power factor is usually taken as

$$\text{Power factor} = \frac{\Sigma V_\phi I_\phi \cos\theta_\phi}{\sqrt{\Sigma(V_\phi I_\phi \cos\theta_\phi)^2 + \Sigma(V_\phi I_\phi \sin\theta_\phi)^2}}$$

where $\Sigma V_\phi I_\phi \cos\theta_\phi = V_a I_a \cos\theta_a + V_b I_b \cos\theta_b + V_c I_c \cos\theta_c$

$$\Sigma(V_\phi I_\phi \sin\theta_\phi)^2 = (V_a I_a \sin\theta_a)^2 + (V_b I_b \sin\theta_b)^2 + \text{etc.}$$

Table 1-4

Orig. P.F.	Final Power Factor																				
	0.80	0.81	0.82	0.83	0.84	0.85	0.86	0.87	0.88	0.89	0.90	0.91	0.92	0.93	0.94	0.95	0.96	0.97	0.98	0.99	1.0
0.76	0.105	0.131	0.157	0.183	0.209	0.235	0.262	0.288	0.315	0.343	0.371	0.399	0.429	0.460	0.492	0.526	0.563	0.604	0.652	0.712	0.855
0.77	0.079	0.105	0.131	0.157	0.183	0.209	0.236	0.262	0.289	0.317	0.345	0.373	0.403	0.434	0.466	0.500	0.537	0.578	0.626	0.686	0.829
0.78	0.052	0.078	0.104	0.130	0.156	0.182	0.209	0.235	0.262	0.290	0.318	0.346	0.376	0.407	0.439	0.473	0.510	0.551	0.599	0.659	0.802
0.79	0.026	0.052	0.078	0.104	0.130	0.156	0.183	0.209	0.236	0.264	0.292	0.320	0.350	0.381	0.413	0.447	0.484	0.525	0.573	0.633	0.776
0.80	0.000	0.026	0.052	0.078	0.104	0.130	0.157	0.183	0.210	0.238	0.266	0.294	0.324	0.355	0.387	0.421	0.458	0.499	0.547	0.609	0.750
0.81		0.000	0.026	0.052	0.078	0.104	0.131	0.157	0.184	0.212	0.240	0.268	0.298	0.329	0.361	0.395	0.432	0.473	0.521	0.581	0.724
0.82			0.000	0.026	0.052	0.078	0.105	0.131	0.158	0.186	0.214	0.242	0.272	0.303	0.335	0.369	0.406	0.447	0.495	0.555	0.698
0.83				0.000	0.026	0.052	0.079	0.105	0.132	0.160	0.188	0.216	0.246	0.277	0.309	0.343	0.380	0.421	0.469	0.529	0.672
0.84					0.000	0.026	0.053	0.079	0.106	0.134	0.162	0.190	0.220	0.251	0.283	0.317	0.354	0.395	0.443	0.503	0.646
0.85						0.000	0.027	0.053	0.080	0.108	0.136	0.164	0.194	0.225	0.257	0.291	0.328	0.369	0.417	0.477	0.620
0.86							0.000	0.026	0.053	0.081	0.109	0.137	0.167	0.198	0.230	0.264	0.301	0.342	0.390	0.450	0.593
0.87								0.000	0.027	0.055	0.083	0.111	0.141	0.172	0.204	0.238	0.275	0.316	0.364	0.424	0.567
0.88									0.000	0.028	0.056	0.084	0.114	0.145	0.177	0.211	0.248	0.289	0.337	0.397	0.540
0.89										0.000	0.028	0.056	0.086	0.117	0.149	0.183	0.220	0.261	0.309	0.369	0.512
0.90											0.000	0.028	0.058	0.089	0.121	0.155	0.192	0.233	0.281	0.341	0.484
0.91												0.000	0.030	0.061	0.093	0.127	0.164	0.205	0.253	0.313	0.456
0.92													0.000	0.031	0.063	0.097	0.134	0.175	0.223	0.283	0.426
0.93														0.000	0.032	0.066	0.103	0.144	0.192	0.252	0.395
0.94															0.000	0.034	0.071	0.112	0.160	0.220	0.363
0.95																0.000	0.037	0.079	0.126	0.186	0.329
0.96																	0.000	0.041	0.089	0.149	0.292
0.97																		0.000	0.048	0.108	0.251
0.98																			0.000	0.060	0.203
0.99																				0.000	0.143
																					0.000
	kvar Required per Kilowatt																				

The capacitance of three-phase lines and equipment is obviously reduced if the system is unbalanced, since one phase will become fully loaded while the other two are partly loaded.

1-9 PHASE SEQUENCE

The time sequence of the phase voltages and currents of a polyphase system is fixed by the direction of rotation of the alternator (source) and the physical arrangement of the phase wires around the alternator. Arbitrarily, the positive direction of the phasors representing the voltages is taken as counterclockwise.

The phase sequence determines the direction of rotation of motors connected to the system. Interchanging any two of the phase wires connected to a motor reverses the direction of rotation of the motor. In an unbalanced three-phase system, interchanging any two of the connections to the unbalanced load will change the magnitude of the load currents. The expression "phase sequence" generally applies to voltages; it is possible that the currents may have a different phase sequence. An induction motor is the simplest device with which to check phase sequence. Any unbalanced three-phase circuit can be used to check phase sequence; usually lamps are used as two of the single-phase loads. The theory is explained in the solutions to the problems that follow.

PROBLEMS

Problem 1-1 Capacitance, inductance, and Q of a coil

Measurements made on the coil shown in the Fig. 1-11 give the following data:

When $C = 0$, resonant frequency $f_0 = 34.0$ kHz, and half-power points are 34.8 kHz and 33.1 kHz.

When $C = 470$ pF, $f_0 = 32.5$ kHz.

When $C = 940$ pF, $f_0 = 31.2$ kHz.

(a) What is the Q of the coil when $C = 0$? (b) What is the distributed capacitance of the coil? (c) What is the true inductance of the coil?

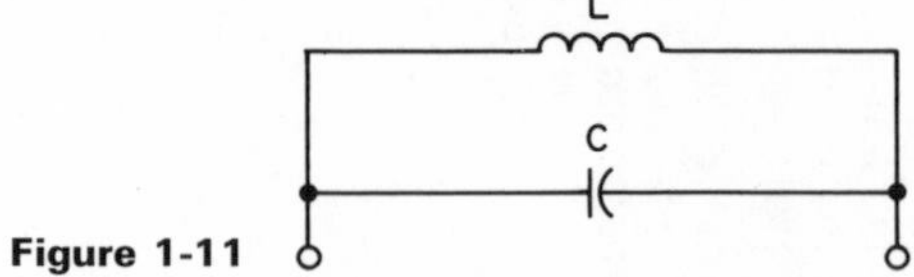

Figure 1-11

Solution:

The equivalent circuit of the coil itself (showing a lumped distributed capacitance) is shown in Fig. 1-12.

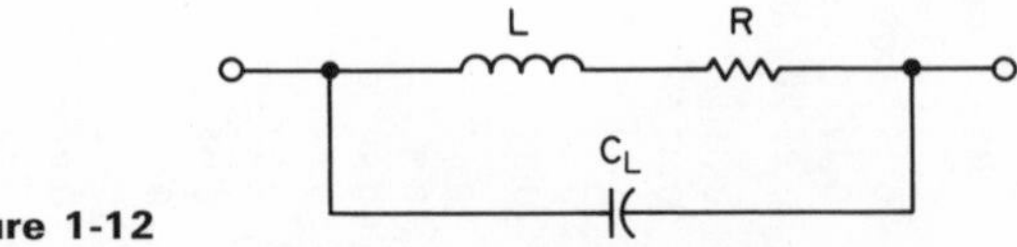

Figure 1-12

(a) The Q of the coil is $\omega_0 L/R$, and

$$\frac{\Delta f}{f_0} = \frac{1}{Q} + \frac{1}{Q}\frac{R_{ar}}{R_g}$$

where R_{ar} = resistance of the circuit of Fig. 1-12 at antiresonance
R_g = resistance of measuring source.

It is customary to vary R_g to obtain maximum power transfer, so that $R_{ar} = R_g$. Then we have $\Delta f/f_0 = 2/Q$. This enables us to calculate the Q of the coil.

$$\frac{\Delta f}{f_0} = \frac{2}{Q}$$

$$\frac{34{,}800 - 33{,}100}{34{,}000} = \frac{2}{Q}$$

$$Q = 40 \qquad \textit{Answer, part (a)}$$

(b, c) The solution of the rest of the problem requires adding the capacitance given to C_L to obtain the additional equations required.

$$f_0 = 34{,}000 = \frac{1}{2\pi\sqrt{LC_L\left(\frac{Q^2+1}{Q^2}\right)}}$$

$$\approx \frac{1}{2\pi\sqrt{LC_L}}$$

$$LC_L = 22 \times 10^{-12}$$

When $C = 470 \times 10^{-12} = C_1$,

$$f_0 = 32{,}500 \approx \frac{1}{2\pi\sqrt{L(C_L + C_1)}}$$

$$LC_L + LC_1 = 24 \times 10^{-12}$$

When $C = 940 \times 10^{-12} = C_2$,

$$f_0 = 31{,}200 \approx \frac{1}{2\pi\sqrt{L(C_L + C_2)}}$$

$$LC_L + LC_2 = 26 \times 10^{-12}$$

Solving, $C_L = 5170$ pF *Answer, part (b)*
$L = 0.00425$ H *Answer, part (c)*

Problem 1-2 Kirchhoff's equations in network analysis

In the circuit of Fig. 1-13, voltage sources E_1 and E_2 are sinusoidal at a frequency of 1000 Hz. Their rms values are 100 volts, and E_2 leads E_1. The voltage across E_1 and E_2 in series is 150 volts rms. How much power does each source supply for the following impedances? Z_1: R = 30 ohms, L = 4.5 mH. Z_2: R = 50 ohms. Z_3: R = 40 ohms, C = 3.2 μF.

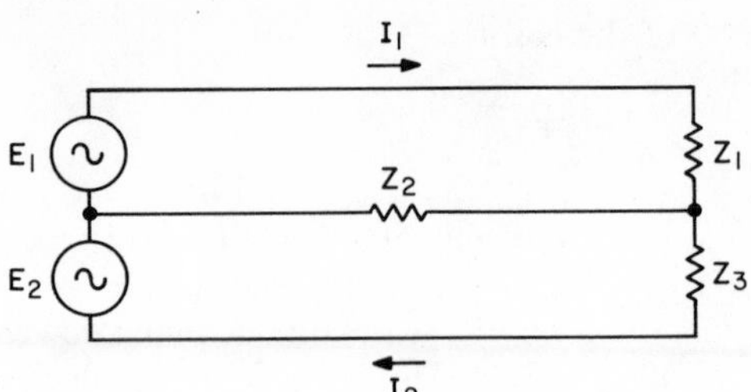

Figure 1-13

Solution:

Obtain voltages in complex form, solve for currents using Kirchhoff's laws (or mesh equations), then

$$P_1 = E_1I_1 \cos \theta_1 \qquad \text{and} \qquad P_2 = E_2I_2 \cos \theta_2$$

Let $E_1 = 100 + j0$

$$(E_1 + E_2 \cos \alpha)^2 + (E_2 \sin \alpha)^2 = (150)^2$$

$$(100 + 100 \cos \alpha)^2 + (100 \sin \alpha)^2 = (150)^2$$

$$\sin^2 \alpha = 1 - \cos^2 \alpha \qquad \text{and} \qquad \cos \alpha = 0.125$$

$E_2 = 100\underline{/82.8°} = 12.5 + j99.2$ See Fig. 1-14.

$$I_1 = \frac{\begin{vmatrix} E_1 & -Z_2 \\ E_2 & (Z_2 + Z_3) \end{vmatrix}}{\begin{vmatrix} (Z_1 + Z_2) & -Z_2 \\ -Z_2 & (Z_2 + Z_3) \end{vmatrix}} \qquad \text{and} \qquad I_2 = \frac{\begin{vmatrix} (Z_1 + Z_2) & E_1 \\ -Z_2 & E_2 \end{vmatrix}}{\begin{vmatrix} (Z_1 + Z_2) & -Z_2 \\ -Z_2 & (Z_2 + Z_3) \end{vmatrix}}$$

where $X_L = \omega L = 28.2$ ohms

$X_C = 1/\omega C = 50$ ohms

$Z_1 = 30 + j28.2 = 41.2\underline{/43.3°}$

$Z_2 = 50 + j0 = 50\underline{/0°}$

$Z_3 = 40 - j50 = 63.9\underline{/-51°}$

Solving, $I_1 = 1.52\underline{/13.2°}$ and $\theta_1 = 13.2°$

$I_2 = 1.4\underline{/82.4°}$ and $\theta_2 = 82.8° - 82.4°$

Therefore, $P_1 = 100 \times 1.52 \cos 13.2° = 148$ watts

$P_2 = 100 \times 1.4 \cos (82.8° - 82.4°) = 140$ watts *Answer*

Problem 1-3 Mesh currents

What value of detector resistance R will give the maximum power in the detector of Fig. 1-15?

Solution:

This is not a case of maximum power transfer, in which case the input impedance of the bridge as seen by the source and its impedance would equal 10 kΩ (or E/I_1

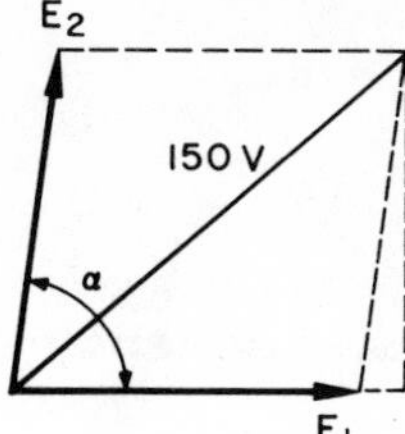

Figure 1-14

would equal 20 kΩ). Rather, the problem in effect asks under what condition would I^2R be maximum, where I is the difference between mesh currents I_2 and I_3?

Write the mesh equations as follows:

$$\begin{aligned} 10 &= 40I_1 - 20I_2 - 10I_3 \\ 0 &= -20I_1 + (30 + R)I_2 - RI_3 \\ 0 &= -10I_1 - RI_2 + (20 + R)I_3 \end{aligned}$$

where R is in kilohms, and I_1, I_2, and I_3 are in milliamps.

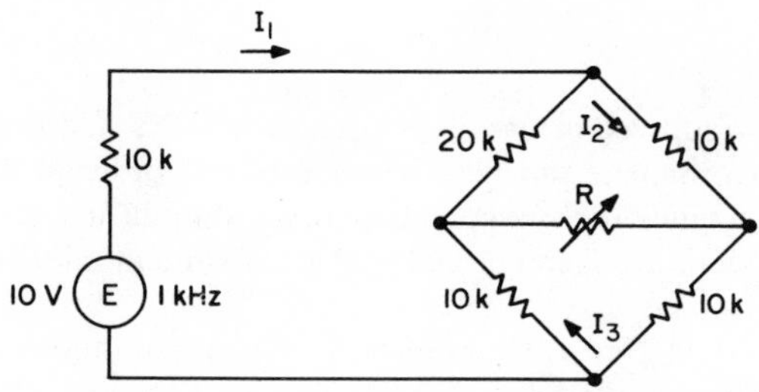

Figure 1-15

$$I = I_2 - I_3 = \frac{\begin{vmatrix} 40 & 10 & -10 \\ -20 & 0 & -R \\ -10 & 0 & (20+R) \end{vmatrix} - \begin{vmatrix} 40 & -20 & 10 \\ -20 & (30+R) & 0 \\ -10 & -R & 0 \end{vmatrix}}{\begin{vmatrix} 40 & -20 & -10 \\ -20 & (30+R) & -R \\ -10 & -R & (20+R) \end{vmatrix}}$$

This reduces to: $I = \dfrac{100}{110\,R + 1300}$ milliamps

$$\text{and } I^2R = \frac{100\,R}{(11R + 130)^2} = P \text{ (milliwatts)}$$

$$\frac{dP}{dR} = \frac{(11R + 130)^2(100) - (100)(R)(242R + 2860)}{(11R + 130)^4}$$

$= 0$ for maximum power in the detector

$R = 11.8$ kohms *Answer*

$$I^2R = \frac{100\ R}{(11R + 130)^2}$$

$= 0.0175$ milliwatts

Problem 1-4 Reactance vs. frequency curve for complex RLC circuit

Sketch the reactance vs. frequency curve for the circuit of Fig. 1-16.

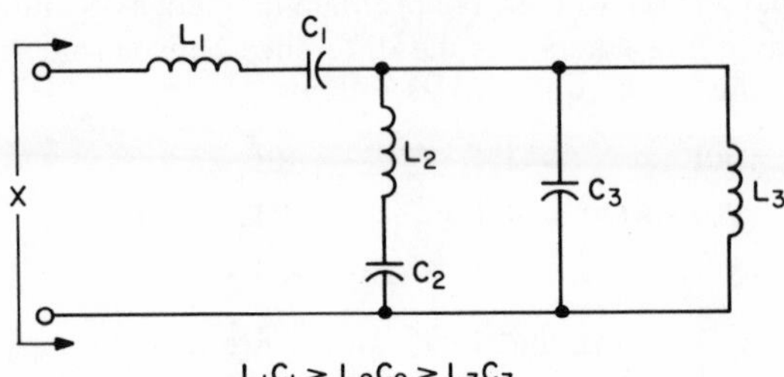

Figure 1-16

Solution:

In series, reactances are additive; in parallel, susceptances are additive. Relative magnitudes of the various branches are given to permit an "order of magnitude" sketch. Frequency vs. reactance (or susceptance) curves should first be drawn for each branch; resonance points are then marked so that zero and infinity points along the abscissa can be determined.

Step 1: Sketch X vs. f for the L_1C_1 branch. This is a continuous asymptotic curve, zero reactance for $f_1 = 1/(2\pi\sqrt{L_1C_1})$, and negative at the lower frequencies.

Step 2: Sketch B vs. f for the L_2C_2 branch. This is a discontinuous curve, infinite susceptance for $f_2 = 1/(2\pi\sqrt{L_2C_2})$, and positive at the lower frequencies.

Step 3: Sketch B vs. f for the L_3C_3 branch. This is a continuous asymptotic curve, zero susceptance for $f_3 = 1/(2\pi\sqrt{L_3C_3})$, and positive at the higher frequencies.

Step 4: Sketch a composite B vs. f curve, combining the values from Steps 2 and 3. This is a discontinuous curve, zero susceptance at f_4 and f_5 values that satisfy:

$$\omega C_2 - \frac{1}{\omega L_2} = \frac{1}{\omega L_3} - \omega C_3$$

Step 5: Sketch X vs. f from the values obtained in Step 4. Add these reactance values to those obtained in Step 1. (See Fig. 1-17.) Note that the resultant curve is discontinuous and infinite at f_4 and f_5.

Problem 1-5 Resistance values for universal meter for voltage readings

The circuit diagram of Fig. 1-18 is the plan for a universal meter that will indicate rms values of sine-wave voltages. The milliammeter has a d'Arsonval movement.

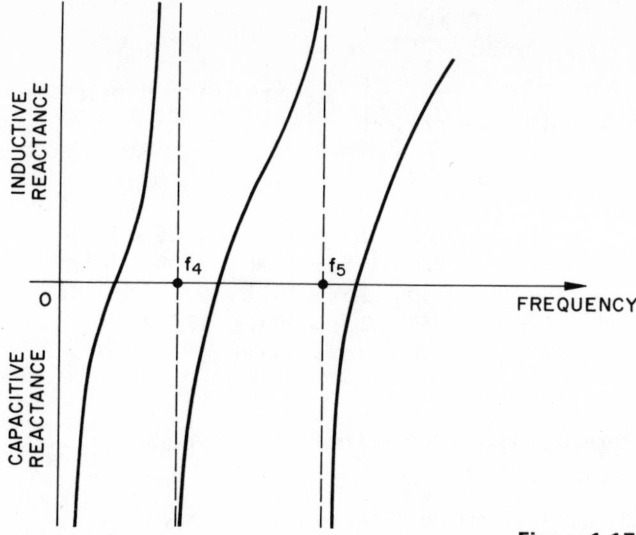

Figure 1-17

Resistors R_A and R_B are to be adjusted to such values that an rms voltage of 2.5 volts connected between a and b will give full-scale deflection on the milliammeter. Meter loading on the circuits to which it is connected is to be 1000 ohms/volt.

Determine the resistance and power ratings of five resistors to be used in the meter.

Solution:

Figure 1-19 simplifies the problem and defines the required calculations. Note that the 2.5 volts is in series with the voltage drop across the resistors external to a-b.

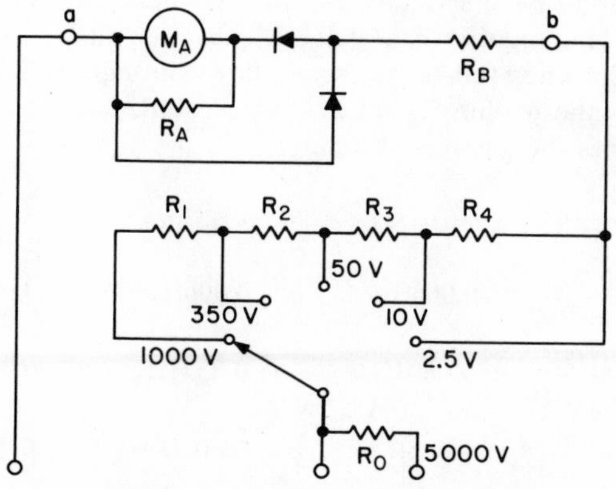

Figure 1-18

Figure 1-19

Range	R_x
5000V	$(5000 - 2.5) \times 1000$ or $4.998 \times 10^6\Omega$
1000V	$(1000 - 2.5) \times 1000$ or $0.998 \times 10^6\Omega$
350V	$(350 - 2.5) \times 1000$ or $0.3475 \times 10^6\Omega$
50V	$(50 - 2.5) \times 1000$ or $47{,}500\Omega$
10V	$(10 - 2.5) \times 7500\Omega$
2.5V	

$R_0 = (4.998 - 0.998) \times 10^6$ or 4.000 Meg *Answer*

$R_1 = (0.998 - 0.3475) \times 10^6$ or 0.6505 Meg *Answer*

$R_2 = (347{,}500 - 47{,}500)$ or 0.3 Meg *Answer*

$R_3 = (47{,}500 - 7500)$ or 40,000 ohms *Answer*

$R_4 = 7500$ ohms *Answer*

Power ratings: Since the design is based on 1000 ohms/volt, and since power = V^2/R, the power rating of each resistor (in watts) is the resistor value in megohms.

Problem 1-6 Resistance values for multirange ammeter

A multirange ammeter is to be constructed with a 6-ohm, 10-mA d'Arsonval type meter, resistors, and a switch. The multimeter ranges are to be 0.1, 1.0, and 10.0 amps, respectively. The resistance of the multimeter on every range must be less than 1 ohm.

Draw the circuit diagram of the multimeter and specify the resistors for resistance and power rating.

Solution:

Recognize that the d'Arsonval meter indicates full-scale deflection when 10 mA passes through 6 ohms. This requires 0.06 volts, which also must be the voltage across the external resistors when full-range current flows through the circuit. Note that the current through the 6 ohms is taken into account. See Fig. 1-20. The following table summarizes the answers.

Range	*Total external resistance*	*Step resistance*	I^2R
0 to 10 A	$\dfrac{0.06}{10 - 0.01} = 0.006\Omega$	0.006Ω	0.6 W
0 to 1.0 A	$\dfrac{0.06}{1 - 0.01} = 0.0601\Omega$	0.0541Ω	0.0541 W
0 to 0.1 A	$\dfrac{0.06}{0.1 - 0.01} = 0.668\Omega$	0.608Ω	0.0049 W

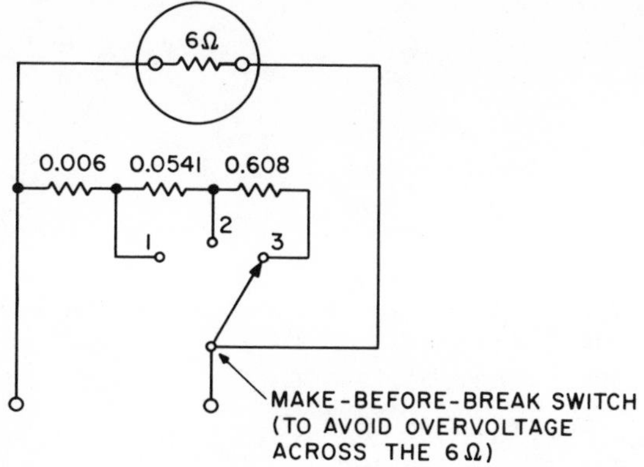

Figure 1-20

Problem 1-7 Bridge for measuring values of resistance, inductance, or capacitance

The circuit elements of the bridge of Fig. 1-21 are $R_1 = 20$ kilohms, $R_2 = 50$ kilohms, $R_3 = 0$ to 10 kilohms (adjustable), $C_1 = 10$ to 150 pF (adjustable), $C_2 = 0.003$ pF, $\omega = 10^5$ rad/sec.

The oscillator that is available to supply this bridge has an output impedance of 50 ohms. An oscilloscope is available as a detector.

Determine the range of the resistance, inductance, or capacitance of the unknown impedance that can be measured with this bridge.

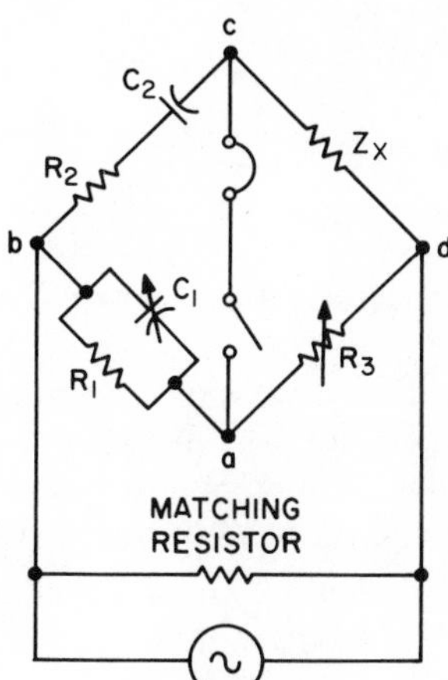

Figure 1-21. *Note:* If the oscillator were to be connected across a and c, under certain values of the variables, there would be a short circuit.

Solution:

This is a variation of the Schering Bridge, frequently used to measure the dissipation factor of a capacitor (the cotangent of the power factor angle). Note that the unknown phase angle is, for the balanced condition, a function of C_1 only.

For balance,

$$\frac{|Z_x| \angle\theta_x}{R_3 \angle 0^\circ} = \frac{|Z_2| \angle\theta_2}{|Z_1| \angle\theta_1} \tag{1-1}$$

$$\theta_x = \theta_2 - \theta_1$$

$$\tan\theta_x = \tan(\theta_2 - \theta_1) = \frac{\tan\theta_2 - \tan\theta_1}{1 + \tan\theta_1 \tan\theta_2}$$

$$\begin{aligned}
\tan\theta_1 &= -\omega C_1 R_1 \\
&= -0.02 \qquad \text{(for 10 pF)} \\
&= -0.3 \qquad \text{(for 150 pF)} \\
\tan\theta_2 &= -1/\omega C_2 R_2 = -10^6/15 = -66{,}700 \\
\tan\theta_x &= -3.33 \qquad \text{when } C_1 = 150 \text{ pF} \\
&= -500 \qquad \text{when } C_1 = 10 \text{ pF}
\end{aligned}$$

Expressing balance Eq. (1-1) in terms of reals and imaginaries, and equating the imaginaries

$$R_x = \frac{R_3 C_1}{C_2} + \frac{R_2 R_3}{R_1}$$

$$Z_x = R_x(1 - j\tan\theta_x)$$

For $R_3 = 10\text{K}$,

$$\begin{aligned}
Z_x &= 33 \times 10^6(1 - j500) \\
&\cong -j16{,}500 \times 10^6 \text{ ohms} \qquad \text{when } C_1 = 10 \text{ pF} \\
&\cong -j1650 \times 10^6 \text{ ohms} \qquad \text{when } C_1 = 150 \text{ pF}
\end{aligned}$$

Recapitulating,

$\tan\theta_x$ varies between 33 and 500 *Answer*

Z_x varies between 0 and 16,500 megohms *Answer*

Problem 1-8 Instantaneous quantities and Thevenin's theorem

Indicate the correct answers by circling the correct values:

(a) A voltage $e = 200 \sin\omega t$ volts is applied to the two terminals of a passive device. The current that flows is represented by the equation $i = 0.5 - 7.0 \sin(\omega t + 60^\circ) + 0.9 \cos 2\omega t$ amps. The average power in watts into the device is

100	350	500	700	1000
1200	1400	1750	2100	None

(b) For the above device, the peak value of the instantaneous power component of 4ω angular frequency is

0	30	60	90	150
180	270	300	360	None

(c) For the A, B, C, and D constants of the generalized transmission line (linear, passive, bilateral, 4-terminal network) at constant frequency, indicate the value of

C if the network consists only of a series impedance Z equal to $3.0\angle 10°$. (Subscripts indicate "source" and "receiver.")

$$E_s = AE_r + BI_r$$
$$I_s = CE_r + DI_r$$

0 $\quad 0.17\angle -5°$ $\quad 0.33\angle -10°$ $\quad 0.67\angle -20°$ $\quad 1.0\angle -10°$

$1.5\angle 5°$ $\quad 3.0\angle 10°$ $\quad 6.0\angle -20°$

(d) Two terminals extend from a linear device. A measurement of the voltage between two terminals showed that a d-c voltage of 200 volts exists. When a 300-ohm resistor is connected between the terminals, a current of 0.5 amp flows. If a 100-ohm resistor is connected between the terminals, the current in amperes that flows is

0	0.5	1.0	1.5	2.0
2.5	3.0	4.0	5.0	None

Solution:

(a and b) First write the equation for the instantaneous value of power; perusal of the component terms will lead to the solution, since the average value of a sine wave is zero.

$$\begin{aligned} p = ei &= 0.5 \times 200 \sin \omega t + 7 \times 200 \sin \omega t \sin (\omega t + 60°) \\ &\quad + 0.9 \times 200 \sin \omega t \cos 2\omega t \\ &= 100 \sin \omega t + 700 (\cos 60° - \cos 60° \cos 2\omega t \\ &\quad + \sin 60° \sin 2\omega t) + 90(\sin 3\omega t - \sin \omega t) \end{aligned}$$

$P_{avg} = 350$ watts *Answer, part (a)*

Zero. There is no 4ω component. *Answer, part (b)*

(c) For a simple series impedance network, A = D = 1, B = Z, and C = 0.
Zero *Answer*

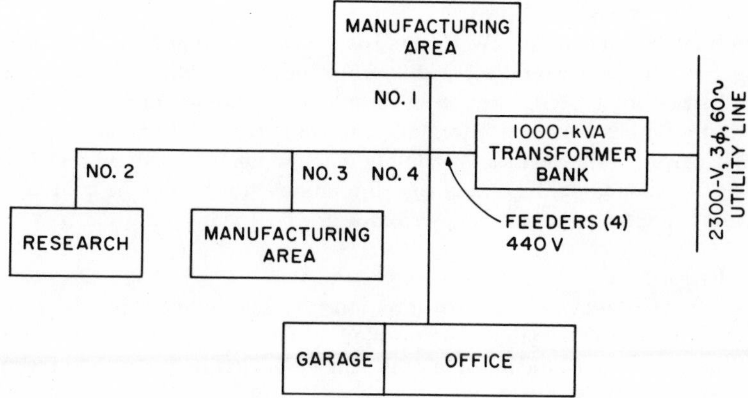

Figure 1-22

(d) This is an application of Thevenin's Theorem, the open-circuit voltage being 200 volts.

When R = 300,

$$E = \frac{200}{Z_s + 300} = 0.5$$

$$Z_s = 100 \text{ ohms}$$

When R = 100,

$$I = \frac{200}{100 + 100} = 1.0 \text{ amps} \qquad \textit{Answer}$$

Problem 1-9 Power factor improvement in industrial plant

In an industrial plant (see Fig. 1-22), the normal load during plant operation on the various feeders was found to be

Circuit	*kW*	*Power Factor (Lagging)*
1	475	0.62
2	100	0.80
3	150	0.68
4	30	0.85

It is necessary to add 200 kW at 0.80 P.F. lagging in the building fed by circuit 1. The overall plant is fed from a main service through a transformer bank rated 1000 kVA with a secondary voltage of 440 volts 3-phase 60 Hz. It is the desire to provide facility for the existing load without increasing the overload presently existing on the transformer, which is considered safe. An additional advantage can be gained by raising the plant power factor generally, since a penalty in the form of demand charges is in the utility rate structure. This penalty is of the form

$$\text{Demand charges} = \frac{0.85 \times \$1.50}{\text{P.F.}} \times \text{maximum demand}$$

Assume that the maximum kW demand is 1.5 times the normal plant kW load.

Specify how you would solve this problem, giving ratings of equipment (in standard sizes) to be used, location of installations, reasons for picking such locations, and all other pertinent information to support your decision.

Also calculate the savings in monthly demand charges both with and without the 200-kW added load. Explain any limitations that might be placed on the maximum value of corrective kvars from a practical viewpoint.

Solution:

First, the minimum capacitive correction must be determined; then the additional correction that can be economically justified. Finally, the allocation of those kvars among the four feeders, the location of the capacitors in the system, and the method of switching should be specified.

(a) Minimum capacitive kvar required:

Present (and maximum safe) load on transformer:

Circuit	*kW*	*kVA*	*kvar*		
1	475	767	600		
2	100	125	75		
3	150	221	162		
4	30	35	18		
Total	755		855	(1140 kVA)	(0.662 P.F.)
Added load	200	250	115		
New total	955		970	(1360 kVA)	

To reduce this load to 1140 kVA, add capacitive reactance

$$970 - [(1140)^2 - (955)^2]^{1/2} = 346 \text{ kvar}$$

$$\text{New P.F.} = 955/1140 = 0.837 \cong 0.84$$

(b) Correction economically justified:
In the absence of sufficient criteria, assume optimum point occurs when

Cost of kvar = savings in demand charges over 2½ years

Assume: cost of kvar = \$15/kvar (installed). For 955 kW, 0.84 P.F.:

P.F.	*Δkvar*	*Δ\$*	*Demand Charges, \$*	*Δ(Demand Charges), \$ (2½ yr)*
0.94	277	4150	58,250	
0.95	34	510	57,650	−600
0.96	35	525	57,050	−600
0.97	39	585	56,450	−600
0.98	47	705	55,850	−600
0.99	56	840	55,300	−550

Example of determining demand charges:

$$\frac{0.85 \times \$1.50 \times 1.5 \times 955 \text{ kW} \times 30 \text{ months}}{0.94} = \$58{,}250$$

It is apparent that the optimum power factor is 0.97. Therefore, install 731 kvar to reduce the net kvar from 970 to 239 (lagging), giving 985 kVA, 955 kW, and 0.97 P.F.

(c) Capacitors are available in 5-, 10-, 15-, 25-, and 60-kvar ratings at this voltage. Locate the capacitance at the load end of the feeders so as to maintain 0.97 P.F. at all times. This requires connecting some of the capacitors across the load side of the motor starter terminals to avoid leading power factor when the motors are not running.

Some of the capacitors will be connected to the bus bars. In these cases, refer to the National Electrical Code or manufacturers' catalogs for the proper ampere rating of the circuit breakers or switches used.

(d) With no capacitors and the 200-kW load disconnected:

kW = 755 kvar = 855 kVA = 1140 P.F. = 0.66

$$\text{Monthly demand charge} = \frac{0.85 \times 2.25 \times 755}{0.66} = \$2190$$

With 731 kvar,

kvar = 124 kVA = 765 P.F. = 0.986

Monthly demand charge = $1465

Savings = $725/month

(e) With no capacitors and the 200-kW load connected:

kW = 955 kvar = 970 kVA = 1360 P.F. = 0.70

$$\text{Monthly demand charge} = \frac{0.85 \times 2.25 \times 955}{0.70} = \$2610$$

With 731 kvar.

P.F. = 0.97

Monthly demand charge = $1880

Savings = $730/month

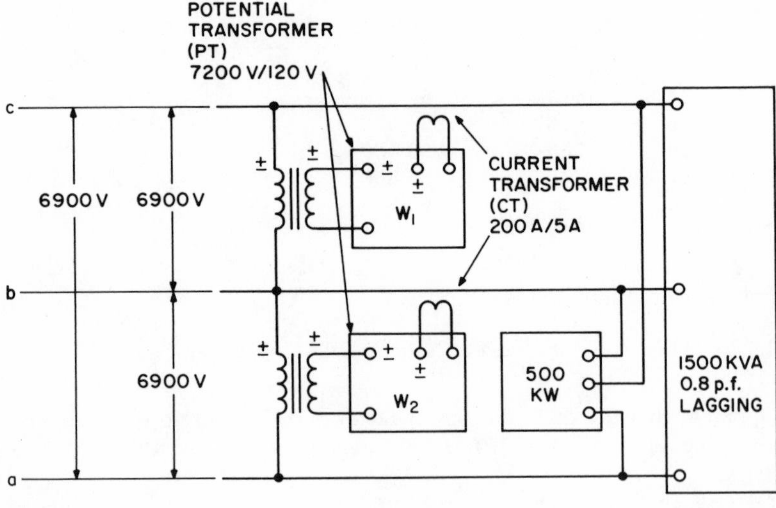

Figure 1-23

Problem 1-10 Two wattmeters on three-phase system (incorrect connection)

Assuming a 3-phase, 3-wire balanced distribution voltage of 6900 volts with the phase rotation as shown and the paralleled balanced loads as shown in Fig. 1-23, calculate the readings of W_1 and W_2. Does the sum of W_1 and W_2 indicate the power (watts) of the load? If not, why not?

Solution:

Draw the phasor diagram of the voltages, lettering them in conformance with the problem. (See Fig. 1-24.) Then write the expression for the wattmeter readings. Do not forget the instrument transformer ratios.

$$\text{Total kW} = 500 + (0.8 \times 1500) = 1700 \text{ kW}$$

$$\text{Total kvar} = 0.6 \times 1500 \text{ or } 900 \text{ kvar (lag)}$$

$$\text{Total kVA} = 1700 + j900 \text{ or } 1920 \text{ kVA}$$

$$\text{Line current} = \frac{1920}{\sqrt{3} \times 6.9} = 161 \text{ amps}$$

W_1 reads $|I_{cc'}||V_{cb}| \cos \theta_1$

W_2 reads $|I_{bb'}||V_{ab}| \cos \theta_2$

$$\cos^{-1} 1700/1920 = 27.7° \cong 28°$$

$$I_{cc'} = 161\underline{/120° - 28°}$$

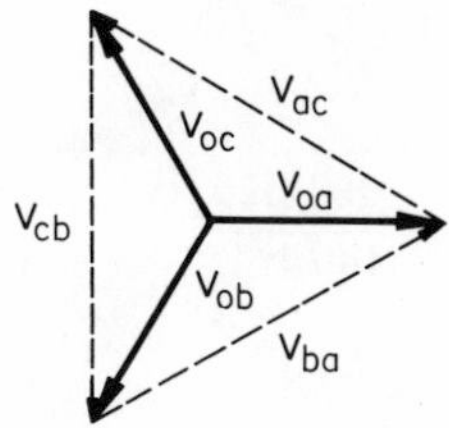

Figure 1-24

$$V_{cb} = 6900\underline{/270°}$$

Hence, W_1 reads 1120 cos − 178° or − 1120 kW. *Answer*

$$I_{bb'} = 161\underline{/240° - 28°}$$

$$V_{ab} = 6900\underline{/210°}$$

Hence, W_2 reads 1120 cos 2° or + 1120 kW. *Answer*

The readings will *not* give the total power when added. The common potential tap should be in the phase that does not contain a current transformer.

(Note: The wattmeter readings will be reduced by the factor $1/(40 \times 60)$ from the figures given above, because of the instrument transformer ratios.)

Problem 1-11 Two wattmeters on three-phase system (correct connection)

The voltages applied to the circuit of Fig. 1-25 are

$$E_{ab} = 208$$

$$E_{bc} = -104 - j180$$

$$E_{ca} = -104 + j180$$

Calculate the indications of each of the wattmeters.

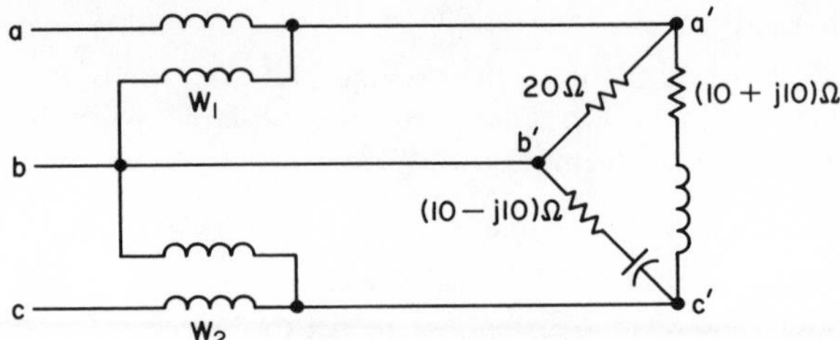

Figure 1-25

Solution:

W_1 reads $|I_{aa'}||E_{ab}| \cos \theta_1$

W_2 reads $|I_{cc'}||E_{cb}| \cos \theta_2$, where θ_1 is the angle between $I_{aa'}$ and E_{ab}, etc. Their algebraic sum is the total power.

$$E_{ab} = 208\angle 0^\circ \qquad E_{cc} = 208\angle 60^\circ \qquad E_{ac} = 208\angle -60^\circ$$

$$I_{aa'} = I_{a'b'} + I_{a'c'} = \frac{208\angle 0^\circ}{20\angle 0^\circ} + \frac{208\angle -60^\circ}{14.14\angle 45^\circ}$$

$$= 6.6 - j14.3 \text{ or } 15.7\angle -65^\circ$$

$$I_{cc'} = I_{c'b'} + I_{c'a'} = \frac{208\angle 60^\circ}{14.14\angle -45^\circ} + \frac{208\angle 120^\circ}{14.14\angle 45^\circ}$$

$$= 28.6\angle 90^\circ$$

W_1 reads $15.7 \times 208 \cos -65^\circ$ or $+ 1380$ watts

W_2 reads $28.6 \times 208 \cos 30^\circ$ or $+5150$ watts *Answer*

Total power $= 1380 + 5150 = 6530$ watts

Problem 1-12 Phase sequence indicator

For the phase sequence indicator shown in Fig. 1-26, determine whether lamp A will be brighter than lamp B with the given phase sequence of the supply or for the reversed phase sequence of the supply. Lamps A and B are identical.

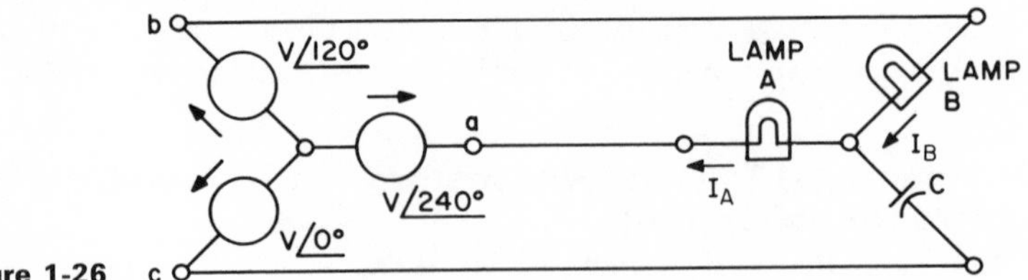

Figure 1-26

Solution:

First draw the phasor diagram of the voltages. (See Fig. 1-27.) Write the equations for the currents through lamp A and lamp B. If the currents are then drawn on the phasor diagram, the one of greater magnitude is obvious.

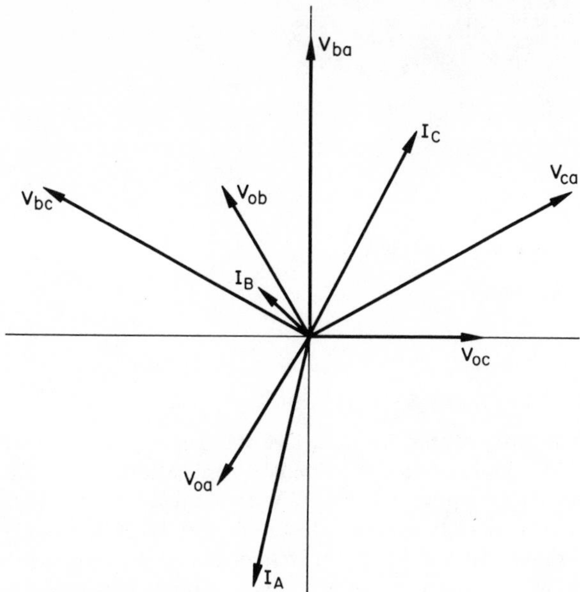

Figure 1-27

Current through lamp A:

$$I_A = \frac{V_{ba}}{2R} + \frac{V_{ca}}{R - jX} \qquad \text{(let R = lamp resistance)}$$

Current through lamp B:

$$I_B = \frac{V_{ba}}{2R} + \frac{V_{bc}}{R - jX}$$

$$V_{ba} = V_{ob} - V_{oa}$$

$$V_{bc} = V_{ob} - V_{oc}$$

$$V_{ca} = V_{oc} - V_{oa}$$

From the phasor diagram, it is apparent that with the phase sequence given, lamp A will be brighter. *Answer*

chapter 2
TRANSFORMERS

The range of applications of transformers is very large, and transformer design and performance criteria depend on the particular application. Power frequency transformers are designed for optimum efficiency and regulation although instrument transformers require special attention to ensure linear performance within a given load (burden) range. Audio and higher frequency transformers are designed for either maximum power transfer or optimum gain, with as constant a response as is possible over a prescribed frequency range; turns ratio is determined by the impedances of the circuits being coupled.

2-1 EQUIVALENT CIRCUITS

Figure 2-1 is the "exact" equivalent circuit of the iron-core transformers, assuming sinusoidal voltages and currents. This assumption is valid for most applications, for a given frequency. Figure 2-2 is the "practical" equivalent circuit, with values of all parameters referred to the load side of the transformer.

In power applications, the hysteresis effect is greater than the eddy current effect, and it is common to assume that the shunt parameters (g″ and b″ in Fig. 2-2) vary inversely with frequency. R_{eq} can be assumed independent of frequency and X_{eq}, of course, varies directly with frequency.

In audio-frequency applications (16 to 20,000 Hz, but more usually 250 to 2750 Hz), iron-core transformers are operated at relatively low flux densities, and further

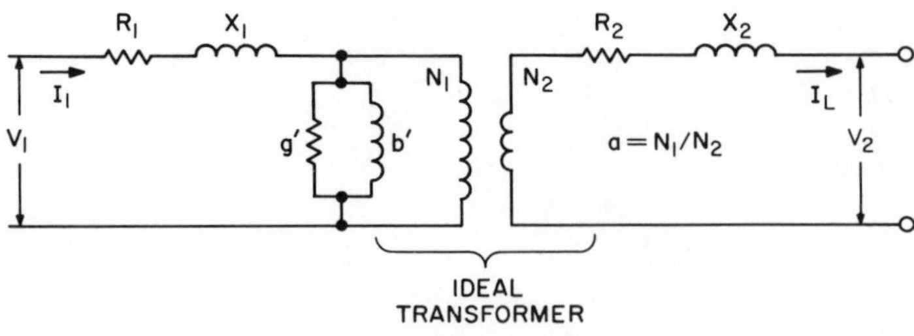

Figure 2-1

simplification of the equivalent circuit of Fig. 2-2 can be performed. The circuits of Fig. 2-3 are applicable (values are referred to the source side of the transformer in these diagrams).

At higher frequencies, air-core transformers are used, and leakage flux and excitation current cannot be ignored at any frequency. Coupled circuit theory is the preferred approach, and the equivalent circuit is rarely used.

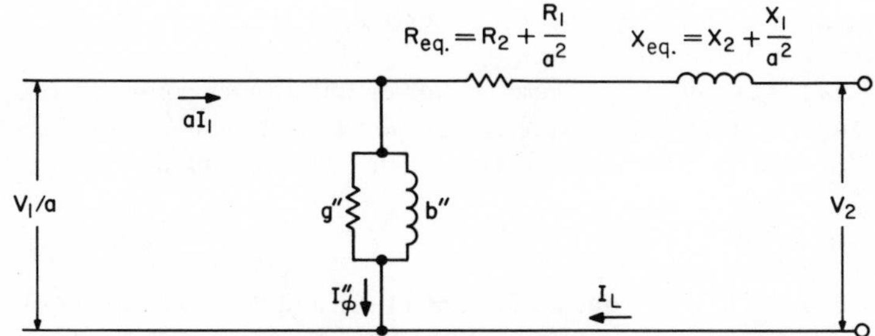

Figure 2-2

2-2 REGULATION AND EFFICIENCY

The phasor diagram corresponding to the "practical" equivalent circuit of Fig. 2-2 is shown in Fig. 2-4. Where I_L is the full load current, the regulation is given by

$$\% \text{ regulation} = 100 \times \frac{V_1/a - V_2}{V_1/a}$$

Total losses of a transformer consist of copper losses and core losses; these are the wattmeter reading of the short-circuit test and the open-circuit (no-load) test, respectively. Efficiency is expressed by

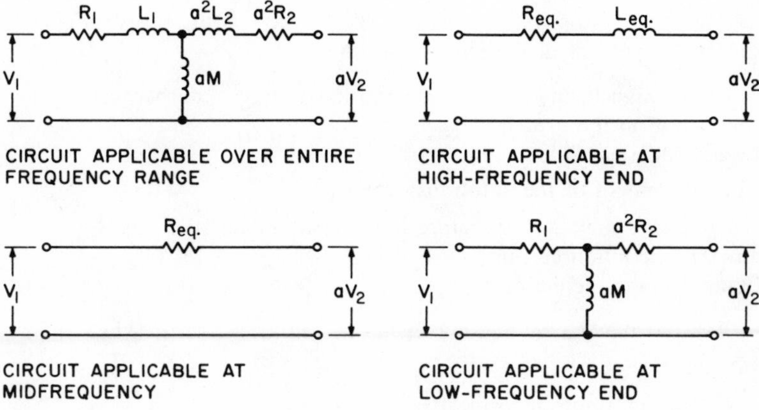

Figure 2-3

$$\% \text{ efficiency} = 100 \times \frac{\text{full-load output (watts) at rated P.F.}}{\text{full-load output} + \text{total losses}}$$

Since R_{eq} and X_{eq} can be obtained from the short-circuit test, the regulation can be obtained readily. The excitation current is ignored, since the test is performed with a very low test voltage and flux density is low.

The shunt parameters are obtained from the no-load test that is performed at rated voltage. The entire current is assumed to be the excitation current. Where primary line regulation is to be determined, the excitation current may be sufficient to justify including it in the calculations.

The total core losses of an iron-core reactor or transformer consist of eddy-current losses and hysteresis losses, expressed as follows (sinusoidal conditions are necessary for the validity of the second term on the right side of the equation):

$$P_c = K_1 \frac{E^n}{f^{n-1}} + K_2 E^2$$

By varying induced emf E and frequency f one at a time, and measuring total losses, the separation of the two components of core loss can be performed.

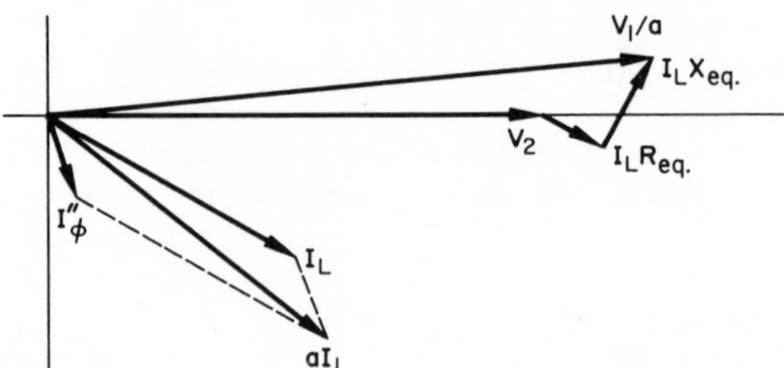

Figure 2-4

2-3 THE AUTOTRANSFORMER

The practical equivalent circuit of the autotransformer is shown in Fig. 2-5. If the rating of an ordinary transformer is x kVA, when connected as an autotransformer, its rating is approximately (a + 1)x, where a is the turns ratio.

The disadvantages of the autotransformer are

1. Need for high insulation level on the low-voltage side because of the direct connection to the primary.
2. Larger short-circuit currents.

The advantages of the autotransformer are

1. Greater efficiency, and therefore lower cost and smaller size.
2. Smaller excitation current.
3. Better voltage regulation.

Little advantage is gained by using an autotransformer when the ratio of primary and secondary line voltages is high (greater than 2).

$$\frac{\%Z \text{ as an autotransformer}}{\%Z \text{ as a two-circuit transformer}} = \frac{V_p - V_s}{V_s}$$

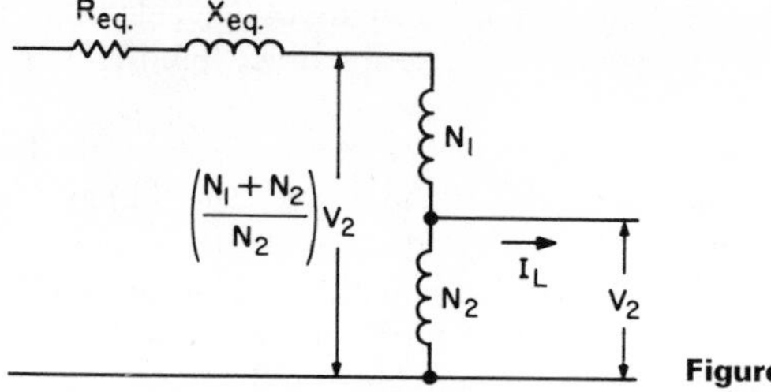

Figure 2-5

PROBLEMS

Problem 2-1 Comparison of audio-frequency and utility power transformers

Transformers of various kinds find wide application in electrical engineering. Answer the following relating to typical transformers for either (1) audio-frequency communications applications or (2) electric power applications. If a particular question does not apply to the classification selected, indicate with a brief explanation.

(a) Designate the classification selected and state briefly the principal function or functions of the type you have selected.

(b) Draw an equivalent circuit representative of the principal electrical features of the transformer, and that retains the identity of each winding.

(c) Draw two approximately equivalent circuits suitable for appropriate load or frequency conditions. State such conditions.

(d) What special circumstances must be investigated if such transformers are operated in parallel?

(e) For what frequency ranges are such transformers commonly designed?

(f) Are thermal considerations a major or minor factor in the design? If major, how is proper cooling accomplished?

Solution:

Answers are given first for audio-frequency applications, then for power applications.

Audio applications:

(a) The principal function is impedance matching for maximum power transfer in output transformers. However, gain (turns ratio) is also a governing factor, as in input transformers. Circuit isolation is a concurrent function for blocking of the d-c component.

(b, c) See Figs. 2-1 to 2-3.

(d) Not applicable; parallel operation of audio transformers is seldom, if ever, called for.

(e) 16 to 20,000 Hz, but normally 250 to 2750 Hz.

(f) Thermal considerations are not a major factor; core losses are low, and heat dissipation of total losses is assisted by proper ventilation of the enclosure of the entire circuit.

Power applications:

(a) The principal function is voltage changing; isolation is a concurrent function to insulate the low-voltage side from the high-voltage side. One exception would be the constant-current transformer for series street lighting.

(b, c) See Figs. 2-1 to 2-3.

(d) For parallel operation of single-phase transformers, the turns ratios should be equal to avoid circulating currents. Transformers should have equal impedances so that the load will be shared in proportion to their respective kvar ratings. It is desirable that the transformers have equal R_{eq}/X_{eq} ratios so that they will carry their kW shares of the load (this is of relatively minor importance).

When three-phase transformers are operated in parallel, a Δ/Δ or a Y/Y transformer should not be paralleled with a Δ/Y or a Y/Δ transformer, since their primary (or secondary) voltages would not be in phase.

(e) Power, distribution, and instrument transformers should be designed for a specific frequency, such as 50 or 60 Hz. With the exception of instrument transformers, a given transformer can be operated on either frequency, although some derating might be necessary. Instrument transformers will suffer in accuracy and range if operated at other than design frequency.

(f) Cooling is a major consideration, and the cooling provision (natural convection liquid or air cooled, forced circulation—liquid or air, etc.) must be appropriate for the intended percent loading, ambient temperature, and direct exposure to sun's rays and other radiant sources.

Problem 2-2 Coefficient of coupling in transformer coils

A transformer consisting of two identical coils is connected to a circuit as shown in Fig. 2-6. Each transformer coil has a self-inductance of 10 henrys and the coefficient of coupling is 0.90. The power source E has a negligible internal impedance and a terminal voltage of 500 volts at an angular velocity ω of 1000 rad/sec. The value of C is 1.0 μF.

Calculate the value of the current in the 1000-ohm load resistor.

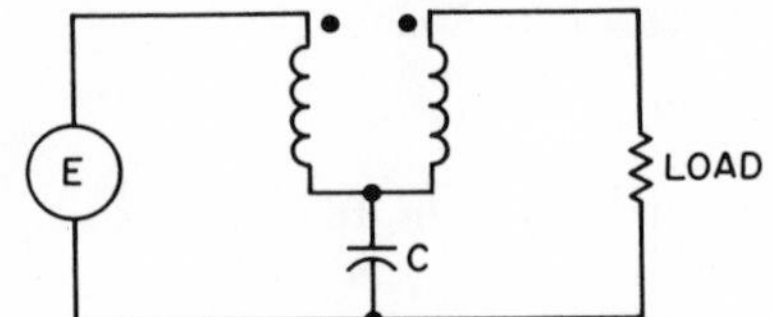

Figure 2-6

Solution:

A convenient solution is to write the mesh equations, treating the mutual inductance as a mutual element. (See Fig. 2-7.)

$$E = j\left(\omega L_1 - \frac{1}{\omega C}\right) I_1 - j\left(\omega M - \frac{1}{\omega C}\right) I_2$$

$$0 = -j\left(\omega M - \frac{1}{\omega C}\right) I_1 + \left(R + j\omega L_2 - j\frac{1}{\omega C}\right) I_2$$

$$E = 500 + j0 \qquad \omega L_1 = \omega L_2 = 10{,}000 \qquad \omega M = 9000 \qquad 1/\omega C = 1000$$

$$500 = j9000 I_1 - j8000\, I_2$$

$$0 = -j8000 I_1 + (1000 + j9000) I_2$$

$$I_2 = \frac{\begin{vmatrix} j9000 & 500 \\ -j8000 & 0 \end{vmatrix}}{\begin{vmatrix} j9000 & -j8000 \\ -j8000 & (1000 + j9000) \end{vmatrix}} = \frac{j4}{-17 + j9} \text{ or } 0.207\underline{/-152°}$$ *Answer*

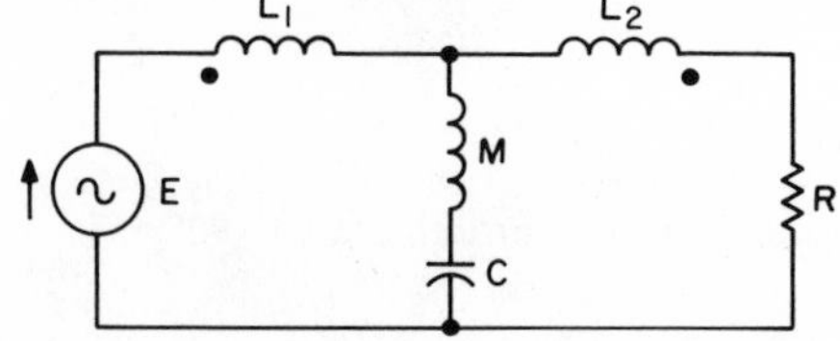

Figure 2-7

Problem 2-3 Transformer open-circuit and short-circuit tests

A 100-kVA, 13.2/2.4-kV 60-Hz transformer was tested to give the following data:

Open-circuit test (power supplied to low-voltage side):

E = 2400 V I = 37 amps P = 1100 watts

Short-circuit test (power supplied to high-voltage side):

E = 450 V I = 8.2 amps P = 1600 watts

The high-voltage side of the transformer is supplied over a transmission line that has a resistance of 10 ohms and an inductive reactance of 35 ohms. A 75-kW load at 80% power factor (lagging) is connected to the low-voltage side of the transformer.

If 2300 volts is desired across the 75-kW load, what must be the terminal voltage of the generator supplying the transmission line?

Solution:

The equivalent resistance and reactance of the transformer are obtained from the short-circuit test data. Since the excitation current is appreciable, the shunt parameters of the transformer should be obtained from the open-circuit test data and used in calculating the line drop. In the following, all quantities are referred to the primary side. (See Fig. 2-8.)

From the short-circuit test,

$R_{eq} = 1600/(8.2)^2 = 23.8$ ohms

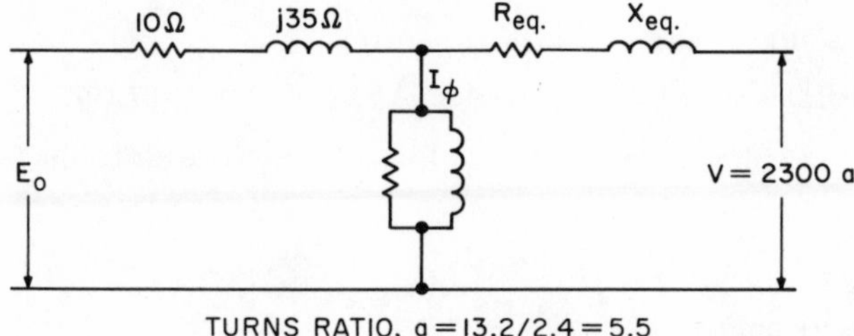

Figure 2-8

$Z_{eq} = 450/8.2 = 55.0$ ohms

$X_{eq} = \sqrt{(55)^2 - (23.8)^2} = 50.0$ ohms

Load current referred to the primary:

$$I_L = \frac{75{,}000}{(a)(0.8)(2300)} = 7.35 \text{ amps, where } a = \frac{13.2}{2.4} = 5.5$$

Excitation current:

$$I_\Phi = 37/a = 6.73 \text{ amps}$$

at an angle $\cos^{-1}[1100/(2400 \times 37)]$ or approximately $-90°$.

Sending end voltage:

$$E_0 = 2300a + 7.35(0.8 - j0.6)(33.8 + j85) - j6.73(10 + j35)$$
$$= 13.4 \text{ kV} \qquad \textit{Answer}$$

Problem 2-4 Efficiency and voltage regulation of transformer

A 1000-kVA, 66/11-kV 60-Hz transformer with 40,000 turns in the primary winding has an equivalent series impedance of 1.0 + j4.9 ohms referred to the low-voltage side, and a no-load loss of 5500 watts at rated terminal voltage.

(a) Operating this transformer at rated secondary voltage and rated frequency, at what kVA output is the efficiency maximum? (b) What is the maximum efficiency? (c) What is the power factor at rated load current to give minimum voltage regulation? (d) Maximum voltage regulation? (e) Discuss the operation of this transformer at 50 Hz and at rated voltage.

Solution:

(a and b) Express the efficiency as a function of load current, and make the derivative of efficiency with respect to current equal zero for the maximum efficiency condition. For the minimum regulation case, regulation would be zero.

Assume 0.8 power factor. Let η = % efficiency and I = secondary current. Then:

$$\eta = \frac{11 \times 0.80\ I}{(11 \times 0.80\ I) + 5.5 + (1 \times I^2)/1000} \times 100$$

$$\text{Let } \frac{d\eta}{dI} = \frac{8.8(0.001\ I^2 + 8.8\ I + 5.5) - (8.8\ I)(0.002\ I + 8.8)}{(0.001\ I^2 + 8.8\ I + 5.5)^2} = 0$$

$$I = 74$$

$\eta = 652/663 \times 100 = 98\%$ *Answer, part (a)*

Output $= 11 \times 74 \times 0.8 = 650$ kW (814 kVA) *Answer, part (b)*

(c) For minimum voltage regulation (see Fig. 2-9; occurs with leading power factor):

At 1000 kVA,

$$I = 1000/11 = 91 \text{ amps}$$

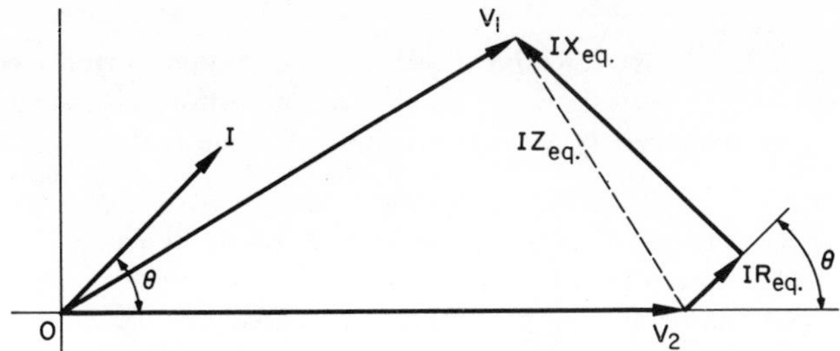

Figure 2-9

$$|V_1| = |V_2| = 11 \text{ kV}$$

$$V_1 = V_2 + 91(\cos\theta + j\sin\theta)(1 + j4.9)$$

$$= V_2 + 91\,(\cos\theta - 4.9\sin\theta) + j91(4.9\cos\theta + \sin\theta)$$

The power factor angle can be readily found by plotting on graph paper:

Step 1: Describe an arc centered at V_2 with radius of $IZ_{eq} = 91 \times 5 = 455$ volts.

Step 2: Describe an arc centered at 0 with radius of $V_2 = 11{,}000$ volts.

Step 3: At the intersection of the arcs, mark V_1.

Step 4: Describe an arc centered at V_1 with radius $IX_{eq} = 91 \times 4.9 = 446$ volts.

Step 5: Draw IR_{eq} and measure θ (= 12°)

Power factor = $\cos\theta = 0.98$ (leading) *Answer*

(d) For maximum regulation, it will be seen that this occurs with lagging power factor when V_1 lies along the horizontal axis, or

$$IR\sin\theta = IX\cos\theta$$

$$\tan\theta = 4.9$$

$$\theta = 78.5^\circ$$

Power factor = $\cos 78.5^\circ = 0.2$ (lagging) *Answer*

(e) If the frequency is 50 Hz,

1. Core loss will be less for the same flux. X_{eq} will be less.

2. Losses will be less and regulation better (lower) for given load and power factor.

Problem 2-5 Open-delta transformer connection on three-phase system

A bank of three 13,200/4160-volt transformers, each rated at 833 kVA, 60 Hz, and connected delta-delta, feeds a short distribution line that is terminated in a bank of three 833-kVA 4160/480-volt transformers with a 1600-kVA, 0.8 power factor lagging load.

(a) If one of the 13,200/4160-volt transformers burns out, what would the voltage, current, and capacitance rating of capacitors on the secondary side of the 4160/480-volt transformers be to prevent overloading of any transformer? (b) What would the capacitor ratings be if connected on the primary side of the 4160/480-volt transformers? Neglect line impedance.

Solution:

(a) In the open-delta connection, line current equals phase current; consequently, the system rating is less than the full-delta connection. If transformer impedance is ignored, a balanced symmetrical system (voltage and current) may be assumed.

Rated current per transformer at 13,200 volts is 833/13.2 = 63 amps.
Actual current per transformer (1600 kVA, 0.8 power factor): $1600/\sqrt{3} \times 13.2 =$ 70.0 amps (with open-delta connection). Therefore, kVA must be reduced to $63/70 \times 1600 = 1440$ kVA.
Real power = $0.8 \times 1600 = 1280$ kW.
Reactive kVA without capacitors = $[(1600)^2 - (1280)^2]^{1/2} = 960$ kvar (lagging).
Reactive kVA with capacitors = $[(1440)^2 - (1280)^2]^{1/2} = 663$ kvar (lagging).
Capacitive kvar required = $960 - 663 = 297 \cong 300$ kvar.

If installed at the 480-volt level, 100-kvar single-phase capacitors are required per phase, for operation at 480 volts, 60 Hz. The current through this capacitor bank will be 100/0.480 = 208 amps per phase. *Answer, part (a)*

(b) If installed at the 4160-volt level, the bank of three 100-kvar capacitors should be specified for operation at 4160 volts line-to-line, ungrounded, and the current will be 24 amps per phase. *Answer, part (b)*

Problem 2-6 Transformer rating to limit motor starting voltage dip

A 500-kVA transformer is used to step down the voltage of a 13.2-kV 3-phase supply to 440 volts. The transformer has a 5% impedance. The transformer supplies a load consisting of a group of induction motors and a lighting transformer.

Because the dip in voltage caused by induction motor starting produces light flicker, it is decided to limit this dip to 3%. The following assumptions are made:

1. The power line voltage remains constant.
2. Circuit resistances are negligible.
3 Motor starting current is six times full-load current.
4. Full-load efficiency and power factor of the motors are 0.90 and 0.83, respectively.

What is the maximum size of motor that can be started without exceeding 3% voltage dip on starting?

Solution:

Since the transformer loading prior to starting is not given, we shall assume that primary taps are provided to permit rated voltage at full load.

The ratio of motor starting kVA to the transformer rating multiplied by the transformer percent impedance must not exceed 3%. Although starting power factor is important in calculating line drop and overall system power factor, it is not required to solve this problem.

Starting kVA of motor:

$$\frac{6 \times 0.746 \times \text{hp}}{\text{Eff} \times \text{P.F.}} = \frac{(6)(0.746)(\text{hp})}{(0.90)(0.83)}$$

$$= 6 \times \text{hp}$$

$$\frac{6 \times \text{hp}}{500} \times 0.05 = 0.03$$

$$\text{hp} = 50 \qquad \textit{Answer}$$

Problem 2-7 Transformer core loss (eddy current and hysteresis)

A test of a transformer yields the following data:

Core loss at 60 Hz: 240 watts (120 volts applied to primary).

Core loss at 25 Hz: 50 watts (50 volts applied to primary).

Calculate the eddy current loss for this transformer when 240 volts is applied to the primary winding at 60 Hz.

Solution:

Core loss = hysteresis loss + eddy-current loss

$$P_c = K_h f B^n_{max} + K_e f^2 B^2_{max}$$

Since $\Phi \propto E/f$, both sets of data are based on the same B_{max}. Therefore, write and solve the two simultaneous equations.

$$P_c(25\ \text{Hz}) = 25\ K_1 + (25)^2 K_2 = 50$$

$$P_c(60\ \text{Hz}) = 60\ K_1 + (60)^2 K_2 = 240$$

$$K_1 = 0.571$$

$$K_2 = 0.0571$$

Eddy-current loss at 60 Hz is $0.0571 \times 3600 = 205$ watts. At 240 volts, flux density has doubled; therefore, the eddy-current loss is $205 \times 2^2 = 820$ watts. *Answer*

chapter 3
THE NATIONAL ELECTRICAL CODE

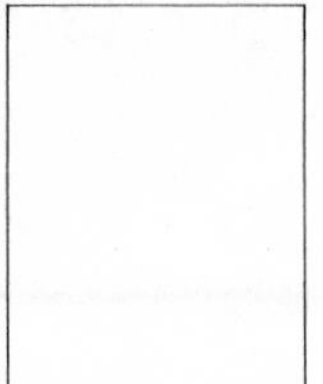

The National Electrical Code is a minimum standard suitable for use by municipal, state, and national regulatory bodies and insurance inspectors. Electrical installations in compliance with this code are not necessarily in compliance with all municipal and state codes. This code is not to be confused with the National Electrical Safety Code (National Bureau of Standards Handbook H30), which is an advisory and suggested mandatory code for electrical supply stations, underground and overhead distribution and transmission lines, industrial installations, and radio receiving and transmitting stations. In some states, the license examinations require familiarity with the National Electrical Safety Code or its state counterpart (for example, in California, General Order No. 95 of the Public Utilities Commission).

Much of the apparent complexity of the National Electrical Code vanishes if the more commonly used articles are understood and tabulated for ready reference.

3-1 QUICK REFERENCE INDEX TO FREQUENTLY USED ARTICLES

Branch Circuits and Taps

Grounding: Article 210–7 (use of cable armor or metallic raceway)
Conductors: Article 210–19
Overcurrent protection: Article 210–20
Devices: Article 210–21 (lampholders)
  Article 210–22 (minimum number of receptacles)
  Article 210–23 (maximum operating load)
  Article 210–24 (connected load)
Branch circuits 220–3 (number required)

Feeders

Feeders connect the incoming supply to the branch circuits.
Calculation of load: Article 220–2 (minimum requirements; total load)

Article 220-4 (permissible demand factors; neutrals)
Article 220-5 (ranges and cooking appliances)
Article 220-7 (simplified method for one-family residences)
Conductor size: Article 215-2
Voltage drop: Article 215-3
Common neutral: Article 215-5

Overcurrent Protection

Overcurrent protection: Article 240
(Table 240-28)
Conductors: Article 240-5
Article 240-6 (fuses)
Article 240-7 (nonadjustable-trip circuit breakers)
Article 240-14 (fuses in multiple)
Article 240-23 (voltage and current ratings)
Article 240-25 (circuit breakers; requirements for noninterchangeable trips)

Grounding

A-c systems: Article 250-5
Article 250-23 (grounding conductor on load side of service switch is not to be connected to grounding electrode)
Article 250-34 to 250-40 (lightning rod clearances)
Equipment grounding: Article 250-42 to 250-45
Ground resistance: Article 250-57, -59, -84.
Size of grounding conductors: Article 250-94, -95

Wiring Methods

(600 volts and less)
Conductor application: Article 310-2
Article 310-8 (minimum sizes)
Tables 310-12 to 310-15 (current-carrying capacities)
Nonmetallic sheathed cable: Article 336 (some local codes forbid this)
Radius of conduit bends: Article 346-10
Electrical metallic tubing: Article 348-1 (this thin-wall tubing is not permitted in many localities)
Clearances of switchboards: Article 384-4 to 384-8
Flexible cords, fixture wire, fixtures and lamp holders, electrical discharge fixtures and transformers: Article 400

Motors, Motor Circuits, and Controllers

Locked rotor kVA: Table 430-7(b)
Motor circuit conductors: Article 430-22 to 430-27
Motor overload protection: Article 430-31 to 430-40
Motor branch-circuit protection: Article 430-52 to 430-59

Controllers: Article 430–81 to 110 (ratings)
Motor full-load current: Tables 430–147 to 430–150

Transformers

Overcurrent protection: Article 450–3

Power Factor Correction

Size and method of discharge: Article 460–5 and 6
Current-carrying capacity (of conductors): Article 460–8

3-2 EXPLANATION OF RULES PERTAINING TO MOTOR PROTECTION

Table 430–37 of the National Electrical Code specifies that "three running overcurrent devices shall be used where 3-phase motors are installed in isolated, inaccessible, or unattended locations, unless the motor is protected by other approved means." This is to protect against single-phasing where the power supply is from wye-delta transformers.

Single-Phasing. If one phase of a 3-phase circuit supplying an induction motor is open and the motor is delta connected, the currents through the overload relays will not change percentagewise as much as the current through the motor winding. Twice normal current would flow in one winding, for normal horsepower, versus 1.73 times normal for the unaffected feeders.

In the case of a wye-connected motor, the change in line current is the same as the change in winding current. The addition of a third overload element will not help this situation; therefore, the overload elements should be sized as closely as is feasible. However, if the power supply is from a wye-delta transformer and if a primary feeder becomes open-circuited, one of the secondary feeders for normal horsepower will have twice normal current. If this happens to be the phase without the overload element, the motor will be greatly unprotected, especially wye-connected motors.

If the motor is delta-connected, two of the phase windings will carry 1.73 times normal current. The basic controller is shown in Fig. 3-1.

3-3 CAPACITOR APPLICATIONS

Caution must be used in applying capacitors. The Institute of Electrical and Electronics Engineers (IEEE) and the National Electrical Manufacturers Association (NEMA) prescribe rules to follow, which may be found in manufacturer catalogs. This information, presented in tabular form, covers

1. Minimum ampere ratings for capacitor switching devices.
2. Maximum kvar ratings that should be associated with squirrel-cage induction motors of given horsepower and NEMA Design Class.
3. Maximum kvar ratings that should not be exceeded when capacitors are

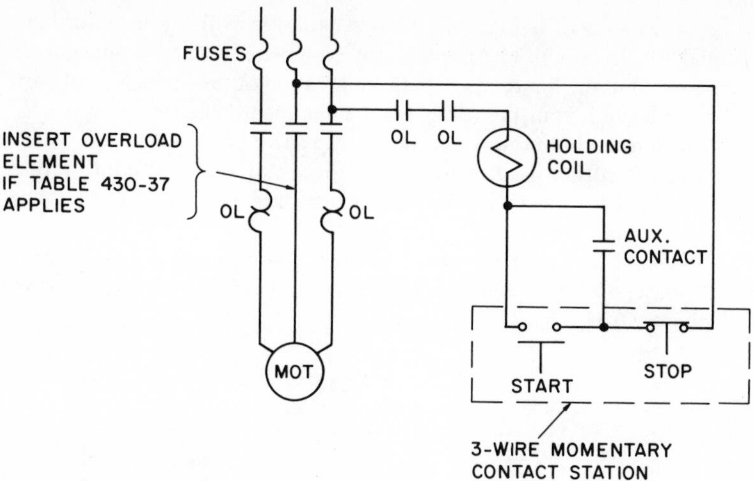

Figure 3-1

installed on the load side of transformers; generally, this value should not exceed 75% of the transformer kVA rating.

Wherever large inertia loads taking power supply from an automatic transfer switch are to be associated with power-factor corrective capacitors, an individual study should be made to ensure against injurious overvoltages or overcurrents incident upon restoration of supply; time delay may be necessary in the transfer switch operation.

3-4 HAZARDOUS LOCATIONS

Article 500 defines areas and conditions, and classifies flammable and explosive substances. The application of this article requires knowledge of practices in the pertinent industries. For example, Recommended Practice 500 of the American Petroleum Institute (API) details a method of classifying Division 1 and Division 2 locations, relative to the source of vapors and to ambient conditions. Most industries and insurance inspectors now subscribe to the following philosophy: Division 2 locations are those in which flammable or explosive substances are not normally present. In such areas, general-purpose nonarcing devices, such as a squirrel-cage induction motor, are deemed acceptable, provided they are protected against weather or other deterioration. Arcing devices, however, must meet the requirements of a Division 1 area, if an ignitable substance could be present under abnormal conditions. In Division 1 locations, even though a device is nonarcing, it must be of a design suitable for Division 1 locations, unless the device is intrinsically safe even under electrical breakdown conditions.

PROBLEMS

Problem 3-1 Design of motor control and circuitry to conform with the National Electrical Code

Two new motors, No. 1 rated at 75 hp and No. 2 rated at 10 hp, are to be installed in a plant location as shown in Fig. 3-2. This installation is to be in accordance with the National Electrical Code. Approximate dimensions of the plant and the smaller room are given in the figure, as well as the location of the main switchboard. Both motors are to be fed from the same main switchboard feeder.

Assume for distances that motors are at the respective corners and the switchboard is located at the corner as shown. Design the installation including ratings of all circuit breakers, disconnect switches, conductor sizes, and any other requirement for this installation.

Motors are 4-pole (1750-rpm) induction motors of a general-purpose type, rated 220/440 volts, 3-phase, 60 Hz, and are to be operated on 220 volts. Service voltage is 240 volts, 3-phase, 60 Hz.

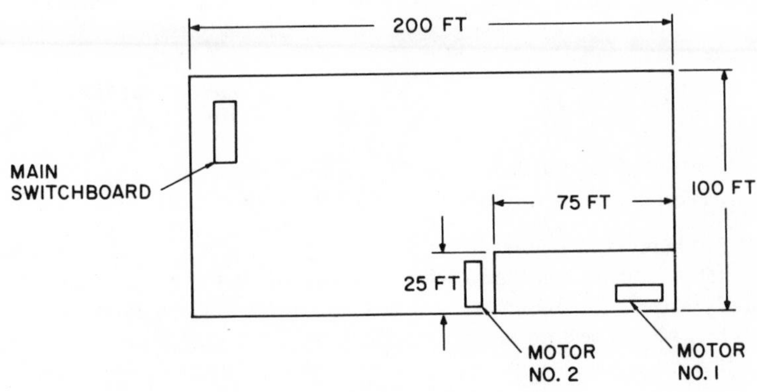

Figure 3-2

Solution:

This is primarily an exercise in applying the pertinent articles of the NEC, with attention paid to the requirement that motor operating devices be visible from the motor location.

Referring to Fig. 3-3,

FLC[1]	*C*[2]	*B*[3]	*A*[4]
10 hp 27 A	35 A	70 A	Refer to fig. 3-4.
75 hp 185 A	250 A	500 A (462)*	

[1] Table 430–150
[2] Table 430–146, column 2 (nonadjustable trip)
[3] Table 430–146, column 4 (circuit breaker)
[4] Article 430–62
* Table 430-153

To obtain motor feeder size,

$27 + (1.25 \times 185) = 259$ amps (Article 430–24)

Use 350 MCM TW (Table 310–12)

Use 3-in. rigid steel conduit (NEC Table 1, Chapter 9)

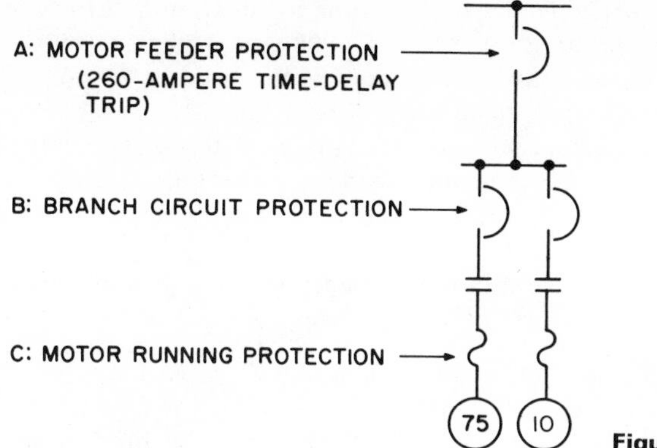

Figure 3-3

Voltage drop check:

0.032 ohms/1000 ft (NEC Table 8, Chapter 9)

$0.3 \times (185 + 27) \times 0.032 = 2.0$ volts

As this is less than 3% maximum specified by Article 215-3, it is satisfactory.

Table 430-153 permits $2.5 \times$ FLC or 462 amps. This is raised to the next higher standard rating in Table 430-146, which is consistent with Articles 240-7 and 430-59. *Note:* If the starting current is more than 300% of FLC, Article 430-52 allows $4 \times$ FLC, which in this case would be 740 amps!

Figure 3-3 and the trip settings given constitute a literal interpretation of the code. Actually, if the conductor size remains unchanged [except for a short length connecting the two starters—see Article 430-53 (b) (5) in Fig. 3-4], only motor running protection need be provided at the motor corner of the building, and the branch circuit protection can be combined with the feeder overcurrent protective device at the main switchboard, as shown in Fig. 3-4.

Problem 3-2 Motor overload protection and voltage drop

A machine that processes chemical materials has an electric motor and a group

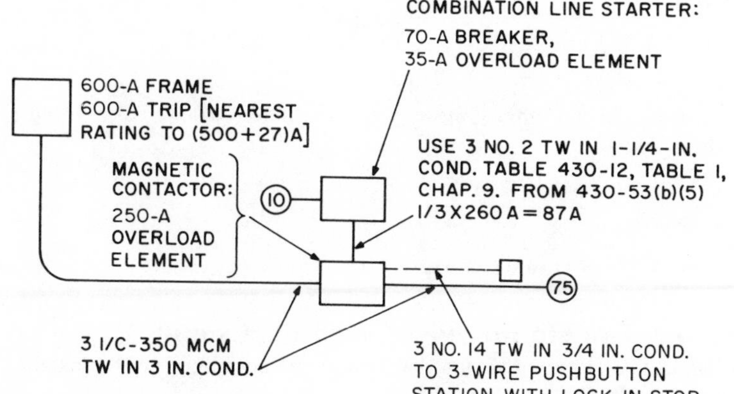

Figure 3-4

of heating elements. The feeder to the motor comes from a distribution center 200 feet away from the motor, where there is a 208-volt, 3-phase, 60-Hz power supply. The motor is a 3-phase class A induction motor rated at 25 hp at 208 volts, 60 Hz. There are three heaters rated at 7.5 kW at 120 volts.

Determine (a) the total power to be supplied to this machine, (b) the wire size to be used in the feeder, and (c) the overload protection.

Solution:

Elements involved here are motor overload protection, branch circuit protection, conductor sizing, and a check of voltage drop.

Motor full-load current (Table 430–150): $1.06 \times 64 = 68$ amps.
Heater current: $7500/120 = 62.5$ amps.
Conductor sizing (Article 430–24): $(1.25 \times 68) + 62.5 = 147.5$ amps.
Wire size (Table 310–12): Use 3/0 RW (unless provision for future expansion is desired).
If heaters are separately switched, use No. 4 neutral wire.
Starting current of motor (Table 430–7b):

$$\text{kVA/hp} = 3.14$$

$$\frac{3.14 \times 25}{\sqrt{3} \times 208} = 218 \text{ amps}$$

Motor running protection (Table 430–146, column 2): 90 amps (nonadjustable).
Branch circuit protection: From Table 430–152, we would use 150% of full-load current; however, this would not handle the starting current. Article 430–52 permits up to 400% of FLC. Assume 200-amp time delay is satisfactory. If we let this device also handle the heaters: $200 + 62.5 = 262.5$ or the nearest trip setting. *Note:* Because of the speed of low-tension devices, this breaker should have adequate short-circuit interrupting capacity (as must also the main-feeder protective device). Protect the heaters with 70-amp fuses.
Total power: Assume 80% power factor for the motor. Motor power requirement is

$$\frac{\sqrt{3} \times 208 \times 68 \times 0.8}{1000} = 19.6 \text{ kW}$$

$$\text{Heaters: } 3 \times 7.5 = 22.5 \text{ kW}$$

$$\text{Total} = 42.1 \text{ kW}$$

Voltage drop (Article 215–3): Ohms/phase is approximately 0.0642 from Table 8, Chapter 9 of the Code.

$$\frac{100 \times (68 + 62.5)(0.0642 \times 0.2)}{120} = 1.4\%$$

As this is below 3%, it is satisfactory.

Problem 3-3 Transformer vault with dual supply

Figure 3-5 indicates the proposed wiring diagram of the equipment to be installed in the transformer vault of a hospital.

Transformer data are

1. Rating: 500 kVA, 3 phase, 60 Hz.
2. The line-to-line supply voltage is 4160 volts.
3. The fuses are to be rated at 80 amps and the feeder cables will be No. 4.
4. Because continuity of service is of prime importance, two feeders, each of which can carry the full load, are brought in from the generating station in underground conduits.
5. There will be 80-amp fuses at the generator end of the feeders.
6. Only one feeder will be connected at a time, and interlocks on the switches will be used to make this certain.

Are there any aspects of this plan which you would refuse to approve? Explain.

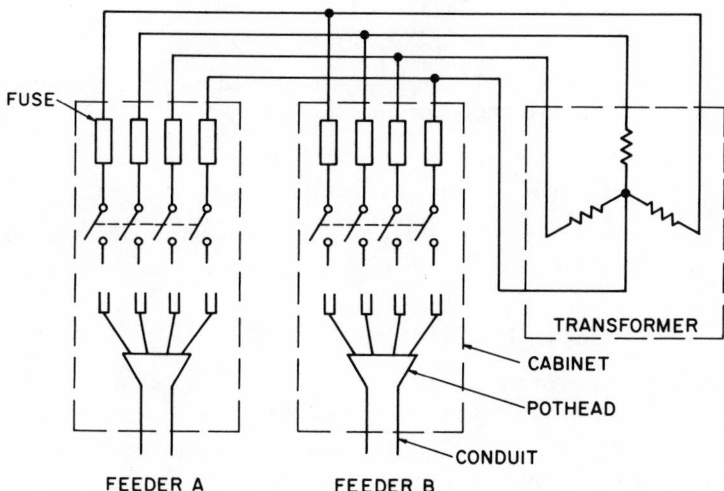

Figure 3-5

Solution:

1. Neutral must not be fused. Blowing of that fuse would cause a rise in voltage to ground.
2. Each set of fused switches should have isolators on the load side to permit safe maintenance.
3. Each set of fuses should be ganged, to prevent single-phasing, if these are load-break switches.
4. If secondary overload protection equal to or greater than 250% of rated transformer capacity is provided, these fuses are unnecessary per Article 450–3b of the code. Fuses at the source end should then be uprated to prevent fuse blowing or deterioration upon surges or motor starting currents. They can be rated at least 4×90 if necessary.
5. A delta-wye transformer is preferred from the standpoint of harmonics and availability. Utilization voltage is probably 120/208. Incoming supply would then be 3-wire.
6. Interrupting duty and fuse-holder rating should be checked.

Problem 3-4 National Electrical Code conductor sizing and voltage class

Indicate the correct answer to the following questions. If the correct answer is not shown, indicate None:

(a) The largest stranded conductor that may be connected by means of screws to terminal plates is AWG No.

4	6	8	10	12
14	16	18	20	None

(b) An AWG No. 10 Type R conductor shall have an insulation thickness in inches of

1/64	1/50	1/32	1/25	3/64
3/50	1/16	2/25	5/64	None

(c) Lampholders in multiple off a single switch installed over highly combustible material should be located above the floor, in feet, by at least

7	7½	8	8½	9
9½	10	11	12	None

(d) The lowest voltage in volts for a class 2 remote-control circuit having overcurrent protection of 3.2 amps is

6	12	18	24	30
36	50	60	80	None

(e) The highest voltage in volts at which Askarel-insulated transformers may be installed indoors without being enclosed in a vault is

2400	4160	6000	6900	8000
10,000	11,000	12,000	15,000	None

(f) By definition, except for certain special cases, a high-voltage circuit is any circuit having a difference of potential in rms volts between any two conductors in excess of

240	300	360	460	500
600	800	1000	1100	None

(g) The highest current density in amps per square inch for bare copper conductor feeders when permitted in ventilated enclosures is

600	800	1000	1200	1400
1600	1800	2000	2400	None

(h) The greatest distance, in feet, that a fixed motor of one horsepower or less in size may be from its terminal enclosure is

2	3	4	5	6
8	10	15	20	None

(i) The smallest AWG conductor size for a 30-amp branch circuit is

16	14	12	10	8
6	4	2	0	None

(j) The smallest AWG conductor size to supply a single professional type motion picture projector is

16	14	12	10	8
6	4	2	0	None

Solution:

The license examination from which this problem was taken referred half of the problems to that state's electrical code. Although the following solution is based primarily on the National Electrical Code, attention is invited to the existence of the National Electrical Safety Code (National Bureau of Standards Handbook H30), which covers grounding, installation of electrical equipment, underground and overhead distribution and transmission lines, operation of equipment and lines, and rules for radio installations. There are minor differences between the N.E.C., the N.E.S.C., and codes issued by some states.

(a) 10 *Answer* (Article 110–13)

(b) 3/64 *Answer* [Table 310–2(b)]

(c) None *Answer* Article 503 refers to Class III (hazardous) installations. The main requirement is that the equipment itself is of the type approved for the location.

(d) 15 *Answer* [Article 725–3, 725–31(b)]

(e) 15,000 *Answer* [Article 450–23]

(f) None *Answer* Most codes refrain from using the term high voltage, but rather classify circuits as low energy, etc., or give rules pertaining to supply circuits up to 750 volts, 7500 volts, etc. Typical pertinent articles are N.E.C.: Article 300–2, 310–2(d)(5), 710, 720, 725; N.E.S.C.: Sec. 1, para. 45 and 47.

(g) 1000 *Answer* [Article 374–6 (*continuous* current in bare copper bus in auxiliary gutters)]

(h) 6 *Answer* [Article 430–145(b)]

(i) 10 *Answer* (Table 210–25)

(j) 8 *Answer* (Article 540–13)

chapter 4
MACHINERY

From Faraday's observation $e = N(d\phi/dt)$, or more generally, $e = d\lambda/dt$, basic expressions are derived for electrical machinery (just as for the transformer $E = 4.44fN\phi_{max}$, where ϕ varies sinusoidally with time and E is in rms volts). The expression for force on a current-carrying conductor in a magnetic field $F = Bli$ is also derived from observation; it is only necessary to use the identity hp = 2π (rpm)(torque)/33,000, and to use a compatible system of units to obtain the necessary formulas for torque and power for an electromagnetic-mechanical system. These formulas are then modified to compensate for armature reaction and the nonlinear characteristics of the magnetic circuit. It is convenient, dependent on the type of machine under consideration, to vary the approach (flux cutting, change-of-linkages, or transformer action) for analysis; the basic premise remains Faraday's law.

Regardless of the type of machine, for a torque to be developed, two conditions must exist: There must be an angle in space between the axes of the opposing mmf's, and this angle must remain essentially constant.

4-1 D-C MACHINES

For a d-c motor or generator, the induced emf in the armature is

$$E = \frac{Z}{a} p\phi \frac{n}{60} = k_1\phi n$$

where ϕ = flux per pole, webers

a = number of armature paths in parallel

Z = number of armature conductors

n = rpm

p = number of poles

If the armature is lap-wound, a = p = the number of brushes required; for a wave-wound armature, a = 2, and the number of brushes required is 2 although more are generally used to reduce the current at the segment undergoing commutation.

The expression for torque is

$$T = \frac{60}{2\pi} k_1 \phi I_a = k_2 \phi I_a$$

where T = torque, newton-meters; and I_a = armature current.

It is assumed that flux distribution in the air gap surrounding the rotor is uniform, approximating a square wave. This wave is distorted by the armature mmf, and this armature reaction limits the short time rating of d-c (especially shunt-wound) machines. Shifting of the brushes helps to overcome this effect by shifting the axis of the armature mmf. Also, compensating field windings are inserted in the pole faces.

Interpoles are usually inserted between the main poles to counteract the induced emf that exists in the coil being commutated.

The equivalent circuit of a d-c machine is shown in Fig. 4-1. Figure 4-2 shows the power flow diagram.

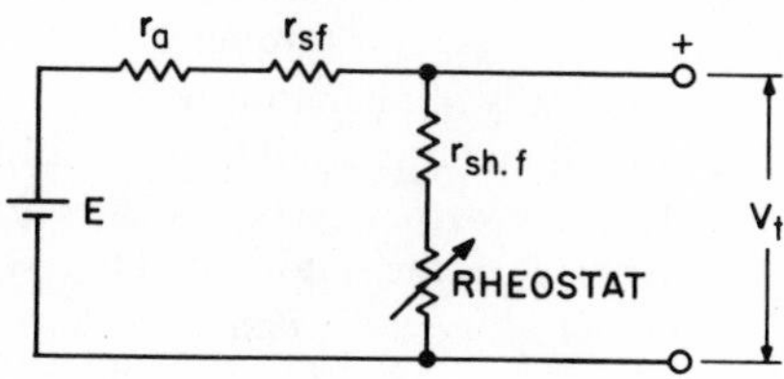

Figure 4-1. *Note:* Subscript a is the armature; sf is the series field; and sh. f is the shunt field. V_t is the terminal voltage.

The magnetization curve of a d-c machine is generally a plot of E (volts/rpm) versus field ampere-turns per pole.

The primary consideration in the control of a d-c motor is that under no condition may the armature be energized if the field circuit becomes open-circuited or if the field current becomes dangerously low. With the exception of fractional horsepower motors, full voltage is never impressed across the motor terminals at standstill or before the field is energized. Both the automatic starter and the manu-

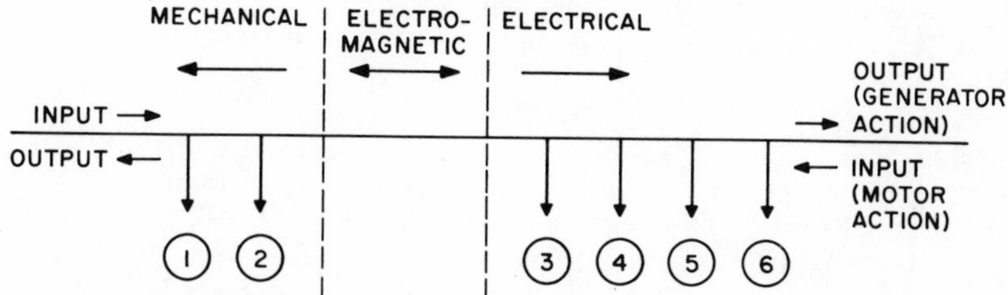

Figure 4-2. Power flow in a d-c machine. *Note:* 1 is the no-load rotational losses (includes core loss); 2 is the stray losses; 3 is the $I_a^2 r_a$ (armature copper loss); 4 is the brush loss; 5 is the series field copper loss; and 6 is the shunt field copper loss.

ally operated four-point starter include the necessary protective device. In the case of the series motor, the driven equipment must never be disconnected from the motor when the latter is energized.

The primary consideration in the operation of a self-excited generator is that the field circuit resistance be below the critical value to permit the buildup of rated terminal voltage.

4-2 THE POLYPHASE INDUCTION MOTOR

When a polyphase winding, wrapped around the stator of a machine, is energized, the resultant field rotates at a speed in rpm equal to 120f/p (the synchronous speed). The mmf of the rotor current set up by the induced voltage in an induction motor rotates at this same speed with respect to the stator under all conditions. The axis of this rotating mmf is displaced from the axis of the stator field, and the basic condition for torque exists at all times. The rotor itself rotates at $(1 - s) \times$ synchronous speed, where s is the *slip*. The slip can never become unity, since there would be no induced rotor emf and hence no torque.

At standstill, the induction motor is electrically similar to a transformer with a short-circuited secondary. Under other conditions, it is similar to a transformer under load. Its equivalent circuit, with values shown per phase, is shown in Fig. 4-3. From Fig. 4-3, I_s is the stator (input) current; R_s is the stator winding resistance; X_s is the stator leakage reactance; R_c is the core-loss equivalent resistance; X_ϕ is the magnetizing equivalent reactance; V_t is the terminal voltage; I_e is the excitation current (about 30% to 40% of full-load current); E is the induced emf in the rotor at standstill (referred to the stator in accordance with the turns ratio); R_r is the total rotor circuit resistance (referred to the stator); X_r is the rotor leakage reactance at standstill (referred to the stator); and I_{LOAD} is the rotor current (referred to the stator).

For determining the expected performance of an existing machine, it is usually adequate to use the simplified equivalent circuit of Fig. 4-4; parameters can be obtained by a few simple measurements. From Fig. 4-4,

$$V_t' = V_t - I_{NO\ LOAD}(R_s + jX_s)$$

where $I_{NO\ LOAD}$ = stator current at no load

$(R_s + jX_s)$ = synchronous impedance

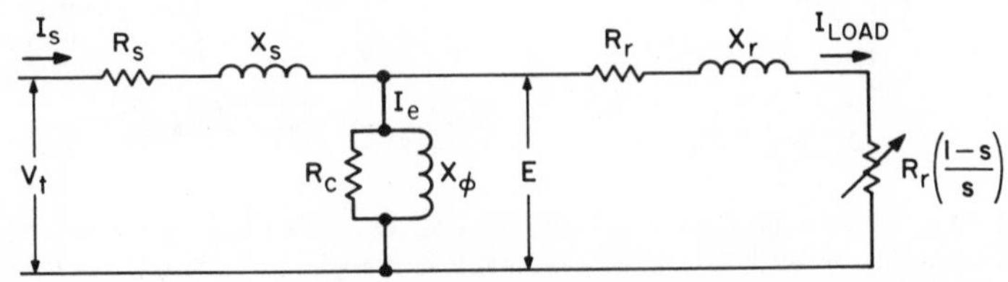

Figure 4-3. Equivalent circuit of the polyphase induction motor.

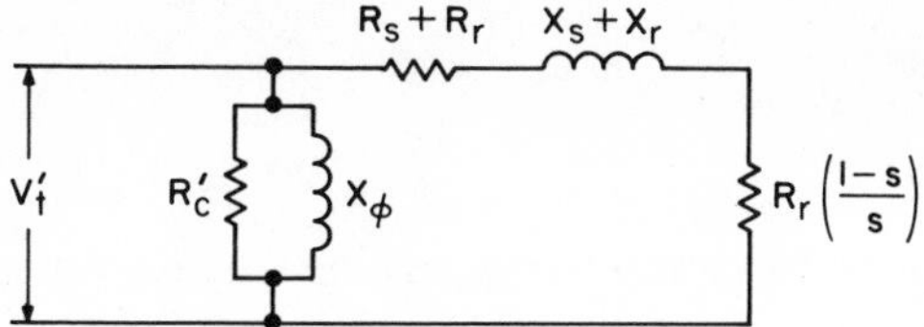

Figure 4-4

and $R_c' = R_c$ plus an equivalent resistance to account for windage, friction, and stray losses.

Using Fig. 4-4, the total power output is

$$P \text{ (watts)} = \frac{3(V_t')^2(1 - s)sR_r}{(sR_s + R_r)^2 + s^2(X_r + X_s)^2} = 3I_r^2R_r\left(\frac{1 - s}{s}\right)$$

The no-load test is similar to the open-circuit test of a transformer. The measured power, less the no-load copper losses, equals the rotational and core losses of the motor.

The locked rotor test is similar to the short-circuit test of a transformer, and is performed with a low impressed voltage. If P_{lr} is the measured power input, V_{lr} is the line voltage, and I_{lr} is the measured line current, then the per-phase values of the series parameters are

$$R_s + R_r = P_{lr}/3\ I_{lr}^2$$

$$X_s + X_r = \sqrt{\left(\frac{V_{lr}}{\sqrt{3}\ I_{lr}}\right)^2 - (R_s + R_r)^2}$$

The circle diagram, see Fig. 4-5, is useful to determine the performance data for varying load conditions. The vertical ordinates represent the real components of current; they can also represent real power, or torque, using the proper constants of proportionality (voltage and synchronous speed, respectively).

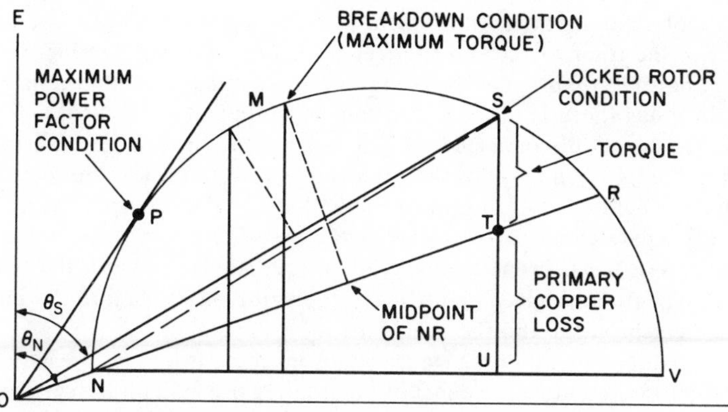

Figure 4-5. Circle diagram of the induction motor.

Example

Primary I^2R loss with a locked rotor is

$$[(OS)^2 - (ON)^2] \times R_s$$

If R_s is per phase, then the above value is divided by the terminal voltage per phase and plotted as UT on the circle diagram.

Example

Locked rotor torque can be obtained from

$$\frac{ST \times \sqrt{3}E \times 33{,}000}{746 \times 2\pi N_s} \text{ lb-ft}$$

where N_s = rpm.

To construct the circle diagram of Fig. 4-5, the following data is required:

1. The terminal voltage (direction is along OE).
2. The no-load current and phase angle (ON and θ_N).
3. The locked-rotor current and phase angle (OS and θ_s).
4. The stator resistance (R_s; use direct current).
5. The stator copper loss (calculate this to locate point T on line SU).

To construct the diagram, draw a circle through N and S, centered on NV. Locate point T.

4-3 THE SYNCHRONOUS MOTOR

Since there are two independent variables (load and excitation), a circle diagram as used for the induction motor is not adequate. However, most problems of motor application can be solved through the use of a simplified equivalent diagram and V-curves.

The synchronous motor itself has no starting torque, since the angle between the axes of the two mmf's is not constant. It must, therefore, be connected as an induction motor for starting. Amortisseur or damping windings are inserted in the pole faces of the rotor to act as a squirrel-cage rotor winding. During the starting period, the normal rotating field windings are discharged through a resistor. When near-synchronous speed is reached, d-c voltage is applied to the field and then the discharge resistor is disconnected. When synchronous speed is almost reached, considering the low frequency of the rotor mmf (with respect to the rotating stator field), the two field axes during the positive half of the low-frequency cycle are substantially separated in space to establish the condition for "pull-in" torque. When the motor acts as a synchronous motor, the torque angle (between the two mmf's rotating at synchronous speed) must reach the value of 90° before the motor will pull out of synchronism and the motor must be shut down.

The equivalent circuit of the synchronous machine is that of a reactor in series with voltage E representing the effect of the rotating d-c field on the stator windings (see Fig. 4-6).

Unfortunately, stator leakage reactance X_s is not constant because of the

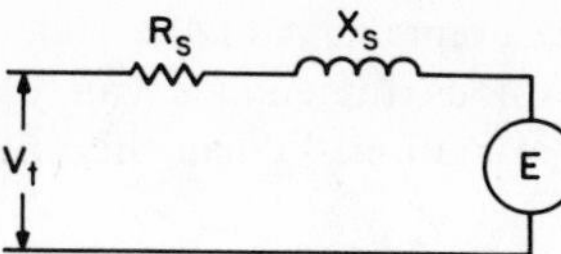

Figure 4-6. Equivalent circuit of the synchronous machine. *Note:* R_s is the stator winding resistance; X_s is the self-inductive reactance of the stator winding only; and $R_s + jX_s$ is the synchronous impedance.

nonlinearity of the magnetic circuit. Also, the saliency of the rotor structure introduces a *reluctance torque* that is superimposed on the normal torque of the synchronous machine. For estimating purposes, X_s is adjusted for the operating point in question. An open-circuit characteristic (saturation) curve can be determined experimentally by opening the stator winding and measuring V_t for various values of field current.

The total power transferred from the stator to the rotor is given by

$$P = 3 \times \frac{V_t E}{X_s} \sin \delta$$

where δ = angle between V_t and E.

V-curves can be obtained experimentally or by computation from the equivalent circuit. This family of curves should be obtained from the manufacturer when a synchronous machine is purchased. See Fig. 4-7.

Leading power factor is obtained by increasing excitation. The phasor relationship is shown in Fig. 4-8. *Note:* Assume a Y-connected machine and use

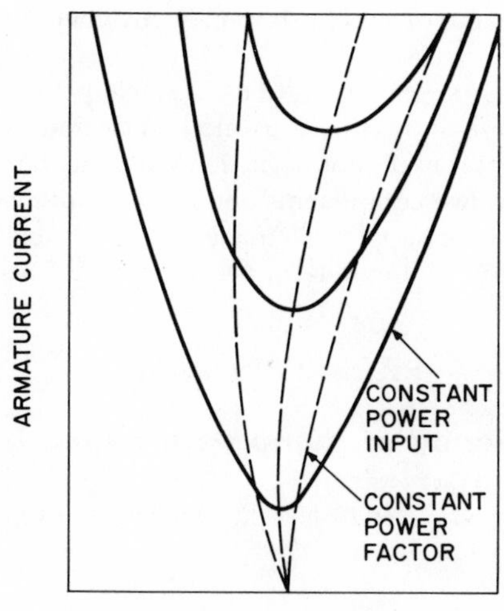

Figure 4-7

Figure 4-8. V-curves of a synchronous motor.

per-phase values. Resistance is obtained by direct measurement. Add the stator core-loss component to obtain R_s (effective). Synchronous impedance can be obtained from short-circuit tests for various values of excitation. X_s can then be calculated.

$$IZ_s = V_t - E \qquad \text{(phasor quantities)}$$

For efficiency calculations, windage and stray losses are obtained by subtracting armature copper losses from input at no load. Field copper losses should not be overlooked.

4-4 OTHER TYPES OF MOTORS

From the foregoing, it is evident that the type of motor to be selected depends on the service required. For integral horsepower sizes, the d-c motor accommodates itself to various load-speed requirements. The polyphase induction motor is a relatively inexpensive, essentially constant-speed motor that is offered in various NEMA designs to suit starting torque and starting current requirements (the wound rotor offers a form of speed control, if efficiency is no obstacle, and provides a means of lowering the starting current). The synchronous motor, besides its constant-speed characteristic, constitutes an excellent power factor corrective device. In addition, there is the a-c series motor (single-phase) that is used in 25-Hz traction service. Unfortunately, commutation of alternating current introduces difficulties that prohibit use of this motor from normal power, frequency applications except in fractional horsepower high-speed (1500 to 15,000 rpm) applications. The repulsion motor is similar to the series motor except that magnetic coupling is used instead of electrical coupling.

For most fractional horsepower applications, a single-phase motor operating either on the induction motor or synchronous motor principle (or both, one for starting, the other for running) is used. For induction motor action, the single-phase input is deliberately split into two components out of phase with each other so that the machine "sees" a two-phase supply. Characteristics of fractional horsepower motors are briefly summarized in Table 4-1.

PROBLEMS

Problem 4-1 Efficiency of pump determined by direct-current motor

A direct-current shunt motor was used to test the efficiency of a pump. Data taken during the test:

Line voltage	242 volts
Line current	82.8 amps
Armature current	80.0 amps
Speed	1200 rpm
Head of water	9.25 ft
Rate of flow	1200 cu ft/min

The machines were uncoupled and the motor was operated at 1200 rpm with

2.8-amp field current. Data taken during the test:

Armature voltage	160 volts
Armature current	5.6 amps

To measure armature resistance, 80 amps was observed when the voltage across the brush pigtails was 6.2 volts.

Compute the efficiency of the pump.

Solution:

This is an application of the definition

$$\text{Eff} = 1 - \frac{\text{pump losses}}{\text{pump output} + \text{pump losses}}$$

Table 4-1 Characteristics of Fractional Horsepower Motors

	Direct-Current Motors
Series	Adjustable speed, high starting torque. Used for very small (fan) drives.
Shunt and Compound	Adjustable speed, high starting torque. Used in sizes up to $\frac{3}{8}$ hp.
Universal:	
Compensated and uncompensated	Varying speed, nonreversible, high starting torque. Used in light-weight machinery and portable tools in sizes up to $2\frac{1}{2}$ hp.
Governor-controlled	Constant speed (adjustable), nonreversible. Made only in very small sizes for special applications.
	Alternating-Current Motors
Single-Phase:	
Capacitor-start, induction run	Constant speed, high starting torque; an all-purpose motor. Economical, low starting current. Normally used up to $\frac{3}{4}$ hp.
Capacitor-start, capacitor run	Constant or varying (adjustable) speed, very low starting torque. Used for direct-connected fan drives in sizes up to $\frac{3}{4}$ hp. Characteristics must be accurately matched to the driven equipment.
Split-phase	Constant speed, low-to-medium starting torque. For frequent start applications up to $\frac{1}{3}$ hp. Has low starting current.
Two- or Three-Phase (Shaded Pole)	Adjustable speed, nonreversible, low starting torque. Used in very small sizes; nonswitching components.
Squirrel-Cage	Constant speed, reversible at rest or in motion, medium to high starting torque. An all-purpose motor, where three-phase supply is available.

Unless otherwise noted, all of the motors discussed in this Chapter are reversible only at rest.

$$\text{Output} = \frac{\text{cu ft/min} \times 62.4 \times \text{head (ft)}}{33{,}000}$$

$$= 21 \text{ hp} \times 0.746 \text{ kW/hp} = 15.7 \text{ kW}$$

$$\text{Input} = \frac{242 \times 82.8}{1000} = 20.0 \text{ kW}$$

Total losses $= 20 - 15.7 = 4.30$ kW

Motor losses:

$$\text{Armature loss} = \frac{6.2 \times 80}{1000} = 0.496 \text{ kW}$$

Friction and windage loss (ignore 2.43 watts copper loss) =

$$\frac{160 \times 5.6}{1000} = 0.895 \text{ kW}$$

$$\text{Field loss} = \frac{2.8 \times 242}{1000} = 0.68 \text{ kW}$$

Total motor losses $= 2.07$ kW

Pump losses $= 4.3 - 2.07 = 2.23$ kW

$$\text{Pump efficiency} = 1 - \frac{2.23}{15.7 + 2.23} = 0.876 = 87.6\%$$ *Answer*

Problem 4-2 Motor sizing for escalator

An electric motor is to be selected to drive an escalator. The escalator is 32 in. wide and can accommodate two riders side-by-side; hence the loading can be considered as uniformly distributed with 250 lb/ft. Linear speed is 75 ft/min. The escalator angle is 40° and its lifting height is 20 ft. Mechanical efficiency of the system is 50%.

Determine the motor size to be specified for this escalator.

Solution:

Observe that the escalator lifts the entire burden an *average* height of 20 ft during the complete ascent of one rider.

$$\text{Length} = 20/\sin 40° = 31 \text{ ft}$$

$$\text{Time for ascent} = 31/75 = 0.413 \text{ min}$$

$$\text{Total ft-lb in } 0.413 \text{ min} = 250 \times 31 \times 20 = 155{,}000 \text{ ft-lb}$$

$$\text{Theoretical horsepower} = \frac{155{,}000}{33{,}000 \times 0.413} = 11.36 \text{ hp}$$

$$\text{Actual hp} = 11.36/0.50 = 22.7 \text{ hp}$$

Motor size is specified as 25 hp. *Answer*

Problem 4-3 Energy storage and magnetic effects of field winding in d-c machine

The field of a four-pole d-c machine requires 4.2×10^6 maxwells/pole produced by 2.3 amps from a 225-volt line. The coils are in series and have 2200 turns/pole.

(a) What is the self-inductance of the field circuit?

(b) What is the energy stored in the field when excited?

(c) How much power is required to maintain the flux?

(d) When the circuit was closed on the 225-volt line, what was the initial rate of current increase, assuming no saturation?

(e) What voltage would be induced if the current were cut off in 0.1 sec?

(f) If a resistance of 80 ohms were connected across the field when the circuit was interrupted, what voltage would be induced?

Solution:

In the steady state, the inductance of a coil has no effect on the flow of a d-c current. For the transient state (parts d, e, and f), a further discussion will be found in Chap. 10. Note that in part (e) the rate of decrease of current is not that of a coil freely discharging through its resistance; the current is made to equal zero in 0.1 sec by the opening of the switch.

(a) $LI = N\phi$, where ϕ is in webers. (1 weber $= 10^8$ maxwells)

$$L = \frac{2200 \times 4.2 \times 10^{-2}}{2.3} \text{ henrys/pole} = 40 \text{ henrys/pole}$$

$$= 160 \text{ henrys/4 poles (total)} \qquad \textit{Answer}$$

(b) $W = \frac{1}{2}LI^2$

$$= \tfrac{1}{2} \times 160 \times (2.3)^2 = 425 \text{ joules} \qquad \textit{Answer}$$

(c) $P = EI$

$$= 225 \times 2.3 = 517.5 \text{ watts} \qquad \textit{Answer}$$

(d) $R = V/I = 225/2.3 = 97.8$ ohms

$$T = L/R = 160/97.8 \text{ (time constant)}$$

$$1/T = 0.612$$

$$i = 2.3(1 - e^{-0.612t})$$

$$di/dt = 2.3 \times 0.612e^{-0.612t} \text{ amps/sec}$$

$$= 1.32 \text{ amps/sec for } t = 0.1 \qquad \textit{Answer}$$

(e) $di/dt = 2.3/0.1 = 23$ amps/sec

$$e = L(di/dt) = 160 \times 23 = 3680 \text{ volts} \qquad \textit{Answer}$$

(f) $R = 97.8 + 80 = 177.8$

$$1/T = 1.11$$

$$di/dt = 2.3 \times 1.11e^{-1.11t}$$

$$e = L(di/dt) = 160 \times 2.3 \times 1.11e^{-0.111}$$

$$= 366 \text{ volts for } t = 0.1 \qquad \textit{Answer}$$

(This assumes that a make-before-break switch is used to insert the 80 ohms before the switch starts to disconnect the voltage source.)

Problem 4-4 Design of rheostat for d-c shunt motor

It is desired to select a rheostat to control the speed of a shunt motor. Motor data:

Line voltage	240 volts
Shunt field resistance (hot)	73 ohms
Shunt field resistance (cold)	68 ohms
Field current at rated speed	3 amps
Minimum field current:	0.75 amps

Determine the best combination of (a) fixed resistance and (b) variable resistance for controlling the speed of this motor. Specify the current rating of (c) the first and (d) the last step of the rheostat.

Solution:

The fixed resistance is required to limit the rated speed current to 3 amps under normal operating conditions. The rheostat's normal range should be sized to keep the field current from falling below 0.75 amp (when the field winding is hot). The rheostat must also contain a starting increment to permit minimum current when the field winding is cold. (See Fig. 4-9.)

Total normal full-speed resistance of field circuit = 240/3 = 80 ohms
Value of fixed resistor = 80 − 73 = 7 ohms *Answer, part (a)*
For minimum current, total resistance is 240/0.75 = 320 ohms
Total rheostat resistance (field winding is cold) = 320 − 68 − 7 = 245 ohms
Total resistance with starting increment deleted = 320 − 73 − 7 = 240 ohms
Answer, part (b)

Power rating of fixed resistor:

$$I_{max} = \frac{240}{7 + 68} = 3.2 \text{ amps}$$

$$I^2R = 71.7 \text{ watts}$$

Maximum current through first step:

$$\frac{240}{68 + 7 + 240} = 0.76 \text{ amps} \qquad (\text{Power} = I^2R_{step})$$ *Answer, part (c)*

Maximum current through last step: 3.2 amps (Power = I^2R_{step})
Answer, part (d)

Problem 4-5 Speed control for d-c motor-driven centrifugal fan

A 500-hp d-c motor rated at 230 volts is to be operated to drive a centrifugal fan

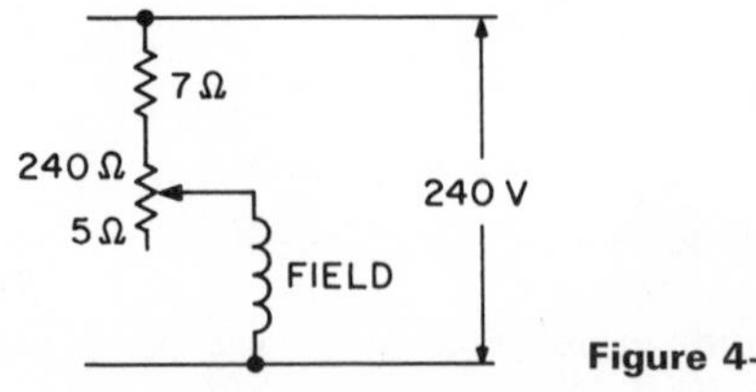

Figure 4-9

over a wide range of speeds. The motor will be directly connected to the fan shaft and the speed-torque requirements are as shown in Fig. 4-10. Motors available are of the four-pole, six-pole, and eight-pole designs. Fan operating speeds desired are as follows: 600 rpm, 1200 rpm, 1800 rpm, and 2400 rpm. Motor characteristics for all of the above pole designs are assumed to be the same and are:

Efficiency at $\frac{1}{4}$ load: 69%
Efficiency at $\frac{1}{2}$ load: 72%
Efficiency at $\frac{3}{4}$ load: 85%
Efficiency at full load: 89%
Efficiency at $1\frac{1}{4}$ load: 85%
Armature resistance: 0.010 ohms at 75°C
Shunt field resistance: 10.0 ohms

For purposes of this problem, neglect any effect of interpoles, compensating windings, armature reaction, and consider that there is no series field. The relation between field current and flux is $\phi = kI_f^{1.2}$. Motors are all general-purpose, continuous-duty type.

(a) Select the base speed of the motor to be used from the three ratings given, and explain why this particular speed was selected.

(b) Determine the method of speed control to be used to obtain each of the four operating speeds. Calculate the resistances required, in ohms, and the wattage ratings of any such resistances for each of the cases.

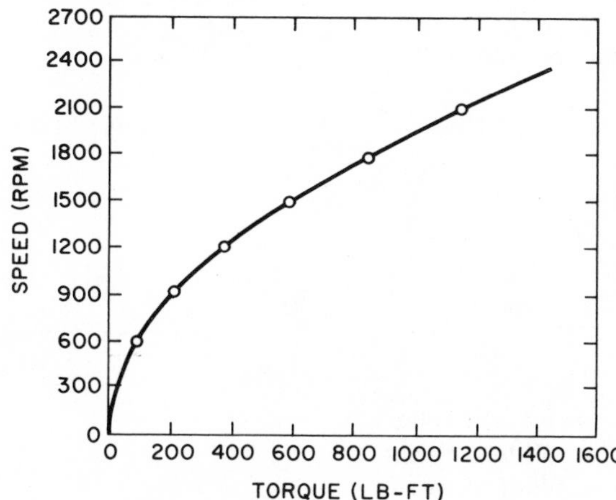

Figure 4-10. Speed-torque requirements for fan drive.

Solution:

(a) Requirement (a) is misleading; the number of poles of a d-c motor does not fix its base speed. The number of poles does establish the flux/pole for a given set of operating conditions (voltage, speed, and torque). *Any* of the four-, six-, or eight-pole designs could drive this fan. The four-pole design would generally be expected to be less expensive; the eight-pole, for a given flux/pole, would provide greater torque (and horsepower) at a given speed.

Select the four-pole machine as the least expensive design. *Answer*

Nothing is given in this problem to indicate that it would have insufficient flux/pole at 600 rpm or insufficient torque at 2400 rpm.

(b) In this problem, the greatest horsepower (and torque) is required at the highest speed. Since torque is proportional to total flux times armature current, and armature current decreases with speed in this problem, total flux requirements can be tabulated against speed.

Regardless of the type selected; and from the curve, since power is proportional to speed times torque:

At 2400 rpm:

$$\text{Power} = 2400 \times 1500 = 3600 \times 10^3 \text{ units or } 100\%$$

At 1800 rpm:

$$\text{Power} = 1800 \times 840 = 1510 \times 10^3 \text{ units or } 41.9\%$$

At 1200 rpm:

$$\text{Power} = 1200 \times 380 = 456 \times 10^3 \text{ units or } 12.7\%$$

At 600 rpm:

$$\text{Power} = 600 \times 90 = 54 \times 10^3 \text{ units or } 1.5\%$$

At 2400 rpm, torque requirements are 100%.
At 1800 rpm, torque requirements are 56%.
At 1200 rpm, torque requirements are 25.2%.
At 600 rpm, torque requirements are 6.3%.

Ignoring field losses, but considering efficiencies, armature current in percent of full-load current will be:

At 2400 rpm, 100%.
At 1800 rpm, 52% $\quad (89/72) \times 42.2\% \times 100\%$.
At 1200 rpm, 16% (estimate 65% efficiency).
At 600 rpm, 2.2% (estimate 60% efficiency).

Therefore, since torque $= k\phi I_a$:

At 2400 rpm, total flux is 100% of full-load value.
At 1800 rpm, total flux is 107% of full-load value.
At 1200 rpm, total flux is 157% of full-load value.
At 600 rpm, total flux is 272% of full-load value.

Assuming no field rheostat required at 600 rpm, the field current will be $230/10 = 23$ amps.

Field current required at 1200 rpm:

$$(I_f/23)^{1.2} = 157/272$$

$$I_f = 14.5 \text{ amps}$$

Rheostat = 5.8 ohms *Answer*

Similarly, at 1800 rpm, I_f = 10.6 amps and rehostat = 11.7 ohms. *Answer*
At 2400 rpm, I_f = 10.0 amps and rheostat = 13.0 ohms. *Answer*

Therefore, speed control should be obtained by a shunt field rheostat. Power dissipation will be:

At 2400 rpm: (10 amps)^2 × 13 ohms = 1300 watts. *Answer*
At 1800 rpm: (10.6 amps)^2 × 11.7 ohms = 1320 watts. *Answer*
At 1200 rpm: (14.5 amps)^2 × 5.8 ohms = 1220 watts. *Answer*

The rheostat should be rated at least 1.5 kW. *Answer*

Note: If the problem had presented a torque that varied inversely with speed, consideration would have been given to armature-resistance speed control.

Problem 4-6 Dynamic braking of d-c shunt motor

A separately excited 10-hp, 230-volt d-c shunt motor is operated at rated speed of 1750 rpm with no load, and draws 2.35 amps armature current.

The motor operates at a temperature of 65°C. Armature resistance is known to be 0.175 ohms at 25°C. Assume brush drop to be 2 volts.

When both armature and field are disconnected from the line, the motor coasts to a speed of 500 rpm in 75 seconds.

(a) Specify a resistor to be used for dynamic braking of this machine such that the initial braking torque will not be greater than twice the full-speed rated torque.

(b) Neglecting the brush drop, calculate the time required to brake the unloaded motor from rated speed to 10% of rated speed, using the resistor determined in part (a).

Solution:

(a) The torque of a d-c shunt-wound machine equals the armature current multiplied by a machine constant.

Let T_1 = rated torque at full speed. Thus,

$$hp = \frac{2\pi \times rpm \times T_1}{33{,}000}$$

where T_1 = 30 lb-ft = 40.7 newton-meters

Let T_2 = friction torque. Rotational losses at full speed may be expressed by

$$(230 - 2)(2.35) - (2.35)^2 r_a$$

$$\text{where } r_a = \frac{234.5 + 65°}{234.5 + 25°} \times 0.175$$

$$= 0.202 \text{ ohms}$$

Losses = 537 watts. Torque corresponding to this power (0.722 hp) = 2.94 newton-meters.

Let T_3 = electromagnetic torque required
= $2T_1 - T_2$ = 78.5 newton-meters

At no load, the electrodynamic torque approximately equals the torque corresponding to frictional losses:

$$(T'_3)_{\text{NO LOAD}} = k_1 i_a$$

where $k_1 = \dfrac{\phi Zp}{2\pi a}$. All values are constant at constant-field excitation.

$$\text{Hence,} \quad 2.94 = 2.35k_1$$
$$k_1 = 1.25$$
$$T_3 = 78.5 = 1.25i_a$$
$$i_a = 62.8 \text{ amps} = \frac{230 - 2}{r_a + R}$$
$$R = 3.43 \text{ ohms} \qquad \textit{Answer}$$

(b) The transient condition of the two variable torques (friction and electromagnetic) requires the determination of a time constant, which is a function of inertial moment and other parameters. The use of the mks system of units is convenient.

First find J (angular moment of inertia). Assume T_2 is proportional to the mechanical speed ω_0.

At 1750 rpm, $\omega_0 = 183$ rad/sec.
At 500 rpm, $\omega_0 = 52.4$ rad/sec.
At 175 rpm, $\omega_0 = 18.3$ rad/sec.

$$T_2 = k_2\omega_0$$
$$2.94 = 183k_2$$
$$0.0161 = k_2$$

Acceleration torque $T = J(d\omega/dt)$.

In the problem, friction torque decelerated the machine to 500 rpm in 75 sec, or

$$k_2\omega = J\frac{d\omega}{dt}$$

$$\text{Integrating,} \quad [t]\Big|_0^{75} = \frac{J}{0.0161}[\ln \omega]\Big|_{183}^{52.4}$$
$$J = 0.975 \text{ kg-m}^2$$

Let T_3 = required electromagnetic torque = $k_1 i_a$, but

$$i_a = \frac{\text{generated emf (e)}}{R + r_a} = \frac{k_1\omega}{3.63}$$

$$\text{Therefore,} \quad J\frac{d\omega}{dt} = k_2\omega + \frac{k_1{}^2\omega}{3.63}$$

$$dt = \frac{3.63J\,d\omega}{3.63k_2\omega + K_1{}^2\omega}$$

$$t = \frac{0.975 \times 3.63}{(3.63 \times 0.0161) + (1.25)^2}\int_{183}^{18.3}\frac{1}{\omega}\,d\omega$$
$$= 7.37 \text{ sec} \qquad \textit{Answer}$$

Problem 4-7 Parallel operation of d-c generators

Two d-c generators are connected in parallel. The terminal characteristics of the generators are shown in Fig. 4-11. Determine the terminal voltage and current of each generator for: (a) a combined load of 1.15 ohms, and (b) a combined load of 1.05 ohms. (c) What is the range of load resistance for which both machines operate as generators?

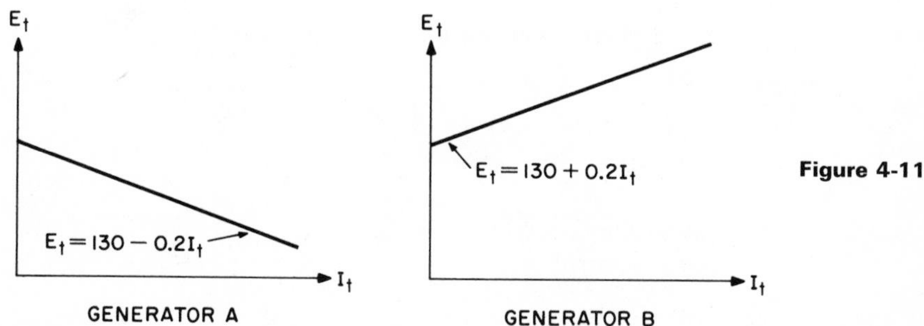

Figure 4-11

Solution:

Using the principle of superposition, no current is found to flow in the neutral of a balanced three-wire generator; actually, no potential difference exists across a load inserted in the neutral. Much the same condition exists here. Note that the terminal voltage equation changes in this problem from generator to motor action (actually under the condition of the problem, neither machine ceases to be a voltage generator).

(a and b) Machine A is a constant-speed d-c generator with a separately excited shunt field. Machine B is an identical machine except that it also has a series field of negligible resistance. The terminal voltage equations with current flowing in the direction of induced emf, are

$$E_T = 130 - 0.2I_A$$
$$E_T = 130 - 0.2I_B + 0.4I_B$$

If machine A continues to be driven at constant speed, its terminal voltage equation, with the positive direction of its current opposite that of its induced emf, is

$$E_T = 130 + 0.2I_A = 130 + 0.2I_B$$
$$I_A = I_B \quad \text{(indeterminate and unstable)} \qquad \textit{Answer}$$
$$I_R = 0 \quad \textit{Answer}$$
$$V_R = 0 \quad \textit{Answer}$$

(c) $130 - 0.2I_A = 130 + 0.2I_B$

$$I_A = -I_B$$

$$R = \infty \quad \textit{Answer}$$

Problem 4-8 Design of resistor for speed control of wound-rotor induction motor

A fan is driven by a 3-phase, 60-Hz, 200-hp wound-rotor induction motor having the following characteristics: full-load slip is 3% with slip rings shorted; resistance between each pair of slip rings is 0.04 ohms; torque-slip curve is a straight line from no load to full load. The required torque of the fan varies as the speed to its 2.5 power.

If it is desired to run the fan at a low speed of 300 rpm, what value of resistance is necessary for use in series with each slip ring to get this speed?

Solution:

Internal torque T of a 3-phase induction motor is given by

$$T = \frac{3pI_r^2R_r}{4\pi fs}$$

where p = number of poles
s = slip
R_r = rotor resistance referred to the stator
I_r = rotor current referred to the stator

$$T = \frac{3p(V_t')^2 sR_r}{[(sR_s + R_r)^2 + s^2(X_s + X_r)^2]4\pi f} \text{ newton-meters}$$

Maximum internal torque T_{max} and corresponding slip s_{max} is

$$T_{max} = \frac{3(V_t')^2}{4\pi f[R_s + \sqrt{R_s^2 + (X_s + X_r)^2}\,]} \text{ newton-meters}$$

$$s_{max} = \frac{R_r}{\sqrt{R_s^2 + (X_s + X_r)^2}}$$

Torque, therefore, can be plotted as a function of slip, and a different curve is obtained for each value of rotor resistance. Such a family of curves, with a torque-speed characteristic of the driven equipment superimposed, would resemble the curves of Fig. 4-12. In this problem, within the region of interest, the motor

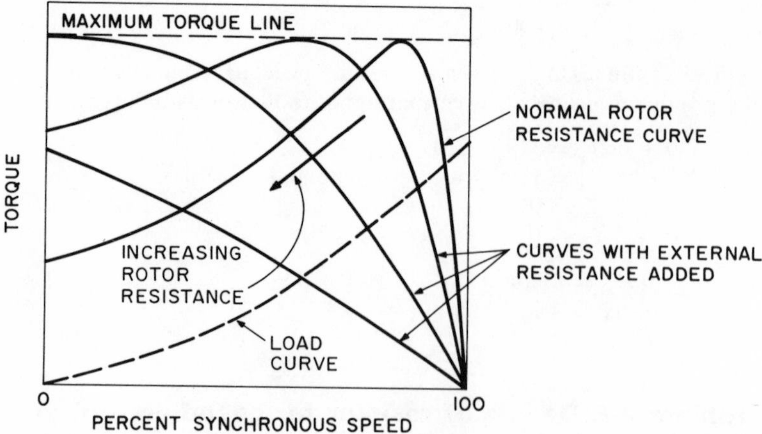

Figure 4-12

torque-slip curve is a straight line for a given rotor resistance. In the absence of further data, the following assumptions are made:

Assume a 16-pole machine.

Assume $T = \frac{s}{R_r(1 + s)^2}$

(A more accurate solution would require stator resistance and reactance, and rotor resistance and reactance referred to the stator; see the discussion above.)

Then

$$\frac{T_{450\ rpm}}{T_{300\ rpm}} = \left(\frac{0.97}{0.667}\right)^{2.5} = \frac{0.03(1.333)^2R'}{0.04(1.03)^2 0.333}$$

$$R' = 0.68 \text{ ohm}$$

where R′ = total rotor circuit resistance required at 300 rpm.
Resistance to be added = 0.64 ohm/phase *Answer*

Problem 4-9 Torque-speed relationship for squirrel-cage induction motor

A 2-pole, 2500-hp, 4160-volt, 3-phase, 60-Hz, squirrel-cage induction motor is used to drive a boiler feed pump in a power plant. The motor speed-torque values at rated voltage are:

% synchronous speed	0	10	30	50	70	90	92	98	99.5
% rated torque	75	75	75	75	80	125	155	240	100
% pump torque	15	0	4	12	26	42	44	87	100

The torque requirements of the pump are expressed in percent of motor rated torque. The drive is started at rated voltage with the discharge valve open but working against a check valve until the pump head equals the system head. The straight-line portion of the pump characteristic between 0% and 10% represents the breakaway requirements. At 92% speed, the check valve opens and there is a discontinuity in the slope of the pump curve. At 98% speed, the motor produces its maximum torque. The inertia of the drive is such that the 5400-kW-sec of energy is stored in the rotating mass at synchronous speed.

(a) How long after rated voltage is applied to the motor will the check valve open? (b) How long will the motor take to reach its maximum torque point?

Solution:

The difference between available torque and running torque (constant velocity) is the torque available for acceleration. If the inertial moment of the rotating mass is known, the time required to reach a given velocity can be calculated.

$$hp = \frac{2\pi \times rpm \times torque(lb\text{-}ft)}{33{,}000}$$

$$T_{FULL\ LOAD} = \frac{2500 \times 33{,}000}{2\pi \times 3600}$$

$$= 3650 \text{ lb-ft}$$

Energy in a rotating mass:

$$W \text{ (kilojoules)} = 0.231J \times (\text{rpm})^2/10^6$$

$$J \text{ (pump and rotor)} = \frac{5400 \times 10^6}{0.231 \times (3600)^2}$$

$$= 1800 \text{ lb-ft}^2$$

Since acceleration torque = (J × rpm/sec)/308, the time required to reach 10% synchronous speed will be determined by the average torque available for acceleration:

$$(0.75 - 0.075)3650 = \frac{1800 \times 360/t_1}{308}$$

$$t_1 = 0.852 \text{ sec}$$

Additional time to reach 30% synchronous speed:

$$(0.75 - 0.02)3650 = \frac{1800 \times 720/t_2}{308}$$

$$t_2 = 1.575 \text{ sec}$$

Similarly, the time to reach 50% synchronous speed:

$$t_3 = 1.74 \text{ sec}$$

Additional time to reach 70% synchronous speed:

$$t_4 = 1.965 \text{ sec}$$

Additional time to reach 90% synchronous speed:

$$t_5 = 1.685 \text{ sec}$$

Additional time to reach 92% synchronous speed:

$$t_6 = 0.136 \text{ sec}$$

Total time to reach check valve opening = 7.95 sec. *Answer, part (a)*

Problem 4-10 Efficiency, power, slip, and torque for wound-rotor induction motor

A 10-hp, 4-pole, 25-Hz, 3-phase wound-rotor induction motor is taking 9100 watts from the line. Core loss is 290 watts; stator copper loss is 568 watts; rotor copper loss is 445 watts; and friction and windage losses are 121 watts. Determine: (a) efficiency; (b) mechanical power output in watts; (c) power transferred across the air gap; (d) mechanical power developed by the rotor; (e) slip; and (f) torque, in lb-ft.

Solution:

Since the rotor induced emf has a very low frequency, all of the core loss is assumed to occur in the stator. Of the total power delivered to the rotor across the air gap, (1 − s) fraction is converted to mechanical power, and the fraction s is dissipated as rotor-circuit copper loss.

(a and b) Total losses = 1424 watts

Output = 9100 − 1424 = 7676 watts *Answer, part (b)*

Efficiency = 7676/9100 = 84.5% *Answer, part (a)*

(c) Power transferred across the air gap is the output plus rotor-circuit copper losses plus windage and friction losses = 8242 watts. *Answer*

(d) Mechanical power developed by the rotor is the output plus friction and windage losses = 7797 watts. *Answer*

(e) s = 445/8242 = 5.4% *Answer*

(f) $\text{Output torque} = \dfrac{\text{output (watts)} \times 60}{2\pi \times 709.5 \text{ rpm}}$ or 103.5 newton-meters *Answer*

Problem 4-11 Two-point starter for induction motor

A one-step, two-point starter is to be designed for a 50-hp, 440-volt, 3-phase, 60-Hz induction motor. The utility company specifies that the starting current shall not exceed 700 amps. At full load, the power factor and the efficiency of this motor are 80% and 90%, respectively. With the rotor locked, the line current is 550% rated current and the power factor is 20%.

Determine the value of the resistor to be inserted in the first step.

Solution:

Calculate the equivalent impedance at starting, and the starter resistance to be added to limit current to 700 amps. This particular problem has a *catch:*

$$\text{Full-load current} = \frac{50 \times 746}{\sqrt{3} \times 440 \times 0.9 \times 0.8} = 67.9 \text{ amps}$$

$$\text{Starting current} = 5.5 \times 67.9 = 373 \text{ amps}$$

Obviously a starting resistor is not required. *Answer*

Note: If the starting current did exceed the permissible value, then assuming a star winding, the equivalent starting impedance per phase of the motor would be

$$\frac{440}{\sqrt{3} \times 373}(0.20 + j\,0.98) = R_m + j\,X_m$$

$$\text{Then, } \frac{400}{\sqrt{3}\,(R_m + R_s + j\,X_m)} = \text{permissible amps}$$

Solve for R_s (ohms per phase).

Problem 4-12 Motor selection for cycling load

A laundry extractor having a total basket and load WK^2 of 400 lb-ft^2 is to be accelerated to approximately 1660 to 1750 rpm, four times per hour. The motor runs for 9 min per start at a load of 2 hp and is manually braked for 3 min. After resting for 3 min while load is removed and the basket reloaded, the cycle is repeated. Graphical representation of the duty cycle is in Fig. 4-13. The speed-torque curve for the load, and typical speed-torque curves for NEMA B and D motors are shown in Fig. 4-14. Assume that for other horsepower ratings, the torques are proportional to the horsepower. See Table 4-2.

The customer requires that the basket be brought up to full speed in less than 2 min.

Select the proper motor for this application to ensure that the acceleration time requirements are met and that the motor will not overheat on this application.

Solution:

Two considerations are involved: the ability of the motor to bring the load to full speed in the allotted time and the ability of the cooling system to dissipate the heat energy developed during the cycle. In this problem, the motor is manually braked; therefore, it is assumed that the kinetic energy of the load (and motor) will be absorbed in a brake that is externally cooled by some means and does not enter into the problem.

$$\text{Average torque (lb-ft)} = 0.194 \times WK^2 \times \text{rev/sec}^2$$

$$= 0.194 \times 400 \times \frac{1800 \text{ (approx.)}}{2 \times 60 \times 60}$$

$$= 19.4 \cong 20 \text{ lb-ft}$$

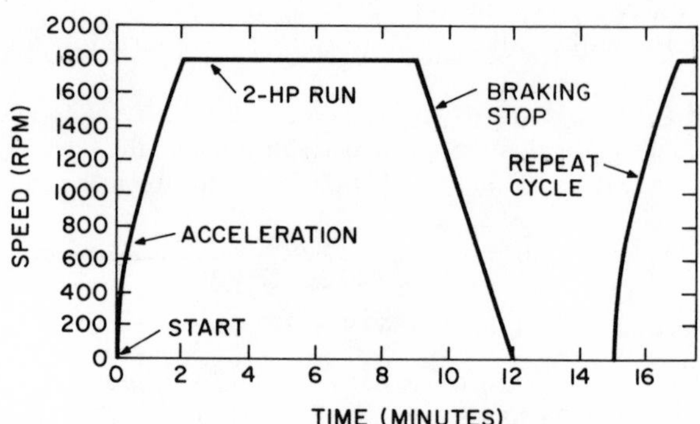

Figure 4-13

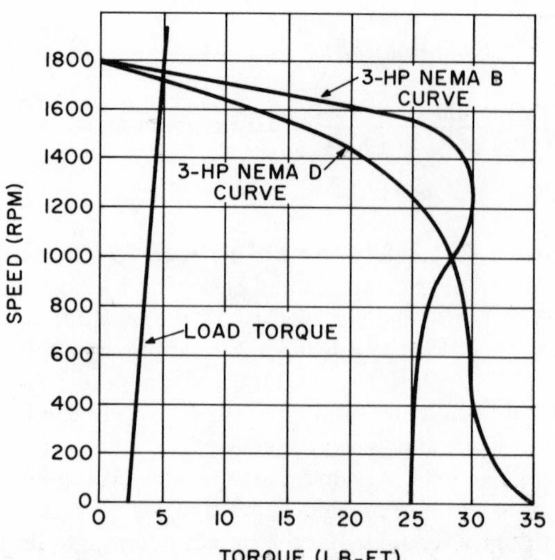

Figure 4-14

Table 4-2

hp	NEMA Type	Poles	Rotor WK^2, lb-ft^2	Full-Load Amps, 440 V	Full-Load rpm	Full-Load Torque, lb-ft	Full-Load Eff, %	Full-Load P.F., %
$1\frac{1}{2}$	B	4	0.17	2.30	1735	4.54	83.5	76.5
$1\frac{1}{2}$	D	4	0.26	2.30	1675	4.70	82.0	71.0
2	B	4	0.20	2.90	1735	6.05	83.0	83.8
2	D	4	0.33	3.10	1670	6.28	76.8	82.2
3	B	4	0.43	4.10	1735	9.09	85.5	83.4
3	D	4	0.41	4.20	1680	9.37	81.3	82.1
5	B	4	0.55	6.4	1735	15.12	87.4	88.3
5	D	4	0.72	7.0	1695	15.5	82.5	85.5

Friction-Windage, W	No-Load Heating, W	Full-Load Heating, W	Rest. T-T@75°C and 440 V	Accel r_1/R_2	Plug r_1/R_2	Heat Dissipation, W RUN	STOP
15	111	205	12.08	1.35	1.22	530	185
20	126	234	12.41	1.045	0.858	570	190
15	120	284	10.82	1.46	1.33	530	185
30	141	372	10.75	0.945	0.769	660	195
35	127	347	6.35	1.24	1.15	890	245
30	158	486	5.90	0.757	0.614	815	205
20	139	521	4.43	1.41	1.23	950	270
60	168	630	3.62	0.821	0.780	1075	280

All motors are 3-phase, 60-Hz, 40°C rise continuous rated, 220/440 volts. Cooling watts during acceleration is assumed to be 67% of cooling watts running.

By inspection of the speed-torque curves, either NEMA B or D would have this average torque, if a 3-hp motor were selected (2 hp would not). Using increments of the torque-speed curve for the 3-hp NEMA B (less costly than D) and observing the average torques over these increments:

From 0 to 1000 rpm:

$$\text{Average torque} = 27 \text{ lb-ft} = 0.194 \times 400 \times \frac{1000}{3600t}$$

$$t = 1.06 \text{ min}$$

From 1000 to 1600 rpm: Average torque = 27.5 lb-ft $\quad$ t = 0.47 min
From 1600 to 1735 rpm: Average torque = 15.2 lb-ft $\quad$ t = 0.18 min
Total time T = 1.71 min

Therefore, a 3-hp NEMA B motor would be acceptable from the standpoint of acceleration.

Note: To match the acceleration curve given in the problem for the load, a 5-hp NEMA D motor would be required. However, it is assumed that this curve was merely to illustrate the duty cycle and not to show the speed-time characteristic of the motor and load.

Proof: Observe that 200 rpm is reached in 0.1 min (6 sec).

$$T_{avg} = 0.194 \times 400 \times \frac{200}{6 \times 60} = 43.1 \text{ lb-ft}$$

Starting torque of 5-hp NEMA B: 5/3 × 25 = 41.5 (inadequate)
Starting torque of 5-hp NEMA D: 5/3 × 35 = 58.2

Heat Balance (for NEMA B, 3-hp motor):
During acceleration,
Heat input = friction and windage losses + I^2R loss + excitation loss

Time: 120 sec
Friction and windage (average): 17.5 watts
Excitation (no-load) losses: 127 watts
Copper losses:
Starting current = approximately four times full-load current
Full-load heating: 347 watts
Approximate $I^2R = \frac{1}{2} \times 4^2(347 - 127) = 1760$ watts
Total input: (17.5 + 127 + 1760)120 = 229,000 joules
Total cooling: 0.67 × 890 × 120 = 71,500 joules

During run:

Time: 420 sec
Friction and windage: 35 watts
No-load losses: 127 watts
I^2R (2-hp load): $(2/3)^2(347 - 127) = 99$ watts
Total input: (35 + 127 + 99)420 = 109,500 joules
Total cooling: 890 × 420 = 373,000 joules

During braking:

Time: 180 sec
Friction and windage: 17.5 watts
Other: None (see assumptions in solution outline)
Total input: 17.5 × 180 = 3150 joules

Total cooling (average): $\frac{890 + 245}{2} \times 180 = 102{,}000$ joules

During rest:

Time: 180 sec
Heat input: None
Total cooling: 245 × 180 = 44,200 joules

Total heat to be dissipated throughout cycle = 341,650 joules
Total heat that can be dissipated = 590,700 joules
Therefore a NEMA B, 3-hp motor would be adequate. *Answer*
Note: This would not be the case if plugging were used and the stored kinetic

energy had to be dissipated by the design cooling capacity of the motor. The energy contained in a rotating mass is given by

$$\text{Joules} = \frac{0.231 \times WK^2(\text{lb-ft}^2) \times (\text{rpm})^2}{10^3}$$

Problem 4-13 Efficiency and line current of three-phase alternator

A 1000-kVA, Y-connected, 3-phase, 3200-volt, 60-Hz 24-pole alternator has an armature resistance of 0.1 ohm from line to neutral. The field requires 100 amps at 120 volts at full load, 0.80 power factor, and the friction and windage losses are 15 kW. The core losses are 20 kW. The inertial moment of the rotor and prime mover is 300 kg-m^2.

Calculate: (a) The line current at full load and 80% power factor; (b) the total armature resistance loss; (c) the efficiency; and (d) the energy from standstill to full speed, neglecting friction and windage.

Solution:

This is an application of

$$\% \text{ Eff} = 100 \times \frac{\text{alternator output}}{\text{alternator input}}$$

Stray losses and excitation losses are not relevant. Assume that part (d) is asking for the stored kinetic energy and not the total input, which would include copper and core losses.

(a) Line current $= I_L = \dfrac{1000 \text{ kVA}}{\sqrt{3} \times 3.2 \text{ kV}} = 180$ amps *Answer*

(b) Copper loss (armature) $= 3 \times 180^2 \times 0.1$ W $= 9.82$ kW *Answer*

(c) Output $= 0.8 \times 1000 = 800$ kW

Losses:
Friction and windage: 15 kW
I^2R: 9.82 (armature) and 12.0 (field)
Core: 20
Total: 59 kW

% Eff $= 100 \times 800/859 = 93.2\%$ *Answer*

(d) Speed (24 poles) $= 300$ rpm

$WK^2 = 300 \times 23.7$ lb-ft^2

$$\text{Energy stored in rotating mass} = \frac{0.231 \times 300 \times 23.7 \times 300^2}{1000}$$
$$= 148{,}000 \text{ joules}$$ *Answer*

Problem 4-14 Terminal voltage of three-phase alternator

A Y-connected, 200-kVA, 440-volt, 3-phase, 3-wire alternator yields 150 volts between line terminals on open circuit. With the field excitation unchanged, the short circuit is 300 amps. The ohmic resistance of this machine between line terminals is 0.10 ohm, and the ratio of effective to ohmic resistance is 1.25.

Calculate the full-load terminal voltage of this machine when the excitation is adjusted to yield a no-load voltage of 500 volts and the power factor is 0.80, lagging.

Solution:

Assume that the effective resistance is unaffected by change in excitation. (Actually this is not so.) The short-circuit current (steady state) equals the ratio of the generated voltage (per phase) to the synchronous impedance.

At full load, the voltage drop per phase in the alternator is the product of the line current and the synchronous impedance per phase.

$$R \text{ (per phase)} = \frac{0.10 \times 1.25}{2} = 0.0625$$

$$I_{sc} = \frac{150}{(R + j\,X_s)2} = 300$$

$$X_s = 0.242 \text{ ohm/phase}$$

At 500 volts (nominal), full-load line current is

$$I_{\text{FULL LOAD}} = \frac{200 \text{ kVA}}{\sqrt{3} \times 0.5 \text{ kV}} = 232 \text{ amps}$$

Let terminal voltage be $V_t\underline{/0^\circ}$ (see Fig. 4-15). Then

$$\begin{aligned} I &= 232(0.8 - j\,0.6) \\ E_{\text{NO LOAD}} &= V_t + 2\,\bar{I}Z_s \\ &= V_t + 2 \times 232(0.8 - j\,0.6)(0.0625 + j\,0.242) \\ &= V_t + 90.4 + j72.4 \\ V_t &= 405 \text{ volts} \quad \textit{Answer} \end{aligned}$$

Problem 4-15 Repulsion-start induction motor

A fractional horsepower motor used to operate an oil burner in a small industrial plant is equipped with a wound rotor, a commutator, and a stator with nonsalient poles from which four leads emanate. The four brushes on the commutator are permanently short-circuited in pairs. A centrifugal device, inoperative at standstill, short-circuits the entire commutator once the machine is started.

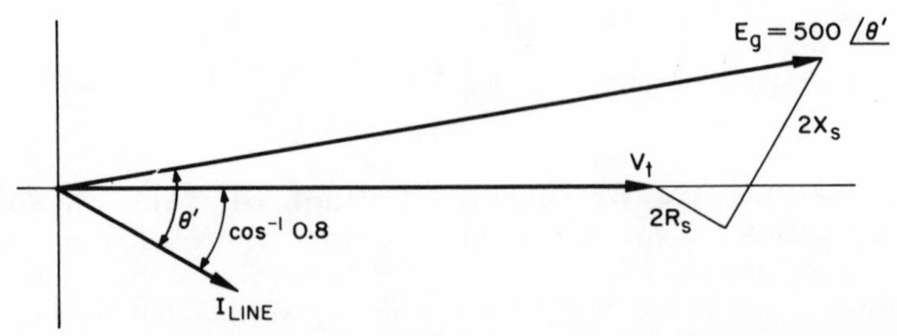

Figure 4-15

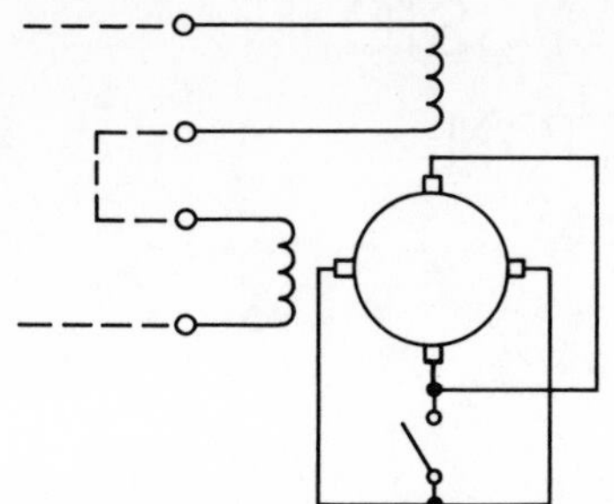

Figure 4-16

(a) What kind of motor is this? (b) Why are four leads supplied? (c) How can the direction of rotation of this machine be reversed?

Solution:

(a) This is a repulsion-start, induction-run, single-phase a-c motor. *Answer*

(b) In addition to the main stator field winding, a supplementary winding is provided so that the direction of the axis of the stator *net* mmf can be reversed instead of the brush axis. *Answer*

(c) The direction of rotation can be reversed by switching the supplementary winding cross-field direction from left to right or vice versa. See Fig. 4-16.

chapter 5
POWER TRANSMISSION AND DISTRIBUTION

5-1 THE PER-UNIT SYSTEM OF NOTATION

The per-unit system of notation was devised primarily as an aid to calculate short-circuit currents. Per-unit reactance is the ratio of the voltage drop across an impedance when carrying rated current to the circuit voltage. For example, if a transformer has a reactance of 10% or 0.10 p.u. (per unit), it will have a voltage drop of 10% or 0.10 p.u. of the circuit voltage when carrying rated current. From this definition of per-unit reactance, the following equation is derived to convert ohms to a per-unit quantity:

$$\text{Per-unit X} = \frac{(\text{reactance in ohms})(\text{rated amperes})}{(\text{rated volts})}$$

$$\text{Per-unit X} = \frac{(\text{ohms reactance})(\text{kVA base})}{(1000)(\text{line voltage in kV})^2}$$

These equations may be used for per-unit reactance, per-unit resistance, or per-unit impedance.

5-2 FAULT CALCULATIONS USING SYMMETRICAL COMPONENTS

The following list summarizes the suggested procedure to calculate fault currents:

1. Obtain a complete single-line diagram for the entire system, including generators, transformers, and transmission lines, and obtain the impedance of each component.
2. Prepare from step 1 the single-line impedance diagram for the positive, negative, and zero sequence networks.
3. Reduce the impedance values of all branches of the networks to a common base.
4. Obtain the single equivalent impedance of each sequence network, also the

equivalent voltage for the positive-phase sequence network (generally assumed 1.0 p.u.) all referred to the proper base.

5. Connect the sequence networks to represent the type of fault under consideration.
6. Determine the component of current of each sequence in the fault.
7. Find the distribution of current in each branch of each sequence network, if necessary for the solution of the problem.
8. Combine the sequence currents at any point to obtain the actual current in per unit.
9. Convert to actual amperes.

Voltages can be obtained at any point in the system in a similar manner by calculating each sequence voltage at a point and combining them in the proper relationship. When voltages and currents are being calculated, phase shift introduced by transformer connections should be taken into account.

5-3 ZERO SEQUENCE IMPEDANCE—TWO-WINDING TRANSFORMER BANKS

The zero sequence impedance for a given transformer connection is determined by whether or not zero sequence current can flow in that connection. For example. consider the wye-wye connection in Fig. 5-1.

At the point n,

$$I_a + I_b + I_c = 0$$

This condition cannot be satisfied if I_a, I_b, and I_c are zero sequence currents, although it is satisfied by positive and negative sequence currents. Therefore, if we apply a zero sequence voltage source to the transformer in Fig. 5-1, no zero sequence current will flow and the zero sequence impedance will be infinite.

Since we know that in per unit, $I_a = I'_a$, $I_b = I'_b$, and $I_c = I'_c$, the zero sequence impedance of a transformer is infinite even if only one side is connected in ungrounded wye, regardless of the connection on the other side.

If we ground the wye on both primary and secondary of the transformer, as is done in Fig. 5-2, a path for zero sequence currents is provided and the zero sequence impedance is simply the winding resistance plus the leakage reactance.

If one side of a transformer is connected in delta, zero sequence currents cannot flow in the lines on the side connected to the delta, since no return path exists for these currents. Zero sequence currents can, however, circulate in the delta. This condition is shown in Fig. 5-3.

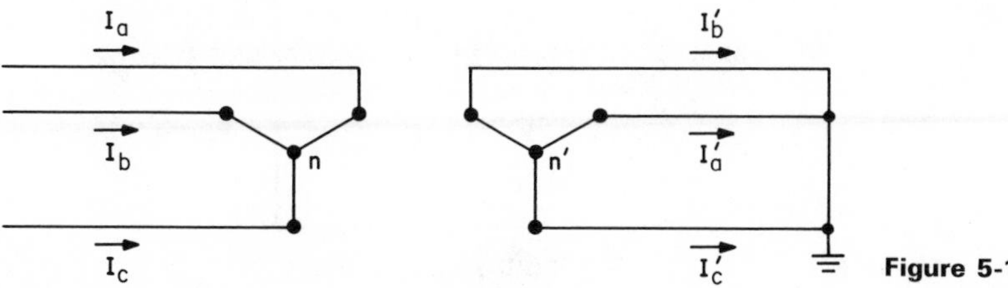

Figure 5-1

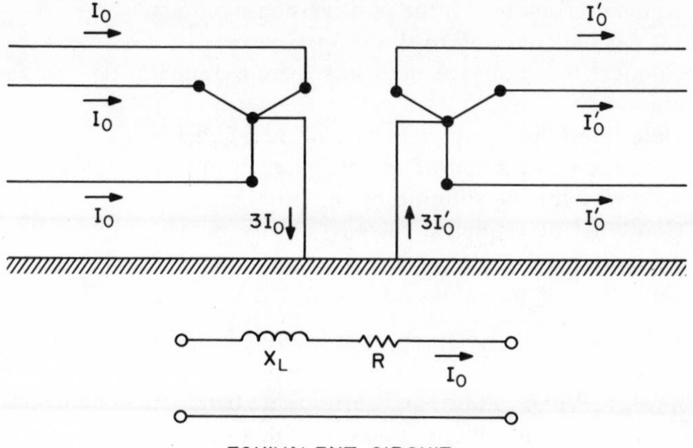

Figure 5-2

A summary of zero sequence transformer connections is shown in Fig. 5-4. There is no phase shift in zero sequence currents and voltages when passing through power transformers.

5-4 POSITIVE AND NEGATIVE SEQUENCE IMPEDANCE—TWO-WINDING TRANSFORMER BANKS

The positive sequence impedance of a transformer consists of its winding resistance and leakage reactance. This impedance may be used regardless of how the bank is connected (delta-wye, delta-delta, wye-wye, etc.). In a transformer, as in all balanced 3-phase static devices, the negative sequence impedance is equal to the positive sequence impedance. Obviously, it makes no difference, as far as the impedance of a static device is concerned, whether three balanced currents and voltages have phase order a, b, c or a, c, b.

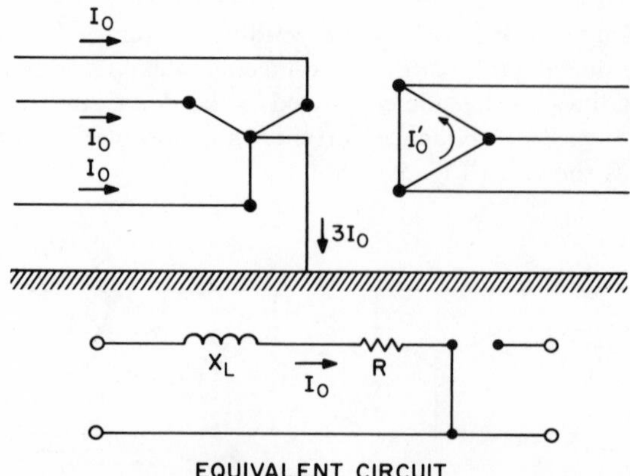

Figure 5-3

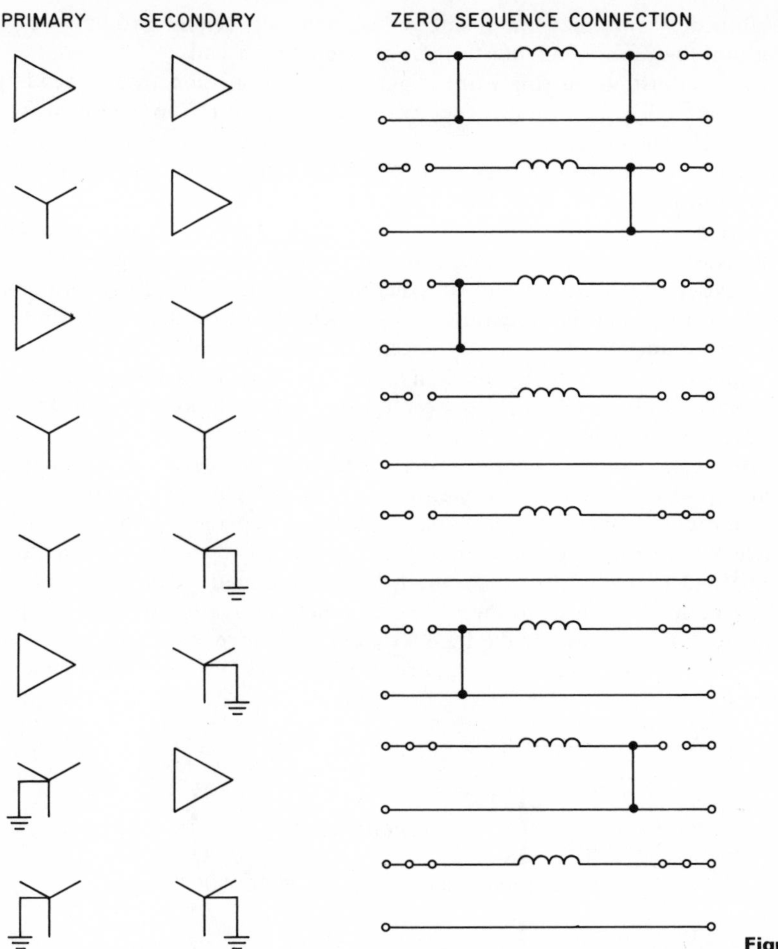

Figure 5-4

Whenever a transformer bank is connected delta-wye or wye-delta, a phase shift in the voltages and currents occurs. This phase shift is different for the three different sequence voltages and currents. The manufacturers of transformers have standardized in calling the phase shift ±30° in all delta-wye and wye-delta banks. However, for calculation purposes, a shift of ±90° is often used because of the convenience of multiplying by ±j.

5-5 TRANSMISSION OF POWER

The simplest case of power transmission is through a series impedance or admittance. Usually this is over a short distance and at such a voltage that the capacitance and charging current between conductors may be neglected. The impedance may be only that of a transmission cable or overhead line connecting two buses or connecting any two selected points of a system, or it may also include the series impedance of other equipment in the circuit between the two buses, such as current-limiting reactors or transformers at one or both ends.

Figure 5-5 illustrates a single-line diagram of transmission from a sending end bus (S) through a series impedance (Z) or admittance (Y) to a receiver bus (R) and to a load. The impedance Z (or admittance Y) includes all series impedances of equipment between the two buses, such as cable, overhead line, current-limiting reactors, transformers, etc.

The load at the receiver end may be a static load or it may be a synchronous load. A static load may consist of induction motors and heating or lighting loads, but must have a negligible amount of synchronous machine load. Synchronous machines have to remain in synchronism with each other in order to transmit or receive power. Induction motor theory necessitates that induction motors *not* run at synchronous speed. Therefore, induction motors are classed as static loads, meaning that they do not have to maintain a certain speed in order to convert electrical power to mechanical power.

If a severe fault occurs on the system, before it can be removed, there is considerable probability that the synchronous machines will lose synchronism or fall out of step with each other. If they do not fall out of step, they will have changed phase angle with respect to each other, so that the load taken changes considerably both during and immediately after a fault. With static loads, as soon as voltage is restored, the load again is on the system at practically its former value unless the voltage dropped too low, or the time required to remove the fault was so long as to cause low-voltage relays to disconnect a percentage of the induction motor load.

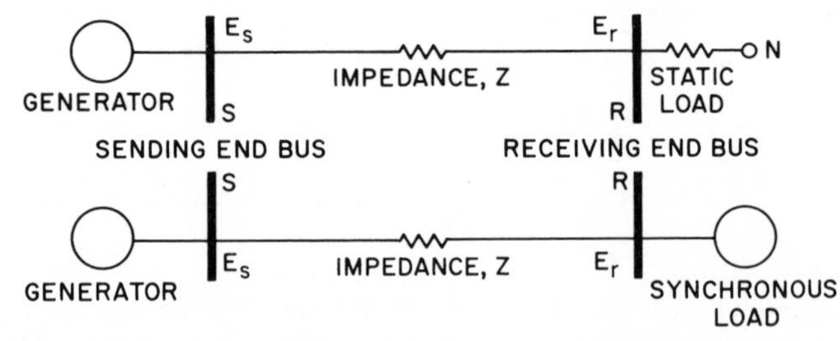

Figure 5-5

For simplicity, a static load is usually considered a constant-impedance load and the magnitude of load impedance does not change during a fault, so that the load current varies directly with the voltage, and the kVA varies as the square of the voltage. For a short duration fault, this assumption does not introduce excessive error, but if a more exact solution is required, the load is divided into two parts and the induction motor part is considered as a constant-kVA load, namely, with decrease in voltage, the current increases, while lighting load kW is considered as varying with the square of the voltage.

At the receiver end of a transmission system, there is usually a combination of static load and synchronous load as shown in Fig. 5-6. The circuit is reduced by means of T to pi conversion equations (see Fig. 5-7):

Pi to T Conversion Equations:

$$Z_s = \frac{Z_{sr}Z_{sn}}{Z_{sr} + Z_{sn} + Z_{rn}}$$

$$Z_r = \frac{Z_{sr}Z_{rn}}{Z_{sr} + Z_{sn} + Z_{rn}}$$

$$Z_n = \frac{Z_{sn}Z_{rn}}{Z_{sr} + Z_{sn} + Z_{rn}}$$

T to Pi Conversion Equations:

$$Z_{sn} = \frac{Z_sZ_n + Z_sZ_r + Z_rZ_n}{Z_r}$$

$$Z_{sr} = \frac{Z_sZ_n + Z_sZ_r + Z_rZ_n}{Z_n}$$

$$Z_{rn} = \frac{Z_sZ_n + Z_sZ_r + Z_rZ_n}{Z_s}$$

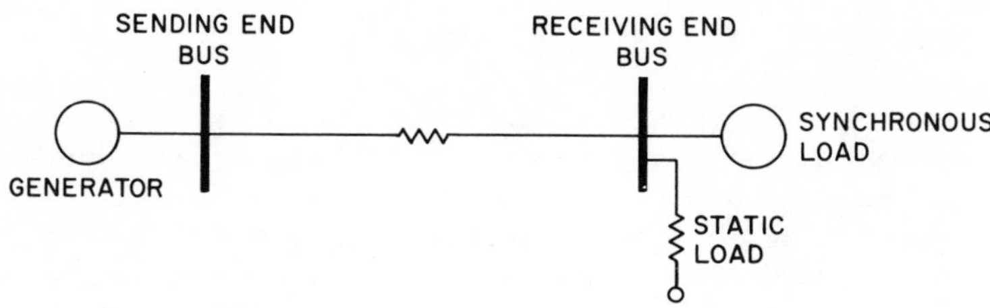

Figure 5-6

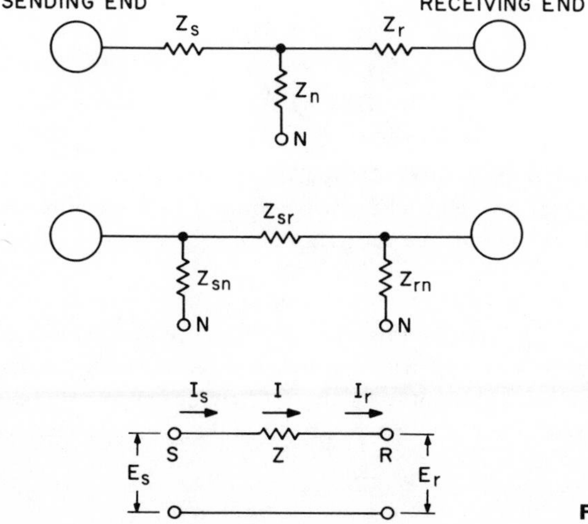

Figure 5-7

In the following analysis, the impedances Z_{sn} and Z_{rn} are neglected, and the power transfer is considered through the simple series impedance Z_{sr}. In the usual case, the inclusion of the shunt impedances will alter the results only slightly.

The phasor equations for power are based on the product of the voltage and the conjugate of the current. The conjugate of a phasor is obtained by changing the sign of the imaginary component (e.g., if phasor $I = 2 - j3$, then $\hat{I} = 2 + j3$).

$$P + jQ = E\hat{I}$$

where Q = reactive power
+ = lagging reactive power
− = leading reactive power
P = real power
E = a phasor quantity
$\bar{E}$ = absolute magnitude of quantity
$\hat{E}$ = conjugate of phasor quantity

$$P_s + jQ_s = \frac{\bar{E}_s^{\,2}}{\hat{Z}} - \frac{\bar{E}_s\bar{E}_r \angle\theta}{\hat{Z}}$$

$$P_r + jQ_r = -\frac{\bar{E}_r^{\,2}}{\hat{Z}} + \frac{\bar{E}_s\bar{E}_r \angle -\theta}{\hat{Z}}$$

The sending- and receiving-end real and reactive power is the sum of two phasor quantities. Furthermore, if the voltages E_s and E_r are held constant, there is only one remaining variable, θ. These equations are plotted as the power circle diagrams shown in Fig. 5-8. From the figure, P_s is positive when true (real) power is flowing into the network at the sending end; Q_s is positive when lagging reactive power is flowing into the network at the sending end; P_r is positive when real power is flowing out of the network at the receiver end; and Q_r is positive when lagging reactive power is flowing out of the network at the receiver end.

In the preceding equations, θ is the angle between the sending-end voltage E_s and the receiver-end voltage E_r, and θ is positive when the sending-end voltage is ahead.

PROBLEMS

Problem 5-1 The per-unit system of notation

Figure 5-9 shows a typical problem where it is required to determine the 3-phase fault current at the 66-kV bus on the receiving end.

Solution:

First select a common kVA base. In this case, 20,000 kVA looks reasonable, since the reactance of the generator and transformers is already given on that base. It is also necessary to select a common kV base. Assume 66 kV to be the base. According to the base selected, it is necessary to make the following corrections to the reactances:

Corrected transformer reactance (generator end) = $(0.10)(69/66)^2 = 0.11$

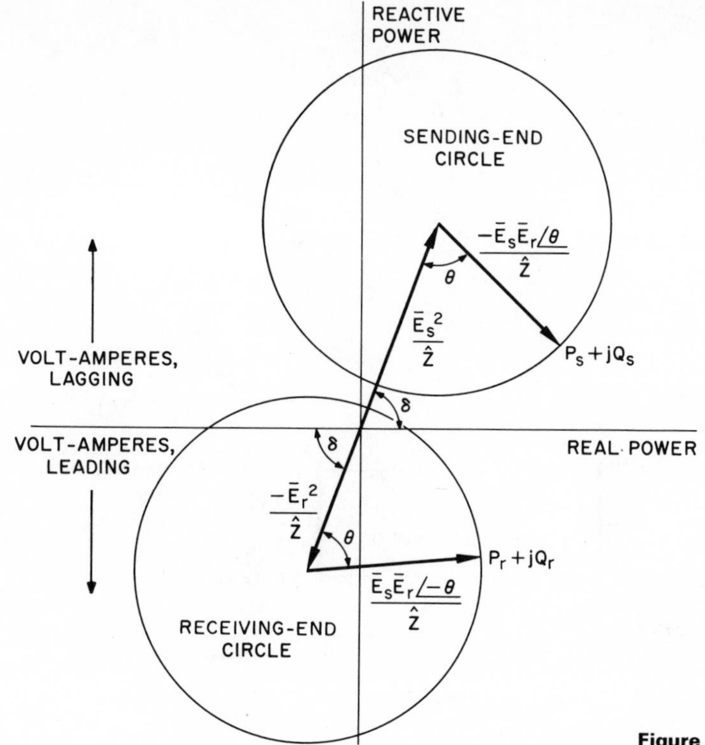

Figure 5-8

With 66 kV on the high side of the generator transformer, the base voltage on the low side is determined by the transformer ratio:

$(66/69)(13.2) = 12.6$ kV

Since the generator is rated 13.8 kV, its corrected per-unit reactance becomes

$(13.8/12.6)^2(0.10) = 0.12$ p.u.

The remaining step is to convert the ohmic reactance of the 66-kV line into per-unit reactance:

$$\text{Per-unit reactance} = \frac{\text{(ohms reactance)(kVA base)}}{\text{(1000)(line voltage in kV)}^2} = \frac{(24)(20{,}000)}{(1000)(66)^2}$$

$$= 0.11 \text{ p.u.}$$

Total reactance from generator to fault:

Generator	0.12 p.u.
Two lines in parallel	0.055 p.u.
Transformer	0.11 p.u.
	0.285 p.u.

Total reactance from motor to fault:

Motor	0.12 p.u.
Transformer	0.10 p.u.
	0.22 p.u.

The short-circuit contribution from the generator end is 20,000/0.285 = 70,000 kVA. *Answer*

The short-circuit contribution from the motor end is 20,000/0.22 = 91,000 kVA. *Answer*

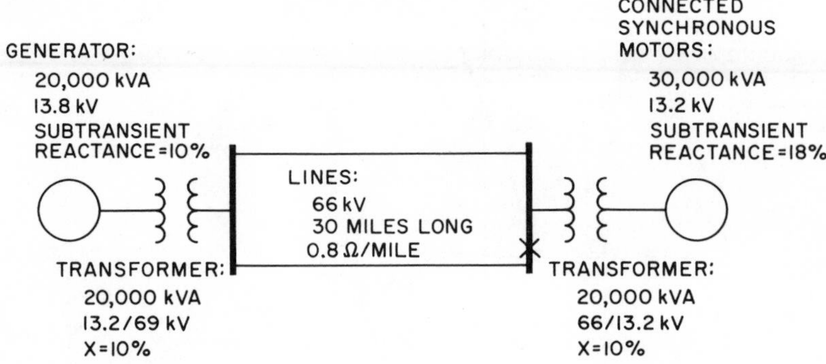

Figure 5-9

Problem 5-2 Fault-current calculation by symmetrical components

Given the system shown in Fig. 5-10, calculate the current in the fault and the current through OCB's (oil circuit breakers) No. 1 and No. 2 for: (a) a 3-phase fault on

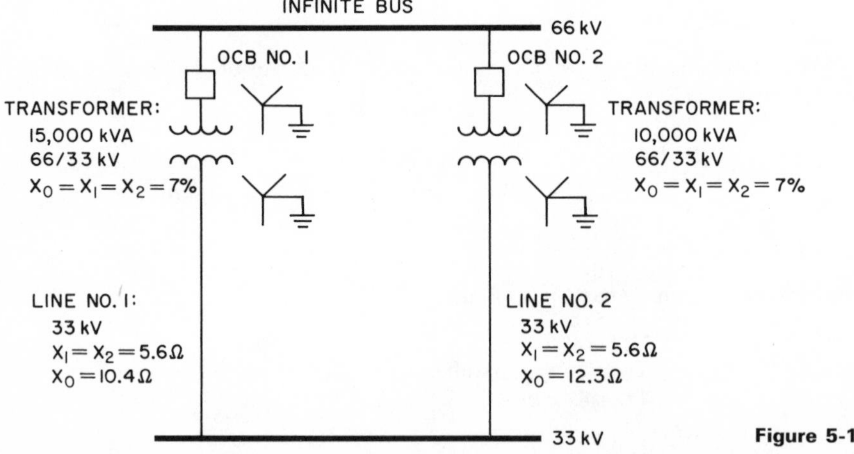

Figure 5-10

the 33-kV bus; (b) a line-to-line fault on the 33-kV bus; and (c) a line-to-ground fault on the 33-kV bus.

Solution:

The term *infinite bus* used to describe the 66-kV bus in this problem is merely a way of stating that X_1, X_2, and X_0, measured from the bus back to the generators are so small as to be considered negligible. Thus, theoretically, a fault on this bus would result in an infinitely large current flow.

The procedure for fault calculations as outlined will be used to solve this problem.

1. The single-line diagram is given in Fig. 5-11.
2. The sequence networks are shown in Fig. 5-11.
3. Calculations are all on a 10,000-kVA base, 66- and 33-kV bases.

Sequence Quantity	*Equipment*	*Calculation*	*p.u. Impedance*
X_1, X_2, and X_0	15,000-kVA transformer	$\frac{(10{,}000)(0.07)}{(15{,}000)}$	0.047
X_1, X_2, and X_0	10,000-kVA transformer	—	0.070
X_1 and X_2	Line No. 1 and line No. 2	$\frac{(5.6)(10)}{(33)^2}$	0.051
X_0	Line No. 1	$\frac{(10.4)(10)}{(33)^2}$	0.095
X_0	Line No. 2	$\frac{(12.3)(10)}{(33)^2}$	0.113

4. The reduced networks appear in Fig. 5-12.

5 and 6. For a 3-phase fault, only the positive sequence network is considered:

$$I_1 = E/Z_1 = 1.0/j0.054 = 18.5 \underline{/-90^\circ}$$

For a line-to-line fault, the positive and negative sequence networks are connected in parallel. Refer to Fig. 5-13.

$$I_1 = \frac{E}{Z_1 + Z_2} = \frac{1.0}{j0.108} = 9.3\underline{/-90^\circ}$$

$$I_2 = -I_1 = 9.3\underline{/90^\circ}$$

For a line-to-ground fault, the three sequence networks are connected in series. Refer to Fig. 5-14.

$$I_1 = I_2 = I_0 = \frac{E}{Z_1 + Z_2 + Z_0} = \frac{1.0}{j0.189} = 5.3 \underline{/-90^\circ}$$

7. The division of the various sequence currents for the three fault conditions are shown in Fig. 5-15. Each sequence current is inversely proportional to the branch impedances in its sequence network.

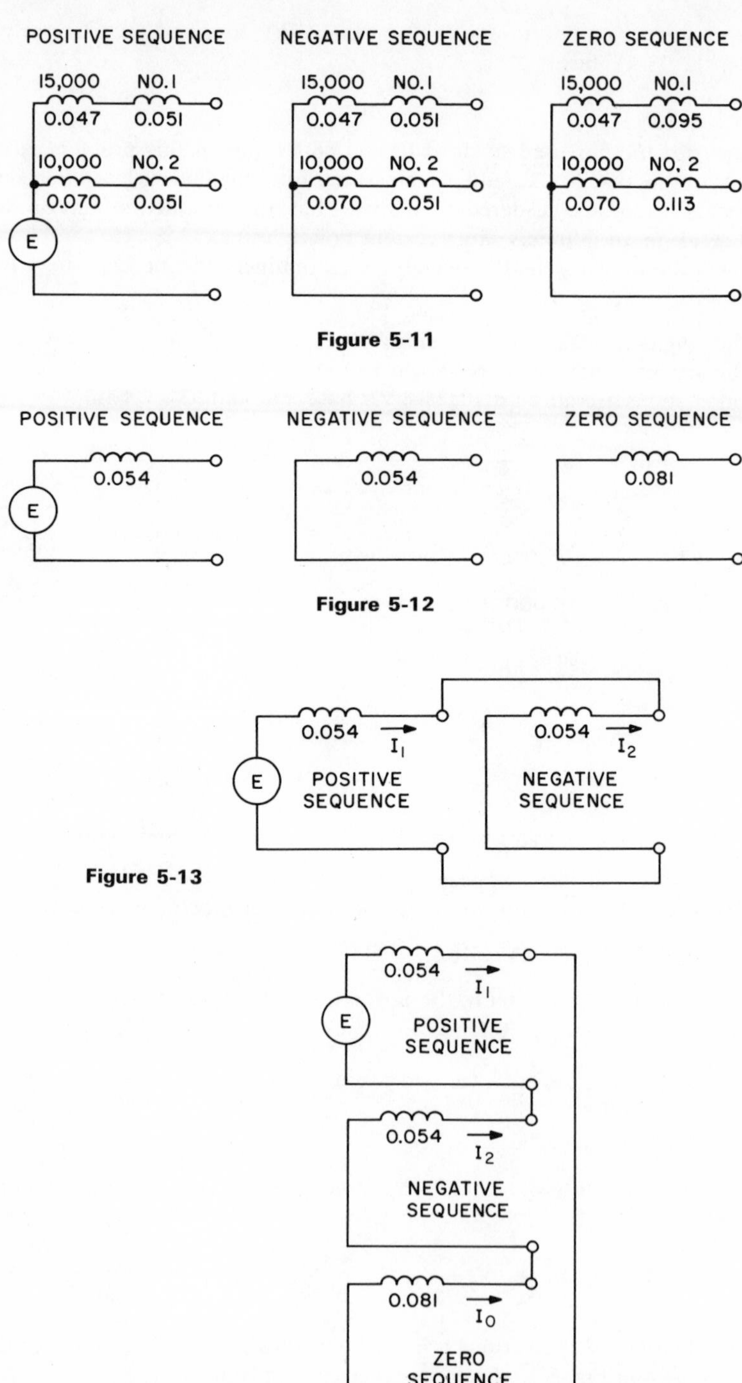

Figure 5-11

Figure 5-12

Figure 5-13

Figure 5-14

THREE-PHASE FAULT

POSITIVE SEQUENCE NEGATIVE SEQUENCE ZERO SEQUENCE

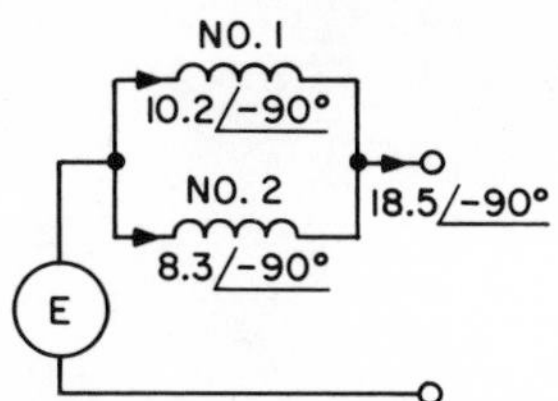

LINE-TO-LINE FAULT

POSITIVE SEQUENCE NEGATIVE SEQUENCE ZERO SEQUENCE

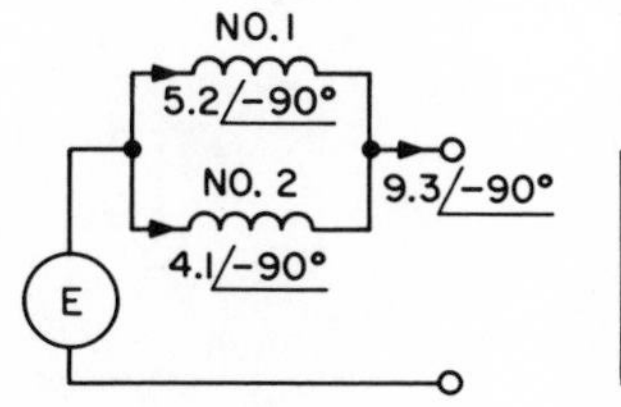

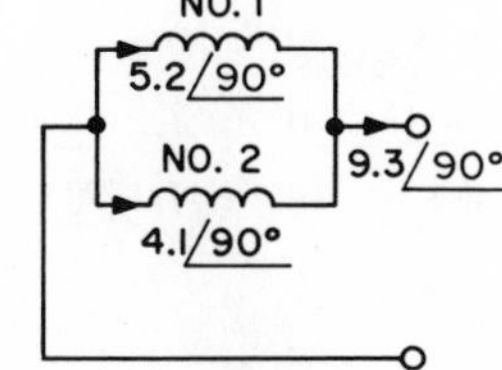

LINE-TO-GROUND FAULT

POSITIVE SEQUENCE NEGATIVE SEQUENCE ZERO SEQUENCE

NO. 1
2.9/-90°
NO. 2
5.3/-90°
2.4/-90°
E

NO. 1
2.9/-90°
NO. 2
5.3/-90°
2.4/-90°

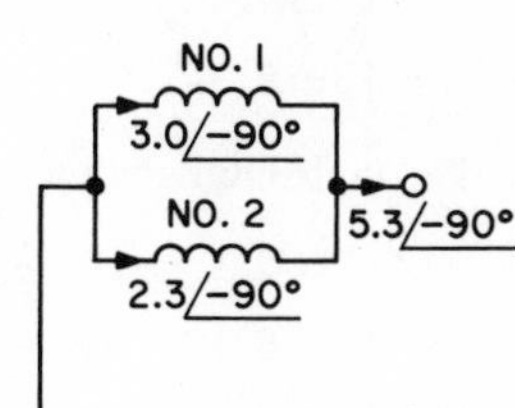

Figure 5-15

8. The sequence components are combined now at each desired place to obtain answers.

(a) Three-phase fault:

At fault,

$$I_a = I_0 + I_1 + I_2 = 18.5 \ \underline{/-90^\circ}$$

$$I_b = I_0 + a^2 I_1 + aI_2 = 18.5 \ \underline{/150^\circ}$$

$$I_c = I_0 + aI_1 + a^2 I_2 = 18.5 \ \underline{/30^\circ}$$

Through OCB No. 1, $I_a = 10.2 \ \underline{/-90^\circ}$ $\quad I_b = 10.2 \ \underline{/150^\circ}$ $\quad I_c = 10.2 \ \underline{/30^\circ}$

Through OCB No. 2, $I_a = 8.3 \angle -90^\circ \quad I_b = 8.3 \angle 150^\circ \quad I_c = 8.3 \angle 30^\circ$

(b) Line-to-line fault:

At fault,

$$I_a = I_0 + I_1 + I_2 = 0 + 9.3 \angle -90^\circ + 9.3 \angle 90^\circ = 0$$
$$I_b = I_0 + a^2I_1 + aI_2 = 9.3 \angle 150^\circ + 9.3 \angle 210^\circ = 16.1 \angle 180^\circ$$
$$I_c = I_0 + aI_1 + a^2I_2 = 9.3 \angle 30^\circ + 9.3 \angle -30^\circ = 16.1 \angle 0^\circ$$

Through OCB No. 1,

$$I_a = 0 + 5.2 \angle -90^\circ + 5.2 \angle 90^\circ = 0$$
$$I_b = 0 + 5.2 \angle 150^\circ + 5.2 \angle 210^\circ = 9.0 \angle 180^\circ$$
$$I_c = 0 + 5.2 \angle 30^\circ + 5.2 \angle -30^\circ = 9.0 \angle 0^\circ$$

Through OCB No. 2,

$$I_a = 0 + 4.1 \angle -90^\circ + 4.1 \angle 90^\circ = 0$$
$$I_b = 0 + 4.1 \angle 150^\circ + 4.1 \angle 210^\circ = 7.1 \angle 180^\circ$$
$$I_c = 0 + 4.1 \angle 30^\circ + 4.1 \angle -30^\circ = 7.1 \angle 0^\circ$$

(c) Line-to-ground fault:

At fault,

$$I_a = I_0 + I_1 + I_2 = 5.3 \angle -90^\circ + 5.3 \angle -90^\circ + 5.3 \angle -90^\circ$$
$$= 15.9 \angle -90^\circ$$
$$I_b = I_0 + a^2I_1 + aI_2 = 5.3 \angle -90^\circ (1 + a + a^2) = 0$$
$$I_c = I_0 + aI_1 + a^2I_2 = 5.3 \angle -90^\circ (1 + a + a^2) = 0$$

Through OCB No. 1,

$$I_a = 3.0 \angle -90^\circ + 2.9 \angle -90^\circ + 2.9 \angle -90^\circ = 8.8 \angle -90^\circ$$
$$I_b = 3.0 \angle -90^\circ + 2.9 \angle 150^\circ + 2.9 \angle 30^\circ = 0.1 \angle -90^\circ$$
$$I_c = 3.0 \angle -90^\circ + 2.9 \angle 30^\circ + 2.9 \angle 150^\circ = 0.1 \angle -90^\circ$$

Through OCB No. 2,

$$I_a = 2.3 \angle -90^\circ + 2.4 \angle -90^\circ + 2.4 \angle -90^\circ = 7.1 \angle -90^\circ$$
$$I_b = 2.3 \angle -90^\circ + 2.4 \angle 150^\circ + 2.4 \angle 30^\circ = 0.1 \angle 90^\circ$$
$$I_c = 2.3 \angle -90^\circ + 2.4 \angle 30^\circ + 2.4 \angle 150^\circ = 0.1 \angle 90^\circ$$

9. It merely remains to convert the calculated per-unit current into amperes.

At 66 kV, 1 p.u. current $= 10{,}000/66\sqrt{3} = 87.5$ amps

At 33 kV, 1 p.u. current $= 10{,}000/33\sqrt{3} = 175$ amps

For OCB's, the current in amps is equal to the per-unit current multiplied by 87.5 amps, since these are at 66 kV.

At the fault, the current in amps is equal to the per-unit current multiplied by 175 amps, since the fault is at the 33-kV bus.

The fault currents in amps are in Table 5-1.

It is interesting to note that a small circulatory current flows through the OCB's. This occurs whenever the ratio of positive sequence impedances in two branches is not equal to the ratio of the zero sequence impedance in those same two branches. The greater the difference in the ratios, the greater the circulating current.

The angles of the various fault currents are not given in the answers because we are generally interested primarily in magnitudes. However, in combining the sequence currents to obtain phase currents, angles must be taken into account or the answer will be incorrect.

The similar values of fault current for line-to-line and line-to-ground faults obtained in this problem are purely coincidental. They are not equal, in general.

Table 5-1 Fault Current (Amps)

		Three-Phase Fault	*Line-to-Line Fault*	*Line-to-Ground Fault*
At fault:	I_a	3240	0	2780
	I_b	3240	2820	0
	I_c	3240	2820	0
OCB No. 1:	I_a	890	0	770
	I_b	890	790	9
	I_c	890	790	9
OCB No. 2:	I_a	730	0	620
	I_b	730	620	9
	I_c	730	620	9

Problem 5-3 Transformer positive and negative sequence impedance

For a line-to-ground fault at the point indicated in Fig. 5-16, calculate the fault current in amperes at the fault.

Solution:

The first step is to reduce the circuit of Fig. 5-16 to its positive, negative, and zero sequence networks. This is illustrated in Figs. 5-17, 5-18, and 5-19.

For a line-to-ground fault, the three equivalent networks are arranged in series, as shown in Fig. 5-20.

$$X_{total} = j0.1925 + j0.2290 + j0.1000 = j0.5215$$

$$I_{sc} = E/X = j1.00/j0.5215 = 1.92 \text{ p.u.} = I_1 = I_2 = I_0$$

$$I_a = I_1 + I_2 + I_0 = (3)(1.92) = 5.76 \text{ p.u.}$$

$$I_{normal} = \frac{100{,}000{,}000 \text{ VA}}{(\sqrt{3})(13{,}800 \text{ V})} = 4180 \text{ amps}$$

I_a at fault = (5.76)(4180) = 24,100 amps *Answer*

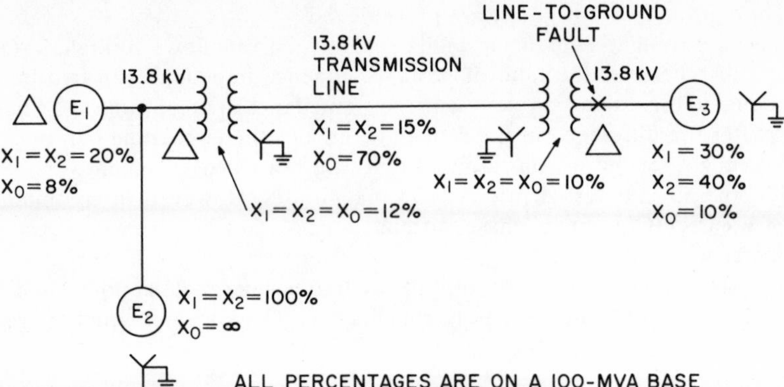

Figure 5-16

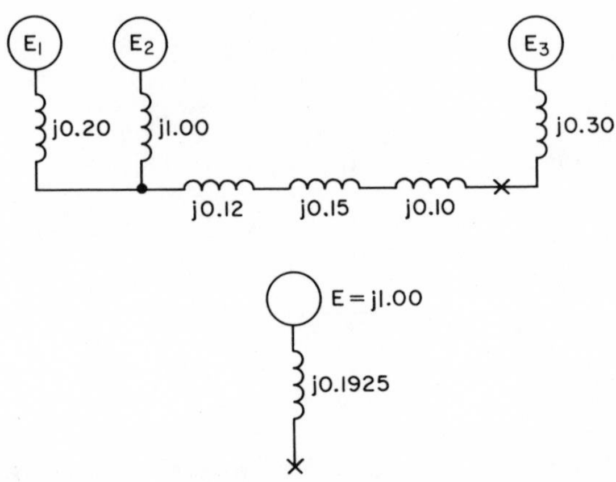

Figure 5-17

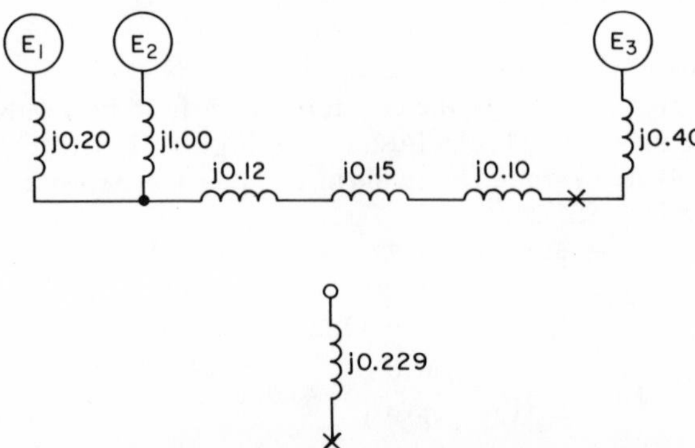

Figure 5-18

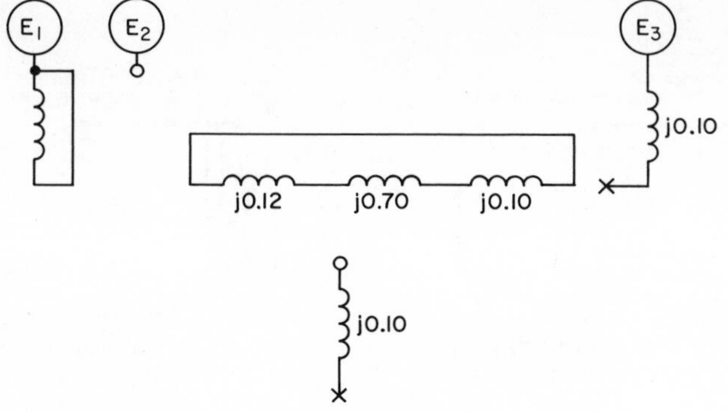

Figure 5-19

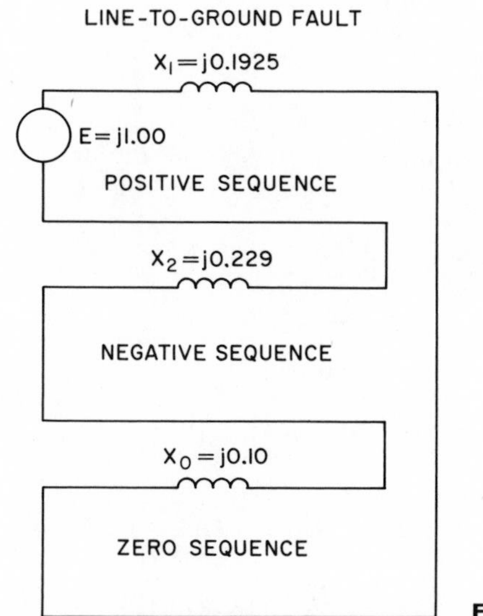

Figure 5-20

Problem 5-4 Power circle diagrams

For Fig. 5-21, assume:

1. The Port Jefferson–Holbrook ties are open.
2. All load impedances are neglected.
3. Northport (66-kV) bus is the sending end.
4. Brookhaven (66-kV bus) is the receiving end.
5. All impedances are expressed in percent on a 100-MVA base.

Draw the sending-end and the receiving-end power circles for the following conditions:

$E_s = 100\%$

$E_r = 85\%, 90\%, 95\%, 100\%,$ and 105%

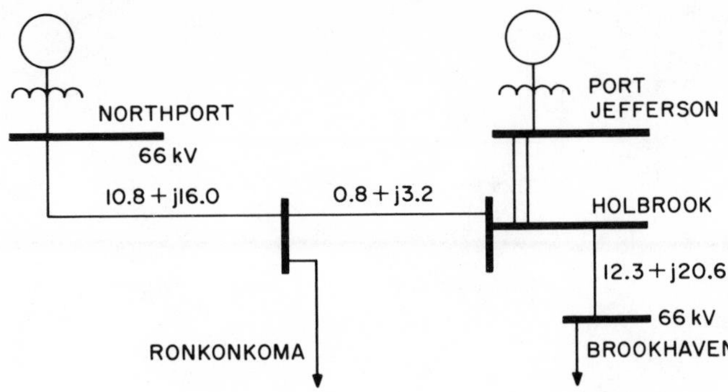

Figure 5-21

From the circle diagrams, determine the real and reactive powers in MW and Mvar at each end of the system when

$$\theta = 10^\circ \qquad E_s = 100\% \qquad E_r = 90\% \text{ and } 100\%$$

Solution:

The total impedance between the Northport bus and the Brookhaven bus is

$$\begin{array}{l} 10.8 + j16.0 \\ 0.8 + j\ 3.2 \\ \underline{12.3 + j20.6} \\ 23.9 + j39.8 = 46.5\ \underline{/59.0^\circ}\% = 0.465\ \underline{/59.0^\circ}\ \text{p.u.} \end{array}$$

When $\bar{E}_s = 1.00$ p.u. and $\bar{E}_r = 1.00$ p.u.,

$$\frac{\bar{E}_s^{\,2}}{\hat{Z}} = \frac{(1.00)^2}{0.465\ \underline{/-59^\circ}} = 2.15\ \underline{/59^\circ} = 1.11 + j1.84$$

$$-\frac{\bar{E}_r^{\,2}}{\hat{Z}} = \frac{-(1.00)^2}{0.465\ \underline{/-59^\circ}} = -\ 2.15\ \underline{/59^\circ} = -\ 1.11 - j1.84$$

$$\frac{\bar{E}_s\bar{E}_r}{\hat{Z}} = \frac{(1.00)(1.00)}{0.465\ \underline{/-59^\circ}} = 2.15\ \underline{/59^\circ} = 1.11 + j1.84$$

Data for the circle diagrams are given in Table 5-2.

Table 5-2 Data for Circle Diagrams (all values in per units)

$\bar{E}_s$	$\bar{E}_r$	$\bar{E}_s^{\,2}/\hat{Z}$	$\bar{E}_r^{\,2}/\hat{Z}$	$\bar{E}_s\bar{E}_r/\hat{Z}$
1.00	0.85	1.11 + j1.84	−0.80 − j1.33	1.83
1.00	0.90	1.11 + j1.84	−0.90 − j1.49	1.93
1.00	0.95	1.11 + j1.84	−1.00 − j1.66	2.04
1.00	1.00	1.11 + j1.84	−1.11 − j1.84	2.15
1.00	1.05	1.11 + j1.84	−1.22 − j2.02	2.26
		Center of sending-end circle	Center of receiving-end circle	Radius of circle

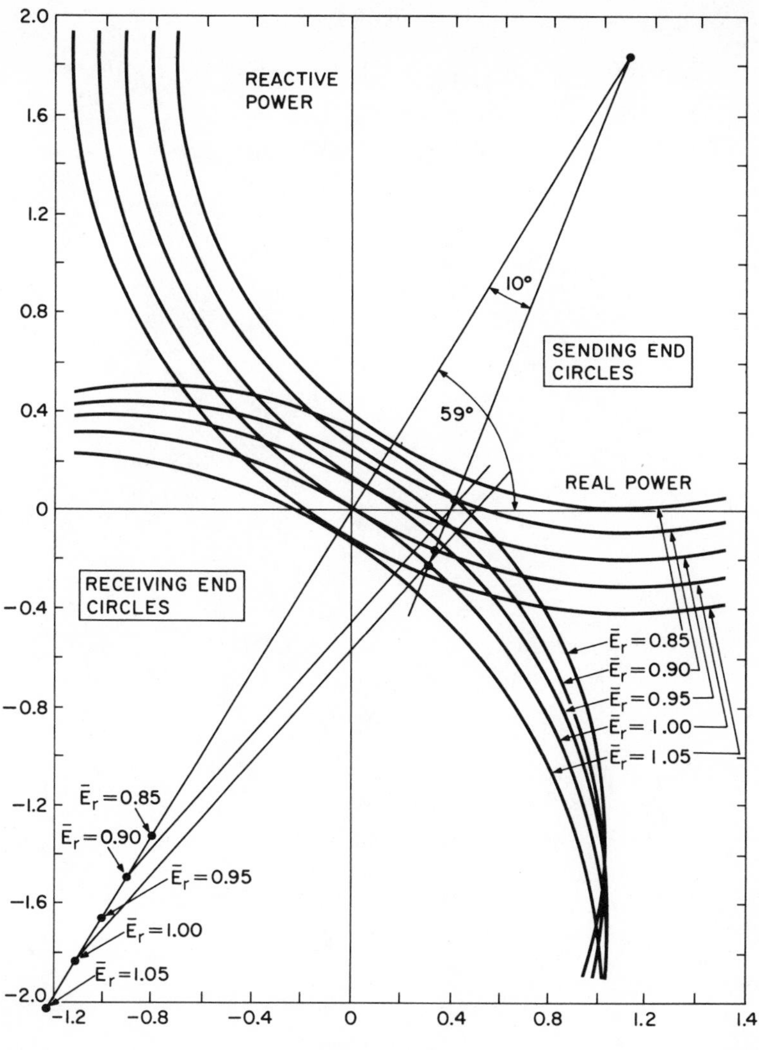

Figure 5-22

The following answers may be read from Fig. 5-22.

When $\theta = 10°$, $\bar{E}_s = 100\%$, and $\bar{E}_r = 100\%$,

$$P_s + jQ_s = 0.33 \text{ p.u.} - j0.16 \text{ p.u.} = 33 \text{ MW} - j16 \text{ Mvar} \qquad \textit{Answer}$$

When $\theta = 10°$, $\bar{E}_s = 100\%$, and $\bar{E}_r = 90\%$,

$$P_s + jQ_s = 0.42 \text{ p.u.} + j0.05 \text{ p.u.} = 42 \text{ MW} + j5 \text{ Mvar} \qquad \textit{Answer}$$

When $\theta = 10°$, $\bar{E}_s = 100\%$, and $\bar{E}_r = 100\%$,

$$P_r + jQ_r = 0.31 \text{ p.u.} - j0.22 \text{ p.u.} = 31 \text{ MW} - j22 \text{ Mvar} \qquad \textit{Answer}$$

When $\theta = 10°$, $\bar{E}_s = 100\%$, and $\bar{E}_r = 90\%$,

$$P_r + jQ_r = 0.36 \text{ p.u.} - j0.04 \text{ p.u.} = 36 \text{ MW} - j4 \text{ Mvar} \qquad \textit{Answer}$$

It may also be noted that the maximum value of $P_r + jQ_r$ (when $\bar{E}_s$ and $\bar{E}_r$ are each 100%) is 1.04 p.u. – j1.80 p.u. = 104 MW – j184 Mvar. In this case, the operating angle is approximately 59°.

chapter 6 ILLUMINATION

The proper design of a lighting installation, indoor or outdoor, should include a detailed analysis of flux distribution and consideration of glare, contrast, and esthetic factors. There is insufficient time in an examination to select the optimum equipment and arrangement. The examiner does, however, look for evidence of knowledge of the fundamentals.

Either the *I.E.S. Lighting Handbook,* or a comprehensive lighting handbook of a manufacturer, is essential to provide recommended lighting intensities, reflection factors, room indices, spacing-to-mounting-height ratios, and representative flux distribution curves of various lamps, diffusers, and reflectors.

6-1 SELECTION OF LIGHT SOURCES

The three most common types of lamps are:

Incandescent Tungsten Filament Lamps

Representative initial lumens/watt values range from 10 to 23, depending on wattage ratings, with an average life of 1000 hr, depending largely on the actual operating voltage. Cost considerations, in many cases, favor this type of lighting where frequent switching or variable-voltage conditions exist, high-intensity localized lighting is a requirement, or where color is a determining factor. The higher the filament temperature, the greater is the efficiency but the shorter is the life. Although under-voltage operation increases the life and decreases the power consumption, the increased lamp life is not economically justified in view of the decreased light output. Over-voltage operation may be economically justified for infrequently used lighting circuits, if the system is deliberately under designed.

Fluorescent Lamps

Typical, initial lumens/watt values range from 27 to 70, depending on wattage ratings, design voltage, color, and starting circuit. Average life may range from 6000 to 7500 hr, depending on the frequency of switching. This type of lamp can be economically justified when available power or system current-carrying capacity is limited, or heat dissipation is a determining factor. Fluorescent lighting is favored when distributed and uniform lighting is important, when color is not a prohibitive factor, and when the stroboscopic effect can be ignored. This type of lamp gives minimal reflected glare. Ballast losses should be considered when calculating wattage requirements and heat dissipation. Under-voltage *and* over-voltage operation reduce efficiency and lamp life. Light output is adversely affected as the ambient temperature falls or rises from 25°C. Erratic performance of glow-switch starters occurs at low temperatures. Special lamps should be used below 32°F.

Starting systems vary; all electrical discharge lamps must have auxiliary equipment to limit the arc current, since the resistance is negative. Three types of lamp circuits are available:

The Preheat Type. The preheat type requires a thermal switch (starter) to momentarily permit current to heat the lamp electrodes, and a choke (ballast) to limit the arc current. The opening of the starter switch causes a voltage surge that strikes the arc. The most common starter includes a glow tube operated switch (although, for d-c or low-temperature operation, a starter consisting of a small heater and bimetallic switch is used). The starter usually has a capacitor to suppress radio interference. The ballast may be a single-lamp or multilamp type. Uncorrected ballasts operate at a low power factor (45% to 60%), but corrected ballasts are available. Two-lamp preheat ballasts provide a high power factor (above 90%) and greatly reduce the stroboscopic effect.

The Instant-Start Type. The instant-start type requires only a ballast. The ballast is larger than that required for starter-type circuits, and ballast losses are greater. Two types of circuits are employed: lead-lag and series.

The Rapid-Start Type. The rapid-start type can be a single-lamp or two-lamp (series) design.

As a general guide to the selection of the proper circuit, the following comments are pertinent:

Preheat	*Instant-Start*	*Rapid-Start*
Advantages:		
Lowest wattage	Immediate starting	Quick starting
Lowest ballast cost	No starter required	No starter required
Negligible hum		
Disadvantages:		
Starting delay	Heavier ballast	Heaviest ballast
Highest maintenance cost (starters)	Higher wattage	Highest wattage
	More expensive	Most expensive
		Series circuit

Mercury-Vapor Lamps

Typical lumens/watt values vary from 33 to 60, depending on lamp wattage, with an average life from 12,000 to 15,000 hr. Frequent switching will reduce lamp life. There are variations now available that provide incandescent and mercury-vapor lighting within the same enclosure, and there are fluorescent mercury-vapor lamps that convert ultraviolet radiation to luminous frequencies. Cost permitting, mercury lamps are indicated when high output and long life are more important than color. Auxiliary equipment is necessary to limit the arc current.

Luminaires, which hold the light sources and direct or distribute the flux, are selected on the basis of architectural factors (degree of indirect lighting desired, appearance of the fixture, harmony with the decorative scheme, diffusion of the light flux, color, etc.) and engineering considerations (accessibility for cleaning and lamp replacement, mechanical design, maintenance factor, and lighting intensity). There is a seemingly endless variety of fixtures available. Only the thought process can be demonstrated in the representative problems given in this chapter.

6-2 METHODS OF CALCULATION

Two methods of calculation are used: the lumen method and the point-by-point method. They are briefly described below.

Lumen Method

The basic formula for the lumen method is

$$N = \frac{A \times FC}{L \times n \times CU \times MF}$$

where N = number of luminaires
n = number of lamps per luminaire
FC = lighting intensity required.
A = area, sq ft
CU = coefficient of utilization, which is the fraction of lumen output effectively utilized by the luminaire when clean.
MF = maintenance factor, which is a figure indicating whether the maintenance of the lamp and luminaire surfaces in a clean condition will be good, medium, or poor.
L = number of lumens per lamp

Procedure for Interior Lighting Design:

1. Determine the illumination level required.
2. Select the lighting system desired (direct, semidirect, general diffused, semi-indirect, or indirect). Consider supplementary (local) lighting.
3. Determine the coefficient of utilization corresponding to the room ratio.

$$\text{Room ratio} = \frac{\text{width} \times \text{length}}{(\text{mounting height above work plane}) \times (\text{width} + \text{length})}$$

For semi-indirect and indirect lighting,

$$\text{Room ratio} = \frac{3 \times \text{width} \times \text{length}}{2 \times (\text{ceiling height above work plane}) \times (\text{width} + \text{length})}$$

4. Estimate the maintenance factor.

5. Calculate the number of lamps and luminaires.
6. Determine the location of the luminaires.

Procedure for Exterior (Floodlighting) Design:

1. Determine the level of illumination required.
2. Select the type and location of floodlights. A series of trials may be necessary.
3. Determine the coefficient of beam utilization.
4. Estimate the maintenance factor.
5. Determine the number of floodlights required.
6. Check for coverage and distribution.

Point-by-Point Method

When the lighting intensities at specific points are required, the lumen method, which gives average intensities on a plane, is not accurate. The point-by-point method is used. This method recognizes that the lighting intensity from a point source at some point P is inversely proportional to the square of the distance from the source to point P. In Fig. 6-1, a point source is shown shedding its light on a horizontal surface and on a vertical surface. The formulas for flux intensities normal to the surfaces are:

For the horizontal surface,

$$\mathrm{FC} = \frac{\mathrm{CP} \times \cos\theta}{\mathrm{D}^2}$$

$$= \frac{\mathrm{CP} \times \mathrm{H}}{\mathrm{D}^3}$$

For the vertical surface,

$$\mathrm{FC} = \frac{\mathrm{CP} \times \sin\theta}{\mathrm{D}^2}$$

$$= \frac{\mathrm{CP} \times \mathrm{S}}{\mathrm{D}^3}$$

where CP is the candlepower of the light source in the direction from the source to point P.

Tables appear in handbooks that enable one to read directly the intensities from a point source to variously located points on horizontal and vertical surfaces.

Although an incandescent lamp or a light source in a small globe can be

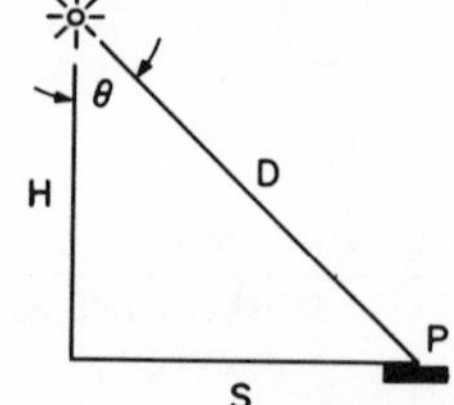

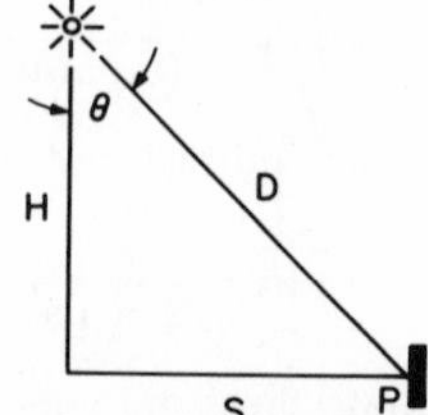

Figure 6-1

considered, with good accuracy, to be a point source, a linear source (such as a fluorescent tube) or a surface source (such as a ceiling panel) cannot be so considered, unless the distance from the source to the point in question is at least five times the greatest dimension of the distributed source. Otherwise, the intensity at point P varies (approximately) inversely as the distance from a linear source, and does not vary at all with the distance from a surface source. When short distances are involved, these factors must be considered. Further, for sources having directional variations in candlepower (projector or reflector lamps, etc.), catalogs and handbooks give illumination intensity tables for distances between the source and the points within the area being illuminated.

PROBLEMS

Problem 6-1 Illumination design for areas in an industrial plant

An industrial plant contains the following areas to be lighted. Cost of installation and cost of operation are both important. The plant has no regular lighting maintenance program.

1. 40-×-100-ft machine shop with 16-ft truss height; a typical galvanized sheet iron building. Task performed there is the precision machining of small metal parts.
2. 40-×-100-ft room of same construction as for 1. Task performed there is the bench assembly of commercial radio and TV sets.
3. 60-×-80-ft drafting office with 10-ft acoustical ceiling. Task performed there is ordinary drafting; no extra fine work.
4. 30-×-40-ft cafeteria and kitchen area combined, with 9-ft ceiling.

For each area, specify the following:

(a) The illumination level to be provided. State how much general and how much supplementary lighting would be provided. Do *not* design the system.
(b) The type of luminaire to be used for general and for supplementary lighting. Draw a cross-sectional sketch. State the type of lamp used.
(c) Briefly list the characteristics of the luminaire that make it particularly suitable for each application.

Solution:

This problem emphasizes the importance of a balance between general and supplementary lighting, the wide range of lighting intensities recommended for various seeing tasks, and the part played by the physical environment. There is more than one acceptable solution.

1. (a) The minimum desirable intensity at the working plane could be as high as 500 fc. Of this, 50 fc to 60 fc of general lighting should be provided.
   (b) See Fig. 6-2.
   (c) Fluorescent lighting is chosen for general illumination to provide the greatest lumens/watt/investment dollar and still obtain flux distribution. Direct reflectors are indicated because of the absence of a reflective ceiling. Lead-lag

ballasts will minimize the stroboscopic effect. Instant-start lamps will eliminate starter maintenance. A high level of supplementary lighting is necessary, since it would be economically prohibitive, and undesirable from the standpoint of glare, to provide 500 fc of general illumination in a building of this type. For local lighting, mercury (standard white or high-output white) lamps can give the greatest lighting intensity per watt; incandescent lamps completely eliminate the stroboscopic effect, which can be a factor at some machine tool speeds.

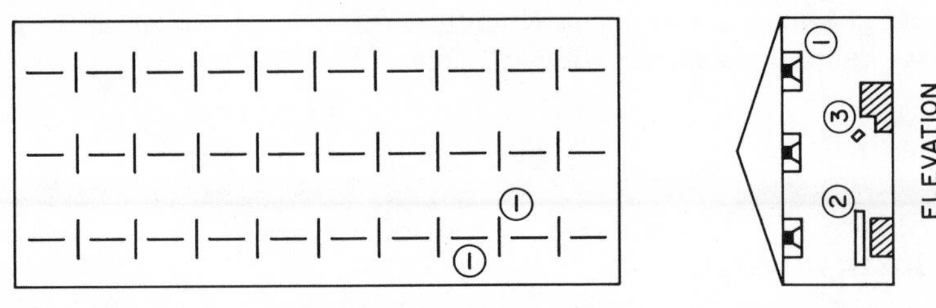

Figure 6-2. *Note:* 1: Two-lamp fluorescent, 4-ft open-end direct reflectors for general illumination. Use lead-lag ballasts and instant-start circuit. 2: Multi-lamp (fluorescent or fluorescent-mercury) troffer with diffuser panel. 3: Projector or spot lamp (incandescent) with circular louvers.

2. (a) 100 fc could be the minimum desirable intensity on the benches. About 40 fc of general lighting should be provided.
   (b) See Fig. 6-3.
   (c) Fluorescent lighting with lead-lag ballasts and instant-start circuits are recommended for the reasons stated in 1.(c). (High-bay, wide-distribution mercury lamps would not be suitable for this relatively low ceiling height.) Troffers are recommended for supplementary lighting rather than spot reflectors, because moderate intensity is acceptable, and a larger working area is involved than in area 1. Diffusers are necessary to avoid reflections from the work.
3. (a) 150 fc (minimum) is recommended; all of this should be general lighting.
   (b) See Fig. 6-4.

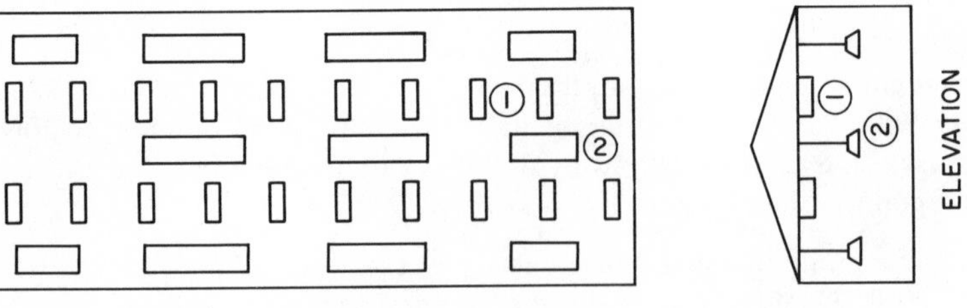

Figure 6-3. *Note:* Two-lamp (fluorescent) open-end direct reflector for instant-start lamps. Use lead-lag ballasts. 2: Multi-lamp troffers with ribbed-glass or checkerboard louvers mounted (say 7 ft) over benches.

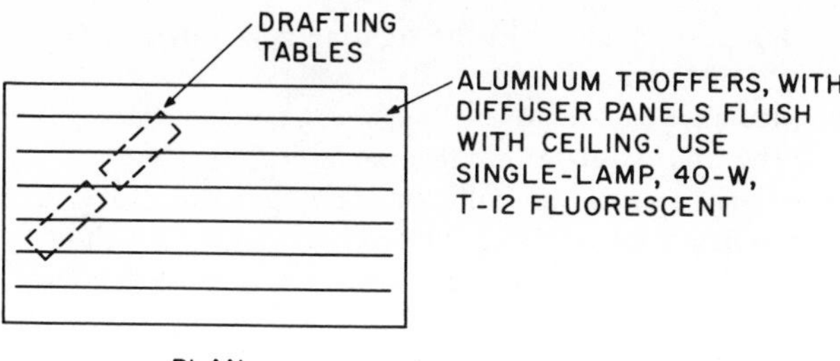

Figure 6-4

(c) In a drafting room, shadows and reflected glare should be minimized. This calls for an approach to an infinite number of low-intensity light sources. Slanting the tables, both horizontally and vertically, will minimize shadows and reflected glare. (Slanting the fixture is not recommended if the room is to be converted to another use in the future.)

An alternate solution would be to suspend semidirect aluminum reflectors, with closed ends, with say 2-to-40-watt fluorescent lamps in each fixture.

4. (a) 50 fc of general illumination is recommended for the kitchen area and for the cafeteria. No supplementary lighting is necessary.

(b) In the kitchen area, install deluxe, cool-white two-lamp fluorescent fixtures in continuous rows. Fixtures can be semidirect, just below the ceiling. See Fig. 6-5.

In the cafeteria area, install standard, warm-white fluorescent lamps above either a louverall ceiling or transparent diffusing panels in the ceiling. See Fig. 6-5.

(c) For safety, as well as sanitary reasons, every working surface in a kitchen should be well illuminated and glare free. The deluxe, cool-white lamp emits light resembling daylight, and is psychologically desirable in a kitchen. The primary consideration in the cafeteria area is that the lighting be diffused; intensities should be lower than the employees' working area to achieve a "change of pace."

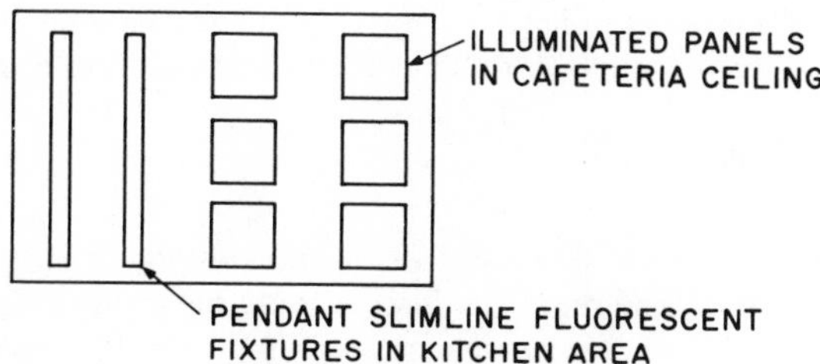

Figure 6-5

Problem 6-2 Illumination design for generating station control room

The control room in a generating station is 40 × 100 ft. Vertical instrument panels are 22 ft apart with 30-in. high control benchboards between. It is desired to maintain 50 fc at the benchboard level. A louverall ceiling will be installed 12 ft above the floor, with lamps 3 ft higher in the lighting cavity and accessible only from below. The room will be ventilated.

(a) Specify the reflectance factors for ceiling, walls, panel surfaces, and floors.

(b) What will be the approximate initial footcandles?

(c) Select a type of lighting from the following, giving reasons for your choice: incandescent, standard fluorescent, slimline fluorescent, and cold cathode.

(d) If the supply is 208 volts, 4-wire, how would you switch the lamps?

Solution:

In this problem, distributed lighting over a large area is required and the watts/sq ft are high. Assumptions must be made with regard to reflection factors, part (a), in order to arrive at the required lamp lumens. Room index, maintenance factor, and coefficient of utilization are taken from the *Westinghouse Lighting Handbook*.

(a) Reflection factors:

Ceiling: 80% (cavity reflectance)
Walls: 30%
Floor: 10%
Panel surfaces: 10%

(b) Assuming good maintenance, the maintenance factor for this type of luminaire would be 0.70. Therefore, the initial intensity of illumination would be about 50/0.70 or 71.5 fc. However, since allowance must be made for decrease in lumen output after say 40% of lamp life, an adequate installation would call for about 75 fc.

(c) Use cold-white, fluorescent, instant-start type lamps. A fluorescent lamp is selected because of its high lumens/watt, its distributed flux, and its long life. Instant start is recommended to avoid the maintenance problem of starter replacement. Rapid start is not desired because of its series connection, since this is a critical lighting service. Stroboscopic effect should be nil with the three-phase supply and with multilamp ballasts. Ventilation will permit the higher ballast losses.

(d) The room index for semidirect lighting, louverall design, and 12½-ft lamp mounting height above the working plane is C or D. For the assumed reflectance factors, the coefficient of utilization is 0.50. The required lumen output is

$$\frac{75 \times 40 \times 100}{0.50} = 600{,}000 \text{ lumens}$$

The instant-start, 40-W-T-12-48-in. lamp has an initial output of 2550 lumens. Approximately 235 lamps would be required. Lamps could be arranged in 12 rows of 20 lamps each, with 3-ft 4-in. spacing between rows. (For louverall design, spacing should not be more than twice the distance between the lamps and the louvers.) Somewhat wider spacing could be used, perimeter lighting decreased, number of rows decreased, and the number of lamps in certain rows increased to reduce the total load and still balance the load between phases. Using two-lamp lag-lead ballasts (16 watts), the total wattage (for 240 lamps) would be 11,520 watts, or say 4000 watts/phase. Six 30-ampere circuits, using two circuits per phase would be satisfactory. Adjacent rows would be connected to different phases. This would permit partial lighting of the room. A multibreaker is recommended.

Problem 6-3 Illumination design for an office

An office area 200 × 100 ft is to have fluorescent lighting of appropriate intensity and of economical design. Go through the complete consideration of this project, giving all data from supply lines to lights on desks. The area may eventually be partitioned with standing walls halfway to the ceiling, which is 14 ft high. All other conditions may be selected or varied to give an ideal installation.

Solution:

Present recommendations for office lighting would call for 100 fc. In order to obtain general lighting of this magnitude with fluorescent lamps, closely spaced rows of continuous fixtures are necessary. The limitation of fluorescent lamps is in their lumens/ft at consumer voltages. Despite this, fluorescent lighting is the most economical method of providing distributed lighting.

At these relatively high levels, the office furnishing (ceiling, floor, wall surfaces, desks, etc.) assumes great importance. In the following solution, 75 fc (minimum) is assumed as an acceptable level commensurate with the office decor.

1. Provide room surfaces to give the following reflectances:

   Ceiling: 0.60 to 0.80
   Walls: 0.50 to 0.60
   Desk tops: 0.30
   Floor: 0.10 or less

2. Select aluminized troffers, with metal cross-louvers, flush with the ceiling, containing three 40-watt, instant-start, standard-white, 48-in. fluorescent lamps with high-power-factor ballast including compensators. (This mounting height should be maintained because of the possibility of partitions being installed in the future.)
3. Mounting height: 11 ft (assuming desk tops are 3 ft from the floor).
4. Room ratio $= \dfrac{200 \times 100}{11 \times 300} = 6$

   Room index: A.
5. Maintenance factor: 0.7 (good maintenance assumed).
6. Coefficient of utilization: 0.62.
7. Mean lumens/lamp (after 40% life): 2400.
8. Number of lamps required:

$$\frac{75 \times 20000}{2400 \times 0.70 \times 0.62} = 1440$$

9. Number of fixtures required: 480. Arrangement: 24 rows, 5-ft spacing between rows, and 24 fixtures per row. (*Note:* The manager's room could be given special consideration. Fixtures could be arranged in continuous rows, in a rectangular pattern, flush with the ceiling, or indirect lighting fixtures could be installed.)
10. Total power required:

1440 lamps at 0.425 amp at 102 volts =	62,000 watts
ballasts (estimated) =	23,000 watts
Total	85,000 watts

Assuming supply is available at 120/208 V, 3 phase, 4 wire, 60 Hz, and assuming 90% power factor, the line current would be 263 amps.

11. Circuit arrangement: Provide a lighting panel consisting of a 300-amp main breaker; 3-pole, solid neutral; with 24 single-pole, 20-amp circuit breakers (including four spare circuits). Each single-pole breaker will supply one row, using No. 12 AWG TW wire in a rigid metal conduit, (or BX cable). Adjacent rows should be connected to different phases so as to approximately balance the loads on the phases.

Problem 6-4 Outdoor illumination of modern building

A modern research laboratory building has walls of light-colored brick and glass windows in narrow metal frames. Its outline and dimensions are as shown in the Fig. 6-6. A well-kept lawn separates the building from the road. There is a distance of 150 ft from the roadway to the nearest point of the building parallel to the road. It is desired to floodlight the three sides of the building that meet the front lawn. The illumination level is to be the lowest satisfactory level for this type of floodlighting. Although poles on the lawn are undesirable, they may be used on the edge of the roadway.

Specify a layout of the required illumination equipment. Compute the total power to be consumed.

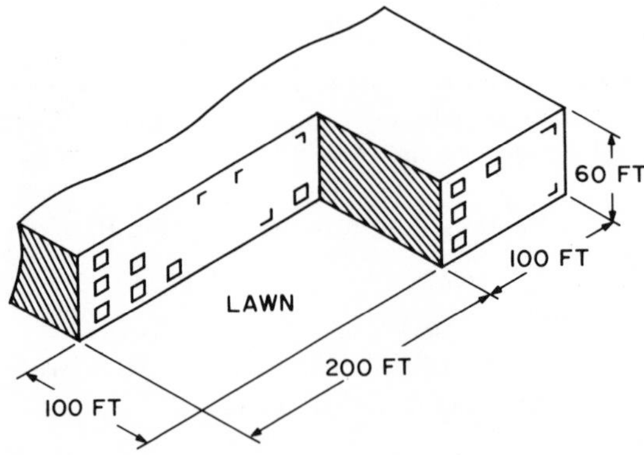

Figure 6-6

Solution:

This is an application of the lumen method in which the following criteria should be considered:

1. Avoid light directed toward the road.
2. Confine light to the building.
3. Overlap corners.
4. Use narrow beams, if possible, to provide uniformity.
5. Increase brightness toward top of the wall.
6. Avoid shadow forming.
7. Each bank of floods should cover an area whose length does not exceed the perpendicular distance from the bank to the building.

A maintained intensity of 5 fc is recommended. Select enclosed heavy-duty floodlights to withstand weather and to have a high maintenance efficiency. Use a maintenance factor of 0.75. Assume that color is not desired; assume dark surroundings. Omit poles, if possible, for appearance considerations.

The coefficient of beam utilization should be between 0.60 and 0.90. A solution would be to use three *banks* of floodlights, A, B, and C as shown in Fig. 6-7. The total wall surface is 400 ft × 60 ft or 24,000 sq ft; however, a portion of this wall will be covered by reflected light. Assume the area to be covered by direct lighting is 95% of this.

Because of the horizontal distances involved, the lens (medium spread) selected would have to be as follows:

	Vertical spread	*Horizontal spread*	*NEMA Class (spread of minor axis)*
A	20°	50°	2
B	20°	40°	2
C	30°	45°	3

The beam lumens for heavy-duty floodlights are:

Watts	500	1000	1500
Lumens	3800	8500	15,000

Assume the coefficient of beam utilization would be 75% for this configuration. The number of floodlights in each bank is

$$\frac{\text{area} \times \text{fc}}{\text{beam lumens} \times \text{CBU} \times \text{MF}}$$

For 1000-watt floodlights:

Bank A:

$$\frac{140 \times 60 \times 5}{8500 \times 0.75 \times 0.75} = 8.8 \cong 9 \text{ floodlights}$$

Bank B:

$$\frac{100 \times 60 \times 5}{8500 \times 0.75 \times 0.75} = 6.3 \cong 6 \text{ floodlights}$$

Bank C:

$$\frac{140 \times 60 \times 5}{8500 \times 0.75 \times 0.75} = 8.8 \cong 9 \text{ floodlights}$$

This solution, therefore, would require twenty-four 1000-watt heavy-duty floodlights, with medium-spread elliptical lenses, consuming a total of 24 kW. Underground (parkway) cable would be used, and the banks would be recessed in the lawn or concealed by decorative shrubs or flowers. *Answer*

Actually, a detailed analysis of flux distribution is desirable with a view toward reducing glare, especially for the bank of floods closest to the road.

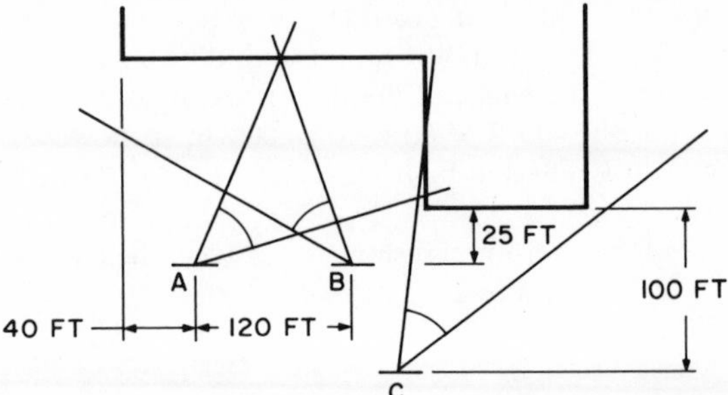

Figure 6-7

Problem 6-5 Outdoor illumination of miniature golf course

Figure 6-8 shows the plan of an outdoor miniature golf course. Design a suitable floodlighting system. There is no limitation on the location of poles, but the pole height should not exceed 25 ft.

Solution:

In applying the beam lumen method, after having determined the illumination intensity required, the most suitable type of floodlight should be selected. Then, by successive trials, the locations and wattage can be determined. The solution illustrates the basic technical approach. However, in actual practice, and depending on funds available, the use of multiluminaire hoods, or of mercury-vapor lamps on appropriate stanchions would be developed.

The minimum intensity should be 10 to 14 fc. A floodlight with a 50° beam spread would be acceptable. Assuming economy governs, use an open, ground-area type. Select a 25-ft mounting height. Beam lumens will be about 10 lumens/watt. Assume a maintenance factor of 65%. The floods should be located and pointed so that the coefficient of beam utilization is over 60%.

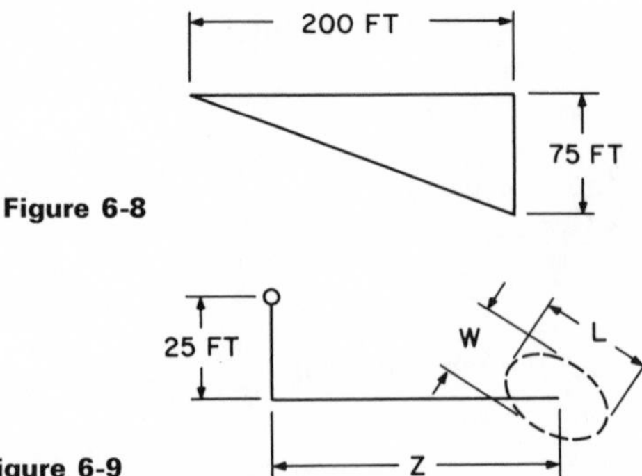

Figure 6-8

Figure 6-9

In Fig. 6-9, the elliptical pattern of the ground that is illuminated is shown Z feet from the pole horizontally; L and W are the major and minor axes of the ellipse. From manufacturers' catalogs, data can be obtained to construct the following table for the floodlight selected:

Z	*L*	*W*	*Area*	*Watts (for 12 fc)*
0	18	18	185	250
30	55	32	970	1500
40	98	42	2300	(excessive glare
50	194	60	6450	and wattage)

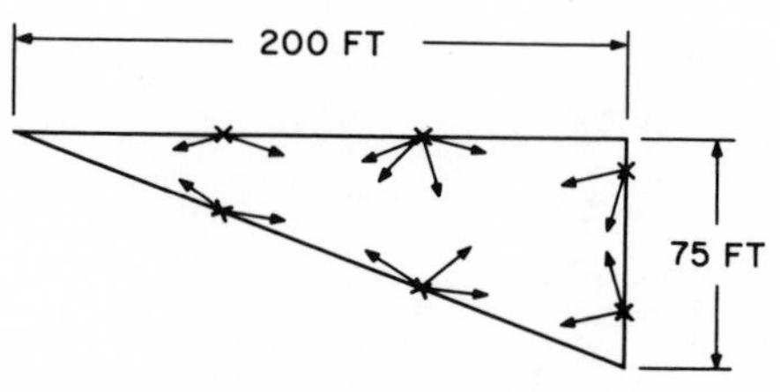

Figure 6-10

Using an average Z of 30 ft and 15 floodlights located on six poles as indicated in the Fig. 6-10, a rough solution can be obtained. *Note:* Area to be illuminated is 7500 sq ft.

$$\text{Watts required} = \frac{7500 \times 12}{0.65 \times 0.60 \times 10} = 23\ \text{kW} \qquad \textit{Answer}$$

Number of floods = 23,000/1500 = 15 *Answer*

chapter 7

WIRE COMMUNICATION

In the discussions of linear circuits (Chap. 1 and Chap. 2) and in the analysis of many electrical power networks, one of the major assumptions is that the basic network parameters (R, L, G, B) are *lumped* and independent of the excitation and response variables (E and I in either order). Actually, the parameters of a line are not lumped but are distributed; this fact must be considered in very long lines. At frequencies appreciably higher than power frequencies, a physically short line can be a very short line electrically. In communication lines, therefore, distributed parameters form the rule rather than the exception. Parameters are expressed in values per unit length of line.

7-1 THE GENERAL TRANSMISSION LINE

By considering a line (i.e., a two-wire circuit) as a series of T-sections and solving the differential equations of the line, expressions containing hyperbolic functions are obtained. From these, convenient concepts and formulas have been developed that permit solution of many communication problems without recourse to tables of hyperbolic functions. The use of these concepts and formulas is demonstrated in the problems at the end of the chapter. However, certain basic terms and expressions follow:

Condition for Maximum Power Transfer: The impedance of the source must equal the conjugate of the impedance of the line connected to the load, or, equivalently, the impedance of the source connected to the line must equal the conjugate of the impedance of the load. Note carefully that one of these impedances is considered fixed (in most cases, the impedance of the source). The conjugate of $Z\underline{/\theta}$ is $Z\underline{/-\theta}$

Gain: By definition, gain (decibels) $= 10 \log P_R/P_S$, where P_R is the power received and P_S is the power sent.

By definition, gain (nepers) $N = \ln V_R/V_S$ (for voltage gain) $= \ln I_R/I_S$ (for current gain), where V and I are the magnitudes (scalar) of the respective voltages and currents. When $V_R/V_S = I_R/I_S$,

$$e^{2N} = 10^{0.1 \times dB}$$

Therefore, 1 neper = 8.686 decibels. This condition exists in properly matched networks.

Propagation Constant (γ): By definition,

$$\gamma = \alpha + j\beta = \sqrt{ZY}$$

where α = attenuation, nepers ($\ln I_S/I_R$)
β = phase shift, radians (1 radian = 57.3°)
Z = series impedance of line, ohms/unit length
Y = shunt admittance of line, mhos/unit length

Characteristic Impedance (Z_0): By definition,

$$Z_0 = \sqrt{Z/Y}$$

This is the required impedance of the receiver (i.e., the terminal impedance) so that the network will appear to the source as an infinite line.

Note: Although it is previously mentioned that parameters Z and Y are values per unit length of line, when the line contains lumped parameters, or for very high frequencies where a rather short length may constitute a circuit element, per-unit parameters cannot be used and Z_0 must be expressed in terms of open-circuit and short-circuit measurements. In terms of measured values:

$$Z_0 = \sqrt{Z_{oc}Z_{sc}} \qquad \text{and} \qquad \tanh \gamma l = \sqrt{Z_{sc}/Z_{oc}}$$

where l = length
tanh = hyperbolic tangent
Z_{oc} = input impedance of network with output terminals open-circuited,
Z_{sc} = input impedance with output terminals short-circuited.

If the receiver (load) impedance is Z_0, then it can be shown that the voltage and current at x distance from the receiver are

$$V = V_S e^{-\gamma x} \qquad \text{and} \qquad I = I_S e^{-\gamma x}$$

Obviously, attenuation is occurring along the line. Since sinusoidal voltages are assumed, the voltage at any one point varies with time; hence, we have a travelling wave (called the incident wave) proceeding toward the receiver, which validates the concept of propagation and propagation velocity.

Velocity of Propagation (v): In an actual line, v is lower than the velocity of light in space (3×10^8 m/sec) because of resistance, inductance, permittivity, and leakage. For the general case,

$$v = \omega/\beta$$

$$\alpha = \beta^2 + RG - \omega^2 LC$$

$$\beta = \sqrt{\frac{\omega^2 LC - RG + [(RG - \omega^2 LC)^2 + \omega^2(LG + CR)^2]^{1/2}}{2}}$$

Various assumptions are made to simplify the above expressions for the low-frequency (audio) line and for the high-frequency line.

Distortion: In an actual line, α, β, and v vary with frequency. All frequencies will not be attenuated equally (amplitude distortion), nor will v be the same for all frequencies (delay distortion). The relationship that must exist for there to be no distortion is

$$L/C = R/G$$

Then, $\alpha = \frac{R}{2}\sqrt{\frac{L}{C}}$

$$\beta = \omega\sqrt{LC}$$

and $v = 1/\sqrt{LC}$

Reflected Waves: When the receiver impedance is other than Z_0, the incident wave is reflected at the receiver back toward the source. The instantaneous voltage at any point along the line is equal to the sum of the instantaneous values of the incident wave and the reflected wave. Further, if the source impedance is not equal to Z_0 of the line, the reflected wave is again reflected at the source. This transfer of energy back and forth results in a line loss. Generally, reflection is not desired. The following terms are frequently used:

$$\text{Reflection coefficient } K = \frac{\text{reflected voltage at the receiver}}{\text{incident voltage at the receiver}}$$

$$\text{Reflection factor } k = \frac{\text{actual current}}{\text{current that would exist if } Z_R = Z_0}$$

A typical sequence to arrive at the dB loss and transmission efficiency of a line not terminated in Z_0 follows:

1. Determine K:

$$K = \frac{Z_R - Z_0}{Z_R + Z_0}$$

2. Determine Z_S:

$$Z_S = Z_0\frac{e^{\gamma l} + Ke^{-\gamma l}}{e^{\gamma l} - Ke^{-\gamma l}}$$

3. Calculate I_S:

$$I_S = E_S/Z_S$$

(It is convenient to assign an arbitrary value of $1\angle 0°$ volt to E_S.)

4. Calculate I_R from:

$$\frac{I_S}{I_R} = \frac{Z_R + Z_0}{2Z_0}(e^{\gamma l} - Ke^{-\gamma l})$$

5. Calculate E_R, which is $I_R Z_R$. Then

$$P_R = I_R{}^2R \qquad \text{and} \qquad P_S = E_S I_S \cos\theta$$

From these values, both the dB loss and the efficiency can be determined.

7-2 TELEPHONE LINES AND LOADING COILS

In the ordinary twisted-pair telephone cable, the values of L and G are negligible, so that the characteristic expressions become

$$\alpha = \sqrt{\omega CR/2} = \beta$$
$$v = \omega/\beta = \sqrt{2\omega/CR}$$

In the open-wire line, if R and C can be considered negligible,

$$v = \frac{3 \times 10^8}{\sqrt{1 - 4 \log a/D}} \text{ m/sec}$$

where a is the conductor radius and D is the conductor spacing.

There is considerable distortion, since both α and v are functions of frequency. To overcome this, the inductance per unit length should be increased. However, it is economically unfeasible to do this, and the next best solution is to insert lumped inductances (loading coils) at intervals along the line. This procedure is called *loading*. The improvement on open-wire lines is usually not sufficient to economically justify loading, but it is quite practicable in telephone cables containing twisted pairs. In practice, complete elimination of distortion is not possible, since L and R are functions of frequency. Considerable improvement is obtained, however, over a limited frequency range. Campbell's Equation is used to calculate the propagation constant of a line consisting of distributed and lumped parameters:

$$\cosh N\gamma' = \frac{Z_c}{2Z_0} \sinh N\gamma + \cosh N\gamma$$

where γ' = new propagation constant per mile, N = number of miles between loading coils, and Z_c = impedance of the loading coil.

7-3 THE HIGH-FREQUENCY LINE

At frequencies of 1 MHz and higher, the internal inductance is zero, ωL is very much greater than R, and G is virtually zero. Depending on the frequency and usage of the high-frequency line, one of two assumptions is used: (a) that the resistance is negligible (the dissipationless line), and (b) that the resistance is small but not negligible (the line of small dissipation). The latter is used when the line is being employed as a circuit element (frequencies in the order of 100 MHz). The Q of such an element is much higher than a conventional coil-capacitor combination, and a quarter or half-wavelength high-frequency line gives a more uniform frequency response, since the inductance of the leads from a conventional capacitor at very high frequencies can make the net reactance of the capacitor inductive. Line characteristics for these two cases are shown in Table 7-1.

For an open-wire line, $Z_0 = 120 \ln D/a = 276 \log D/a$ and $v = 3 \times 10^8$ m/sec.

For a coaxial line,

$$Z_0 = \frac{60}{\sqrt{e_r}} \ln \frac{b}{a} = \frac{138}{\sqrt{e_r}} \log \frac{b}{a}$$

and $v = \frac{3 \times 10^8}{\sqrt{e_r}}$ m/sec

where a = outer radius of inner conductor
b = inner radius of outer conductor
e_r = relative permittivity of dielectric (e_r = 1.0 for air)

The power transmitted along a dissipationless line is easily measured:

$$P = \frac{|E_{max}||E_{min}|}{R_0} = |I_{max}||I_{min}|R_0$$

Table 7-1

	Dissipationless Line	*Line of Small Dissipation*
Z	$j\omega L$	$R + j\omega L$
Y	$j\omega C$	$j\omega C$
Z_0	$\sqrt{\frac{L}{C}} = R_0$ (see note)	$\sqrt{\frac{L}{C}}\left(1 - j\frac{R}{\omega L}\right) \cong \sqrt{\frac{L}{C}}$
α	0	$R/2R_0$
β	$\omega\sqrt{LC}$	$\omega\sqrt{LC}$
γ	$j\omega\sqrt{LC}$	$R/2R_0 + j\omega\sqrt{LC}$
$v = \frac{\omega}{\beta}$	$\frac{1}{\sqrt{LC}}$	$\frac{1}{\sqrt{LC}(1 + R^2/8\omega^2L^2)}$

Actually, the reduction in velocity due to line resistance is much smaller than 1%.

Standing Waves

The combination of the incident wave and the reflected wave results in a standing wave along the line. Although the voltage at any one point is a time variant, oscillating between a maximum value and a minimum value *for that particular point,* measurements will show that at intervals of one wavelength along the line, the maximum voltage will reach its highest value; and at a distance of one-half wavelength, it will reach its lowest value. The following terms are frequently used:

Standing-Wave Ratio: By definition,

$$\text{SWR or } \rho = V_{max}/V_{min} = -I_{max}/I_{min}$$

Tank Circuit: A parallel resonant (antiresonant) circuit.

Matching Stub: A short-circuited or open-circuited quarter-wavelength or half-wavelength (or multiples thereof) section of line used to match the impedance of an incoming circuit to the impedance of a load circuit.

Merit Factor: By definition, the merit factor Q is the ratio of the product two times the maximum energy stored per cycle to the energy dissipated per cycle.

$$Q = \omega L/R_L = R_C\omega C$$

where the resistance is the series resistance of the coil or capacitor. Usually, all the resistance is assumed to be in series with the coil.

The standing-wave ratio is an important entity. It can be shown that

$$\rho = \frac{1 + |K|}{1 - |K|}$$

and $$|K| = \frac{\rho - 1}{\rho + 1}$$

Standing-wave measurements can be made on both open-wire and coaxial lines. In the latter, a longitudinal slot is cut, one-half wavelength or more, to permit the insertion of a probe (vacuum-tube voltmeter connected between the probe and the cable sheath). For the special case when Z_R is resistive (R_R),

$$\rho = R_R/R_0 \text{ for } R_R > R_0$$
$$= R_0/R_R \text{ for } R_R < R_0$$

Use of Transmission Line for Circuit Elements

It is interesting to compare short sections of a high-frequency line. The impedance of a short-circuited dissipationless line is given as

$$Z_{sc} = jR_0 \tan 2\pi s/\lambda$$

where s = length of line, and λ = wavelength (v/f).

In other words, a short-circuited quarter-wavelength line is an inductor and a half-wavelength line is a capacitor. The open-circuited line impedance is given as

$$Z_{oc} = -jR_0 \cot 2\pi s/\lambda$$

An open-circuited quarter-wavelength line is a capacitor and a half-wavelength line is an inductor.

For lines with small but not negligible dissipation (frequencies of 100 MHz and higher), the impedance expressions become more complex, although the sign of the reactance remains that as given above for the dissipationless line.

For a short-circuited line,

Quarter-wave:

$$Z_{sc} = \frac{8R_0^2}{R(2n - 1)\lambda}$$

where n = odd multiple of quarter wavelengths.

Half-wave:

$$Z_{sc} = Rn'\lambda/4$$

where n′ = even or odd multiple of half wavelengths.

For an open-circuited line,

Quarter-wave:

$$Z_{oc} = \frac{R(2n - 1)\lambda}{8}$$

Half-wave:

$$Z_{oc} = 4R_0^2/Rn\lambda$$

The short-circuited $n'\lambda/2$ line and the open-circuited $n\lambda/4$ line behave as a series resonant circuit. The short-circuited $n\lambda/4$ line and the open-circuited $n'\lambda/2$ line behave as a parallel resonant circuit. The quarter-wavelength line permits shorter physical lengths, which in most cases is desirable. As the integers n and n′ increase, they decrease the maxima and increase the minima of the voltages along the line.

The short-circuited quarter-wavelength line is commonly applied as an insulator in supporting high-frequency lines; it is also used for impedance matching.

The Circle Diagram

The basic equation of the high-frequency line, whether or not it contains resistance, is

$$\frac{Z_S}{R_0} = \frac{1 + |K|\underline{/\phi - 2\beta s}}{1 - |K|\underline{/\phi - 2\beta s}} = r_a + jx_a$$

where Z_S = input impedance, ϕ = phase angle of K, and r_a and x_a = arbitrary symbols for convenience.

The circle diagram is a graphical representation of the basic equation for the dissipationless line. Values of r_a and x_a are plotted, giving circles for various values of ρ (standing-wave ratio). To find the input impedance of the dissipationless line, Z_R/R_0 is determined and plotted on the circle diagram. The constant-ρ line passing through this point is followed through an arc βs and new coordinates r_a' and x_a' are read to give the phasor Z_s/R_0, and Z_S is computed.

The Smith Chart provides circles of constant r_a and x_a instead of circles of constant ρ and lines of constant βs. In both diagrams, admittances can be used in lieu of impedances. Some practice is required to properly use these charts.

PROBLEMS

Problem 7-1 Electric field in coaxial cable

A 1,500,000-circular mil, single-conductor, lead-sheath cable has a conductor diameter of 1.412 in. Between the conductor and sheath is a 0.310-in. thick rubber insulation having a dielectric constant of 3.0 and a dielectric strength of 400,000 volts (maximum) per inch.

(a) What is the highest effective or rms voltage that can be applied between the conductor and the sheath without exceeding the dielectric strength of the rubber?

(b) With this particular sheath inside diameter, what conductor diameter would cause the gradient or dielectric stress to be a minimum?

Solution:

(a) It can be shown that for a coaxial cable, the electric field intensity at any point P is

$$\mathcal{E} = \frac{Q}{2\pi r e_r e_0} \tag{7-1}$$

where Q = charge (coulombs) per meter of conductor length
e_r = relative permittivity of the dielectric (in this case, 3.0)
e_0 = permittivity of space = 8.85×10^{-12} in the mks system

and
$$C = \frac{2\pi e_r e_0}{\ln b/a} \text{ farads/m} \tag{7-2}$$

(See Fig. 7-1.) Since Q = CV, where V is the potential difference between inner and outer conductors, substituting Eq. (7-2) in Eq. (7-1),

$$\mathcal{E} = \frac{V}{r \ln b/a}$$

Obviously, the maximum intensity occurs where a = r or

$$\mathcal{E} = \frac{V}{a \ln b/a} \text{ volts/unit length} \tag{7-3}$$

By differentiating, and setting $d\mathcal{E}/da = 0$, $\mathcal{E}$ will be a minimum when ln b/a = 1 or b/a = 2.718.

From Eq. (7-3),

$$\mathcal{E} = 400{,}000 \text{ volts/in.} = \frac{V}{0.706 \text{ in.} \times 0.365}$$

$$V = 102{,}600 \text{ volts}$$

$V_{max} = 0.707 \times 102{,}600 = 72{,}500$ volts (rms) *Answer*

(a) For minimum gradient, given V and b,

2a = 2.032 in./2.718 = 0.747 in. (diameter) *Answer*

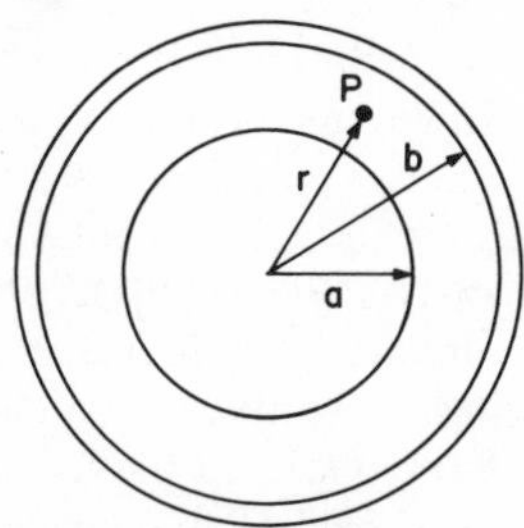

Figure 7-1

Problem 7-2 Resonance of high-frequency transmission line

A communication transmission line has a characteristic impedance Z_0 of 400 ohms and is 0.15 meters long. The line is short-circuited at one end. The attenuation constant α is 0.2 neper/meter.

(a) What value of capacitance must be connected across the open end of the line so that the combination will be resonant at 300 MHz?

(b) What is the Q of the combination if the loss in the capacitor is neglected?

Solution:

This problem falls in the category of the high-frequency line of small but not negligible dissipation. For lengths between zero and $\lambda/4$, a short-circuited section acts as an inductor. The input impedance is

$$Z_{sc} = jR_0 \tan \beta s$$

where $\beta = 2\pi/\lambda$ radians/meter, and s = length of section, meters. It is necessary, therefore, to calculate the inductance, and then the capacitance required for resonance.

The Q of an inductor = $\omega L/R_L$; this is also the Q of the tank circuit, since the problem tells us that the resistance of the capacitance is negligible.

$$\lambda = \frac{f}{v} = \frac{300 \times 10^6}{3 \times 10^8 \text{ (approx.)}}$$
$$= 1 \text{ meter}$$

Hence, s lies between zero and $\lambda/4$.

$$\beta = 2\pi$$
$$Z_{sc} = j400 \tan (57.3 \times 2\pi \times 0.15)^\circ$$
$$= j550 = j\omega L$$
$$L = 0.292 \times 10^{-6} \text{ henry}$$

For resonance, $2\pi f = 1/\sqrt{LC}$.

$$C = 0.97 \times 10^{-12} \text{ farad} \qquad \textit{Answer, part (a)}$$

$$Q = \frac{2\pi \times 300 \times 10^6 \times 0.292 \times 10^{-6}}{R}$$

where R for the high-frequency line is obtained from:

$$\alpha = R/2R_0$$
$$R = 2 \times 400 \times 0.2 \times 0.15 = 24 \text{ ohms}$$
$$Q = 22.9 \qquad \textit{Answer, part (b)}$$

Problem 7-3 Current flow in d-c telegraph line

A d-c telegraph line with ground return has a series resistance of 8.2 ohms/mile and a shunt conductance of 1.5×10^{-5} mho/mile. The length of the line is 140 miles. What current flows through a 900-ohm relay at the receiving end if the sending end is supplied from a 48-volt battery of negligible internal resistance?

Solution:

In this problem, since the series inductance and shunt susceptance are zero (d-c transmission), the propagation constant and characteristic impedance are, respectively,

$$\gamma = \sqrt{RG} \qquad \text{and} \qquad Z_0 = \sqrt{R/G}$$

For a termination in Z_R not equal to Z_0, the receiver current is

$$I_R = \frac{E_S}{Z_R \cosh \gamma l + Z_0 \sinh \gamma l}$$

$$\gamma = \sqrt{8.2 \times 1.5 \times 10^{-5}} = 1.11 \times 10^{-2}$$

$$Z_0 = \sqrt{\frac{8.2}{1.5 \times 10^{-5}}} = 739$$

$$l = 140$$

$$I_R = \frac{48}{900 \times \cosh(1.11 \times 10^{-2} \times 140) + 739 \sinh(1.11 \times 10^{-2} \times 140)}$$

$$= \frac{48}{2223 + 1630} = 12.5 \times 10^{-3}\text{A} \qquad \textit{Answer}$$

Problem 7-4 Design of a T-pad attenuator

A T-pad attenuator is to be designed for a 600-ohm resistance termination from a 600-ohm source. The attenuator is to have two steps: the first step is to give 3 dB attenuation, and the second step is to give 5 dB attenuation.

(a) Lay out the circuit and specify the circuit elements.

(b) If the attenuator is improperly terminated with 500 ohms, how much will the actual attenuation be on each step?

(c) If the resistance of the shunt element in the first section of the attenuator is in error by 10%, what will be the actual attenuation on this step with the 600-ohm termination?

Solution:

Using mesh circuit analysis, formulas have been deduced for the symmetrical T-section and error formulas have also been derived for mismatch conditions.*

(a) See Fig. 7-2 for the circuit. Since

$$R_S = R_R$$

$$k = I_S/I_R = \sqrt{N}$$

$$10 \log N = -3 \text{ dB (first stage)}$$

$$N = 2$$

$$k = 1.414$$

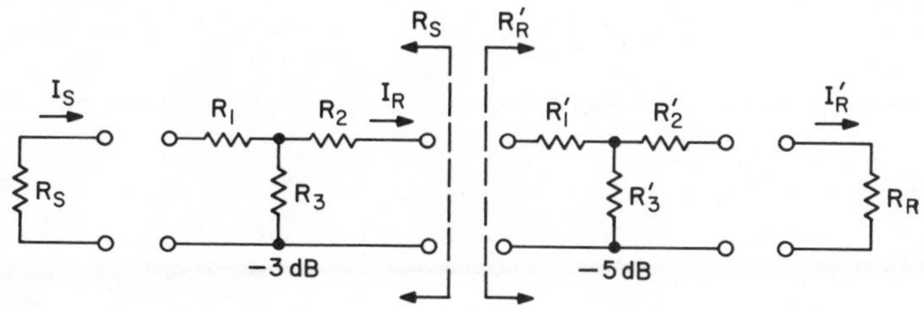

Figure 7-2

---

* *Reference Data for Radio Engineers,* International Telephone and Telegraph Corporation. 5th edition, Indianapolis: Howard W. Sams, 1968.

$$R_3 = \frac{2R_S}{k - 1/k} = 1700 \text{ ohms} \qquad \textit{Answer}$$

$$R_1 = R_2 = R_S\left(\frac{k-1}{k+1}\right) = 105 \text{ ohms} \qquad \textit{Answer}$$

$$10 \log N = -5 \text{ dB (second stage)}$$

$$k = 1.77$$

$$R_3' = 1000 \text{ ohms} \qquad \textit{Answer}$$

$$R_1' = R_2' = R_S\left(\frac{k-1}{k+1}\right) = 167 \text{ ohms} \qquad \textit{Answer}$$

(b) Input Z of second stage:

$$R_R' = R_1' + \frac{R_3' \times (R_2' + 500)}{R_2' + R_3' + 500} = 567 \text{ ohms}$$

First stage:

$$\frac{\Delta k}{k} = \frac{1}{2}\left(\frac{600 - R_R'}{600}\right) \qquad \text{where } k = 1.414$$

$$\text{new } k = 1.46$$

$$= \sqrt{NR_R'/600}$$

$$\text{new } N = 2.25$$

Loss first stage = 3.52 dB *Answer*

Second stage:

$$\frac{\Delta k}{k} = \frac{1}{2}\left(\frac{600 - 500}{600}\right) \qquad \text{where } k = 1.77$$

$$\text{new } k = 1.91$$

$$= \sqrt{N \times 500/600}$$

$$\text{new } N = 4.4$$

Loss second stage = 6.43 dB *Answer*
Overall loss = 3.52 + 6.43 = 9.95 dB

(c) The error for a −10% error in the shunt arm and for a 3-dB design is −0.15 dB (approximately) *Answer*

Problem 7-5 Matching impedance, decibel attenuation, and velocity of propagation on cable

A 19-gage cable has the following coefficients per loop mile:

Resistance: 85.8 ohms
Inductance: 1 millihenry
Capacitance: 0.062 μF
Conductance: 1.5 μmho

The cable is loaded every 6000 ft with coils that have a resistance of 7.3 ohms and an inductance of 88 millihenrys. At 796 Hz, determine: (a) The matching impedance, loaded and unloaded; (b) the decibel attenuation, loaded and unloaded; and (c) the velocity of propagation, loaded and unloaded.

Solution:

First, the characteristic impedance and propagation constant, in complex form, should be determined for the unloaded condition. For the loaded condition, tables for the resultant propagation constant (for the loading in ohms/mile) can be found in such texts as the *Reference Data for Radio Engineers.* If these tables are not available, apply Campbell's Equation, using hyperbolic functions of complex numbers.

$$\omega = 5000$$

$$Z = (85.8 + j5.0) = 86\underline{/3.2^\circ} \text{ ohms/mi}$$

$$Y = 10^{-6}(1.5 + j310) = 310 \times 10^{-6}\underline{/87.2^\circ} \text{ mhos/mi}$$

For the unloaded condition:

$$Z_0 = \sqrt{\frac{Z}{Y}} = \sqrt{\frac{86 \times 10^6}{310}\underline{/-84^\circ}} = 523\underline{/-42^\circ} \text{ ohms} \qquad \textit{Answer, part (a)}$$

$$\gamma = \sqrt{ZY} = 0.162\underline{/45.2^\circ}$$

$$= \alpha + j\beta = 0.114 + j0.115$$

$$\alpha = 0.114 \text{ nepers} = 0.985 \text{ dB/mi} \qquad \textit{Answer, part (b)}$$

$$v = \omega/\beta = 5000/0.115 = 43{,}400 \text{ mi/sec} \qquad \textit{Answer, part (c)}$$

For the loaded condition:

$$Z_c = 6.42 + j387 = 390\underline{/89^\circ} \text{ ohms/mi}$$

$$\cosh N\gamma' = \frac{Z_c}{2Z_0} \sinh N\gamma + \cosh N\gamma$$

where N = number of miles between coils = 1.13.

$$Z_c/2Z_0 = 0.372\underline{/131^\circ}$$

$$\sinh N\gamma = \sinh N\alpha \cos N\beta + j \cosh N\alpha \sin N\beta$$

$$= .129 \times 0.991 + j1.01 \times 0.131$$

$$\cosh N\gamma = \cosh N\alpha \cos N\beta + j \sinh N\alpha \sin N\beta$$

$$= 1.01 \times 0.991 + j0.129 \times 0.131$$

$$\cosh N\gamma' = (0.372\underline{/131^\circ})(0.128 + j0.133) + (1.00 + j0.017)$$

$$= 0.0685\underline{/177^\circ} + (1.00 + j0.017)$$

$$= 0.93 + j0.021$$

$$N\gamma' = 0.021/\sqrt{1 - (0.93)^2} + j \cos^{-1} \tfrac{1}{2}[\sqrt{(0.021)^2 + (1.93)^2}$$

$$- \sqrt{(0.021)^2 + (1 - 0.93)^2}\,]$$

$$= 0.0582 + j0.678$$

$$\gamma' = 0.0515 + j0.6$$

$$\alpha' = 0.0515 \text{ nepers} = 0.457 \text{ dB/mi} \qquad \textit{Answer, part (b)}$$

$$\beta' = 0.6 \text{ radian/mile}$$

$$v = 8350 \text{ mi/sec} \qquad \textit{Answer, part (c)}$$

$$Z_0' = \sqrt{\frac{Z_0 + Z_c}{Y}} = 1140\underline{/-5.2^\circ} \qquad \textit{Answer, part (a)}$$

Problem 7-6 Frequency response of LC circuit

Resonance at 800 Hz is to be obtained by a capacitor in series with a 12.0-μH coil. At this frequency, the Q_0 of the coil is 200 and the dissipation factor of the capacitor is 0.0025.

Determine the frequencies at which the response of this circuit will be (a) 3 dB and (b) 6 dB down from the response at resonance.

Solution:

For the general case, use the relationship between circuit impedance and the deviation from resonant frequency. For the specific case, use the relationship between the overall Q and the bandspread between the frequencies of the half-power points (where the response is 3 dB down from the response at resonance).

$$\omega = 2\pi f = 5 \times 10^6$$

$$f_r = 1/2\pi\sqrt{LC}$$

$$\sqrt{LC} = 1/\omega = 0.2 \times 10^{-6}$$

$$C = \frac{0.04 \times 10^{-12}}{12 \times 10^{-6}} = 0.00333\ \mu F$$

$$d_c = 0.0025 = \omega C R_c$$

$$R_c = \frac{0.0025}{5 \times 10^6 \times 0.00333 \times 10^{-6}} = 0.150 \text{ ohm}$$

$$Q = \omega L/R_L$$

$$R_L = \frac{5 \times 10^6 \times 12 \times 10^{-6}}{200}$$

$$= 0.300 \text{ ohm}$$

$$R_0 = 0.450 \text{ ohm}$$

$$Q_{total} = \frac{\omega L}{R_0} = \frac{5 \times 10^6 \times 12 \times 10^{-6}}{0.450}$$

$$= 133$$

(a) At −3-dB response (half-power points):

$$\frac{f}{f_2 - f_1} = Q_0 = 133$$

$$f_2 - f_1 = \frac{0.8 \times 10^6}{133} = 6000 \text{ Hz}$$

Therefore, the −3-dB points are 803 kHz and 797 kHz *Answer*

(b) At −6-dB response:

$$-6 = -20 \log I_f/I$$

$$I_f/I = 2 = Z/R_0$$

$$R_0 = 0.450 \text{ ohm}$$

$$Z = 0.9\angle\pm 60^\circ \qquad \sin 60^\circ = 0.866$$

$$= R_0[1 - jQ_0\delta(2 - \delta)]$$

$$X = 0.866 \times .9 = R_0Q_0\delta(2 - \delta)$$

$$\delta(2 - \delta) = 0.0129$$

$$\delta = 1.995 \text{ or } 0.005$$

$$f = f_r \pm 0.005f_r = 804 \text{ kHz and } 796 \text{ kHz}$$ *Answer*

Problem 7-7 Standing-wave measurements and stub matching

Standing-wave measurements made on a transmission line with an unknown termination are as follows:

Standing-wave ratio: 2.4
Distance between standing-wave minima: 51 cm
Distance from load end of line to nearest minima: 35 cm
Characteristic impedance of the line: 250 ohms

Neglecting line dissipation, determine: (a) frequency; (b) parameters of the load; (c) power being transmitted; (d) the design and location of a single stub to match the load to the line.

Solution:

If a line is not terminated in its characteristic impedance, a standing wave is established, with voltage and current minima and maxima values at fixed points (nodes) along the line. Connecting a shunt impedance to a line changes its characteristic impedance, and if properly designed, matches the line to the load. The standing-wave ratio is defined as

$$\rho = V_{max}/V_{min}$$

$$\frac{\text{power delivered}}{\text{power reflected}} = \frac{4\rho}{(\rho + 1)^2}$$

Therefore, power delivered is 83% of power sent. *Answer*

Wavelength $\lambda = 1.02$ meters
Frequency $f = 3 \times 10^8/1.02 = 294$ MHz *Answer*

Referring to Fig. 7-3,

$$d = \frac{\cos^{-1}\left(\frac{\rho - 1}{\rho + 1}\right)}{\pi} \times \frac{\lambda}{4} = 0.0930 \text{ meters}$$

$$L = \frac{\lambda}{2\pi} \tan^{-1}\left(\frac{\sqrt{\rho}}{\rho - 1}\right) = 0.1355$$

$L' = \lambda/2 - L = 0.374$ meters *Answer* (d)

To find parameters of the load,

$Z_0 = 250 - j0$ since $R = G = 0$

$$Z_R = Z_0 \left[\frac{1 - j\rho \tan\left(\dfrac{2\pi s'}{\lambda}\right)}{\rho - j \tan\left(\dfrac{2\pi s'}{\lambda}\right)}\right]$$

$$= 307\underline{/-43.5^\circ}$$ *Answer* (b)

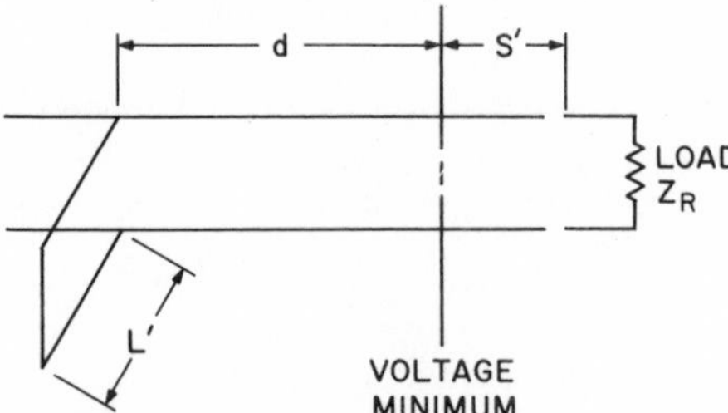

Figure 7-3

Problem 7-8 Decibel power loss in a communication line

A 50-mile communication line has the following parameters:

Series resistance: 21.4 ohms/mi
Series inductance: 1.0 mH/mi
Shunt capacitance: 0.062 μF/mi
Shunt conductance: 0.868 μmho/mi

The frequency is 796 kHz and the line is terminated to avoid reflection.

(a) If the power at the receiving end of the line is to be −20 dB (6 milliwatt reference), what must be the voltage at the sending end?

(b) What will be the dB power loss in the line?

Solution:

The attenuation and phase shift are functions of the line parameters. When the line is terminated in its characteristic impedance (condition of no reflection), the power loss is obtained by converting the voltage attenuation in nepers to power loss in decibels.

Calculate the receiving power:

$20(\text{dB}) = 10 \log P_R/0.006$

$P_R = 0.6$ watt

Calculate the circuit constants per mile:

$Z = R + j\omega L = 22\underline{/13.1^\circ}$ ohms

$$Y = G + j\omega C = 310\underline{/90^\circ} \text{ mhos}$$
$$Z_0 = \sqrt{Z/Y} = 266\underline{/-38.45^\circ}$$
$$\gamma = \sqrt{ZY} = 82.3 \times 10^{-3}\underline{/51.55^\circ}$$
$$= \alpha + j\beta = 0.0512 + j0.0645$$
$$P_S/P_R = P_S/0.6 = e^{50\times 0.0512} = 12.9 \text{ (from tables)}$$
$$P_S = 7.75 \text{ watts} = E_S I_S \cos\theta_0$$

But $I_S = E_S/Z_0$

$$P_S = \frac{E_S{}^2}{Z_0}\cos\theta_0 = \frac{E_S{}^2}{266 \times 50}\cos -38.45^\circ$$
$$E_S{}^2 = \frac{7.75 \times 50 \times 266}{0.7831}$$

$E_S = 362$ volts *Answer, part (a)*

$$\alpha = 0.0512 \text{ nepers} = 0.445 \text{ dB}$$
$$\beta = 0.0645 \text{ radians}$$

Power loss = 0.445 dB/mi

Calculate the power loss for 50 miles and the required sending-end voltage:

Power loss = $50 \times 0.445 = 22.3$ dB *Answer, part (b)*

Problem 7-9 Distortionless two-wire telephone transmission line

A two-wire telephone transmission line has the following parameters:

Series resistance: 10.9 ohms/loop mile
Series inductance: 3.7 mH/loop mile
Shunt capacitance: 0.00812 μF/loop mile
Shunt conductance: 0.3 μmho/loop mile

(a) Find the wavelength, phase velocity, and dB loss per mile at $\omega = 5000$ radians/sec.

(b) What distributed loading/loop mile would be required for the line to be distortionless? Find the new wavelength, phase velocity, and dB loss per mile.

(c) Determine the necessary wire size (in mils) and the wire separation (in inches) necessary to produce the above parameters.

Solution:

First employ the general relationships for a line with distributed constants, then the specific relationships for such a line with no distortion (i.e., attenuation and velocity of propagation independent of frequency).

(a) $Z = 10.9 + j18.5$ ohms/mi

$$Y = (0.3 + j40.6) \times 10^{-6} \text{ mho/mi}$$

$$\gamma = \alpha + j\beta = \sqrt{ZY}$$
$$= 0.030\underline{/73.3^\circ} = 0.00882 + j0.0287$$

$\alpha = 0.00882$ nepers or 0.078 dB *Answer*

$\beta = 0.0287$ radians/mi

$v = \omega/\beta = 5000/0.0287 = 174{,}500$ mi/sec *Answer*

$\lambda = v/f$ where $f = 5000/2\pi$ Hz

$= 219$ mi $= 352{,}000$ m *Answer*

(b) To be distortionless,

$$L/C = R/G$$
$$L = \frac{10.9 \times 0.00812 \times 10^{-6}}{0.3 \times 10^{-6}} = 0.295 \text{ H/mi}$$

Therefore, *add:* $0.295 - 0.0037 = 0.291$ H/mi *Answer*

$$\alpha = \frac{R}{2}\sqrt{\frac{C}{L}}$$
$$= 5.45 \times 10^{-3} \times \sqrt{0.0277}$$

$= 0.908 \times 10^{-3}$ nepers/mi or 7.88×10^{-3} dB/mi *Answer*

$v = 1/\sqrt{LC} = 20{,}500$ mi/sec *Answer*

$\lambda = 41{,}200$ meters *Answer*

(c) If D is the distance between conductors and a is the conductor radius, the inductance of the line in free space is

$$L = (\mu_r + 9.210 \log D/a) \times 10^{-7} \text{ H/meter}$$

where μ_r = relative permeability (= 1.0).

For an inductance of 0.295 H/mi then,

$$D/a = \text{antilog}\left(\frac{\dfrac{10^7 \times 0.295 \times 3.28}{5280} - 1}{9.210}\right)$$
$$= 10^{200}$$

For R = 10.9 ohms/loop mile (1.03 ohms/1000 ft), use 10,400 circular mils or 102 mils diameter *Answer.*

Spacing then would have to be 0.0508×10^{200} in. *Answer.*

Compare this spacing with approximately 12.2 in. for conditions in part (a). It is obviously impracticable to obtain the desired condition by spacing the conductors; further, the capacitance would not then match that in the problem, and the attenuation, wavelength, and velocity of propagation could not be as found in part (b).

The capacitance, in pF/meter is given as

$$C = \frac{12.07\epsilon_r}{\log D/a}$$

where ϵ_r is the relative permittivity (= 1.0).

$$C = 60{,}500\ \mu F/\text{mile}$$

Problem 7-10 Specification of repeater amplifiers for telephone line

A 220-mile open-wire telephone line consists of two conductors of No. 10 B&S gage standard copper wire spaced 12 in. apart. The approximate value of leakage conductance between wires is 0.8 μmho/mi. Repeater amplifiers having a voltage gain of 4 dB are to be installed at equal intervals to maintain the voltage level at the receiving end at or slightly below the voltage level at the sending end.

(a) Specify the minimum number of repeater amplifiers required and the distance between them.

(b) Specify the input and output impedances for the amplifiers.

(c) With the amplifiers installed, calculate the overall loss in dB from the sending end to the receiving end of the line.

Solution:

To determine the overall amplification required, it is necessary to calculate the attenuation constant from the line parameters.* From the values of the line parameters, it is apparent that the frequency is 3000 Hz.

For the 12-in. spacing,

$$R = 10.62\ \text{ohms/mi}$$

$$L = 0.00366\ \text{H/mi}$$

$$C = 0.008\ \mu\text{F/mi}$$

$$G = 0.8\ \mu\text{mho/mi}$$

$$Z = 10.62 + j69 = 69.8\underline{/81.2^\circ}\ \text{ohms/mi}$$

$$Y = 0.8 + j151 = 151 \times 10^{-6}\underline{/90^\circ}\ \text{mho/mi}$$

$$\gamma = \sqrt{69.8 \times 151 \times 10^{-6}\underline{/171.2^\circ}} = 0.103\underline{/85.6^\circ}$$

$$= 0.00785 + j0.1025$$

$$\alpha l = 220 \times 0.00785 \times 8.686$$

$$= 15\ \text{dB}$$

Therefore, three amplifiers are required spaced 55 miles apart. *Answer, part (a).*

$$Z_0 = \sqrt{\frac{69.8 \times 10^6\underline{/-8.8^\circ}}{151}} = 680\underline{/-4.4^\circ}$$

---

* To understand the bridge connection necessary to apply amplifiers without introducing oscillation, see the description of the 22-type repeater in *Standard Handbook for Electrical Engineers* (9th Edition) by Archer E. Knowlton (ed.). New York: McGraw-Hill Book Co., 1957.

This characteristic impedance should be used as the input impedance and output impedance of the amplifier *Answer, part (b).*

The overall loss would be 15 − 12 or a loss of 3 dB *Answer, part (c).*

If the input Z actually available does not equal Z_0, a new αl should be calculated for each section.

Problem 7-11 Detuning of signal generator tank circuit by cable connection

The tank circuit of a signal generator consists of a coil having an inductance of 16.3 μH and a Q of 150. It is tuned to 5 MHz with a capacitor that has a Q of 200.

(a) What is the impedance of this tank circuit?

(b) A 3-ft length of 8 A/U cable that has a characteristic impedance of 50 ohms, an attenuation constant of 0.45 dB/100 ft, and a capacitance of 29.5 pF/ft is connected across the tank circuit. There is an infinite impedance connected to the cable. How much does the frequency of the oscillator shift?

(c) How much is the Q of the tank circuit changed?

Solution:

This problem is primarily a demonstration of the relationships between Q, L, C, and R. When dealing with the resistances of coils and capacitors, care must be taken as to whether series or parallel resistances are being used. Series equivalents are used here. (See Fig. 7-4.)

(a)

$$Q_L = 150 = \omega L/R_L$$

$$\omega = 31.4 \times 10^6$$

$$R_L = 3.42 \text{ ohms}$$

$$X_L = 512 \text{ ohms}$$

$$Q_C = 1/\omega C R_C = 200$$

$$f_0 = 1/2\pi\sqrt{LC}$$

$$C = 62.2 \text{ pF}$$

$$R_C = 2.57 \text{ ohms}$$

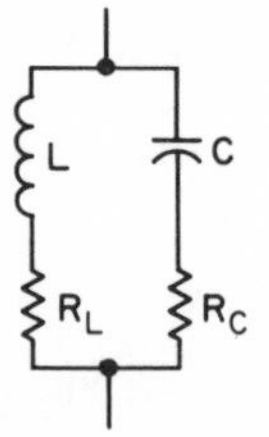

Figure 7-4

$$\text{Overall } Q = \frac{X_L}{R_L + R_C} = \frac{512}{3.42 + 2.57} = 85.7$$

We could also have used:

$$Q = \frac{Q_L Q_C}{Q_L + Q_C}$$

$$\text{Overall } Z = \frac{(3.42 + j512)(2.57 - j512)}{5.99}$$

$$= 44.2 \times 10^3 \text{ ohms} \qquad \textit{Answer}$$

(b) For the high-frequency line of small dissipation:

$$R = \frac{Z_0 \alpha l}{1 - (1 - \alpha^2 l^2)\cos^2 2\pi l/\lambda} \tag{7-4}$$

$$X = \text{capacitive (since } 1 < \lambda/4)$$

$$X = \frac{Z_0(1 - \alpha^2 l^2)\sin 2\pi l/\lambda \cos 2\pi l/\lambda}{1 - (1 - \alpha^2 l^2)\cos^2 2\pi l/\lambda} \tag{7-5}$$

$$\lambda = \frac{v}{f} = \frac{3 \times 10^8}{5 \times 10^6} = 60 \text{ meters}$$

$$\frac{\lambda}{4} = 49.0 \text{ ft}$$

$$\alpha l = \frac{0.03 \times 0.45}{8.686} = 0.00155 \text{ nepers}$$

$$\frac{2\pi l}{\lambda} = \frac{2\pi \times 3}{3.27 \times 60} = 0.096 \text{ radians} = \sin^{-1}0.0959 = \cos^{-1}0.9954$$

$$1 - \alpha^2 l^2 \simeq 1$$

Substituting in Eq. (7-4) (see Fig. 7-5),

$$R = 7.25 \text{ ohms}$$

$$X = 505.0 \text{ ohms}$$

$$C = 63 \text{ pF}$$

$$f_0 = \frac{1}{2\pi\sqrt{16.3 \times 125 \times 10^{-18}}}$$

$$= 3.54 \times 10^6 \qquad \textit{Answer (b)}$$

(c) $\omega' = 22.2 \times 10^6$

$$Q'_T - \frac{\omega' L}{R} = \frac{22.2 \times 16.3}{13.24}$$

$$= 27.4 \qquad \textit{Answer (c)}$$

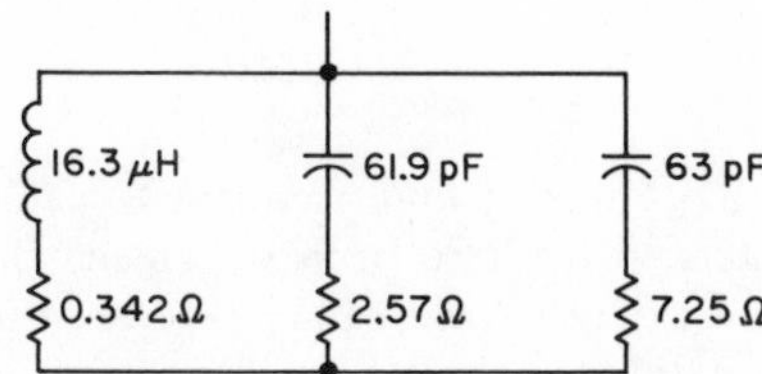

Figure 7-5

Problem 7-12 Design of air-insulated coaxial line

It is desired to construct a rigid air-insulated coaxial line to transmit 250 kW of CW power at 250 MHz. The line is to have a characteristic impedance of 50 ohms and will be properly matched. Operation will be at the highest safe voltage gradient.

(a) Determine the dimensions of the inner and outer conductors. (b) Specify the rated operating voltage. (c) Calculate the attenuation.

Solution:

In this problem, basic formulas for coaxial cables can be used to obtain the ratio of conductor radii, given the characteristic impedance. However, because of the heat dissipation problems, and the factor of safety required to guard against voltage breakdown at the operating frequency, especially in the event of reflected waves that might accidently occur, determining actual diameters and operating voltage must be based on empirical data not readily available to the average examinee. This solution can be only a guide.

$$Z_0 = 50 \text{ ohms} = \frac{60}{\sqrt{\epsilon_r}} \ln \frac{b}{a}$$

where b = inner radius of outer conductor, and a = outer radius of inner conductor.

$\epsilon_r = 1.0$ for air

$b/a = 2.31$

For b, select a 10-in. outer conductor from Andrew Corp. engineering data. The inner conductor would be approximately 4.3 in., and the attenuation about 0.062 dB/100 ft. The curves are based on rather complex formulas, and the values selected are based on unity standing-wave ratio and 23 °C rise of outer conductor temperature over a 40 °C ambient. Radio-frequency voltage is given as $0.247E_p$. E_p is the 60-Hz test voltage (about 50 kV). *Answer* (a), (b), (c)

Problem 7-13 Coaxial tank circuit designed for maximum Q

It is desired to design an air-insulated coaxial tank circuit for a resonant frequency of 300 MHz. One feature of the design shall be maximum Q. The inside diameter of the outer conductor shall be 1 in. At least one side of the tank circuit shall be short-circuited.

Specify: (a) the size of the inner conductor, (b) the overall length of the coaxial unit, (c) the value of Q, (d) the characteristic impedance, and (e) the maximum voltage that can be applied to the unit.

Solution:

Parameters of the air-filled coaxial line at high frequencies can be expressed in terms of the conductor diameters. It has also been shown that for maximum Q, the characteristic impedance must have a fixed value, as must also the ratio of the conductor diameters. It remains then to solve for the missing diameter and the permissible voltage.

(a) For maximum Q:

$Z_0 = 77$ ohms and $b/a = 3.6$

Therefore, $2a = 0.278$ in. = diameter of inner conductor *Answer*

(b) The length of the coaxial cable should be an odd multiple of a quarter wavelength.

$$\lambda = v/f$$

where v = velocity of light in space, and f = frequency (300×10^6 Hz).

$\lambda/4 = 0.818$ ft *Answer*

(c) $$Q = \frac{2\pi Z_0 f}{R\mathcal{E}}$$

where R = line resistance per meter, and $\mathcal{E}$ = velocity of light in meters/sec.

$$Q = 0.0839\sqrt{f}bH$$

where b = inner radius of outer conductor, and H = factor.

Q = 1900 *Answer*

For convenience, this is taken from the curves giving Q for a resonant concentric line when b/a = 3.6

(d) $Z_0 = 77$ ohms *Answer*

(e) For maximum V:

$$E = \frac{V}{a \ln b/a} = 3 \times 10^6 \text{ volts/meter for air}$$

where a is expressed in meters.

V = 27 kV *Answer*

Problem 7-14 Antenna impedance and power input measured by slotted line

It is desired to measure the impedance of, and power input to, an antenna that is 50 ft distant from a transmitter operating at 300 MHz. The transmitter and antenna are connected by a 50-ft length of RG 8 A/U coaxial cable that has an attenuation constant of 4.3 dB/100 ft at 300 MHz. A 50-ohm slotted line designed for measurement purposes is placed at the junction of the transmitter and the cable. The following data are obtained on the slotted line:

Standing-wave ratio: 2.5
Distance between minima: 35 cm (with the cable shorted and also with the antenna attached). The minimum with the antenna attached is nearer to the transmitter than the minimum with the cable shorted.
Voltage at this minimum: 200 volts (rms)

Determine: (a) the impedance of the antenna, and (b) the power supplied to the antenna.

Solution:

This falls in the category of the high-frequency line of small dissipation. Z_0 is essentially resistive. For this case, Z_R (load) is resistive, and equals $2.5 = R_R/R_0$, giving the answer to part (a) after R_0 is determined.

Since the distance from the antenna to the nearest minimum is not given in the problem, an approximation could be made by calculating the power delivered for a dissipationless line and then applying the dB loss.

(a) $R_0 = \sqrt{L/C}$

From tables: $2\pi fL = 50$ ohms/ft and $C = 29.5$ pF/ft.

$$R_0 = 30 \text{ ohms}$$

$$\rho = 2.5$$

$$R_R = \rho R_0 = 75 \text{ ohms} \qquad \textit{Answer}$$

(b) $E_{max} = 2.5E_{min} = 500$ volts (rms)

$$P = \frac{500 \times 200}{R_0} = 3333 \text{ watts}$$

$$dB = 2.15 = 10 \log 3333/P_r$$

$$P_R = 2030 \text{ watts} \qquad \textit{Answer}$$

Problem 7-15 Phase shift and dB loss of line terminated in characteristic impedance

Measurements were made at 796 Hz on a loaded cable that is 5 miles long. Results of these measurements were:

Impedance looking into the sending end with the receiving end open: $Z_{oc} = 650 + j1795$ ohms

Impedance looking into the sending end with the receiving end short-circuited: $Z_{sc} = 267 - j1270$

(a) Determine the dB loss and the phase shift of this line if it is terminated in its characteristic impedance.

(b) Determine the dB loss of this line if it is terminated in a 600-ohm resistor.

Solution:

Attenuation and phase shift can be determined by open-circuit and short-circuit measurements when line constants are known. Phase shift can be determined from the Smith Chart, or by use of hyperbolic functions. When the line is mismatched, the reflection coefficient must be calculated before the power loss can be determined, since:

$$I_S^2/I_R^2 \neq P_S/P_R$$

(a) $Z_0 = \sqrt{Z_{sc}Z_{oc}}$

where $Z_{oc} = 650 + j1795 = 1910\underline{/70^\circ}$

$$Z_{sc} = 267 - j1270 = 1300\underline{/-78^\circ}$$

$$\gamma l = \tanh^{-1}\sqrt{Z_{sc}/Z_{oc}}$$

$$\therefore Z_0 = 1570/-4^\circ = 1560 - j109$$

$$\gamma l = \tanh^{-1} 0.827\underline{/-74^\circ}$$

$$= \tanh^{-1}(0.228 - j0.795)$$

Since:

$$\tanh(A + jB) = \frac{1}{2}\tanh^{-1}\frac{2A}{1 + A^2 + B^2} + j\frac{1}{2}\tan\frac{2B}{1 - A^2 - B^2}$$

$$\gamma l = 0.14 + j0.88 \text{ or } 0.14 + j2.45$$

(Quadrant can be determined from velocity of propagation if known.)

$$\alpha l = 0.14 \text{ nepers}$$

$$\text{dB} = 8.686 \times 0.14 = 1.21 \text{ dB loss}$$ *Answer*

Phase shift $\beta l = 0.88$ radians *Answer*

(b) For

$$Z_R = 600 + j0$$

$$\frac{I_S}{I_R} = \frac{Z_R + Z_0}{2Z_0}(\epsilon^{\gamma l} - K\epsilon^{-\gamma l})$$

$$\epsilon^{\gamma l} = 1.15\underline{/50.5^\circ}$$

$$\epsilon^{-\gamma l} = 0.87\underline{/-50.5^\circ}$$

$$K = \frac{Z_R - Z_0}{Z_R + Z_0}$$

$$= \frac{-960 + j109}{2160 - j109}$$

$$= 0.445\underline{/176^\circ}$$

$$I_S/I_R = 0.77\underline{/-52^\circ}$$

$$Z_S = Z_0\left(\frac{\epsilon^{\gamma l} + K\epsilon^{-\gamma l}}{\epsilon^{\gamma l} - K\epsilon^{-\gamma l}}\right) = 1855\underline{/32^\circ} \quad \text{(referred to } E_S)$$

= input impedance of mismatched line

$$\frac{P_S}{P_R} = \left(\frac{I_S}{I_R}\right)^2 \frac{R_S}{R_R}$$

$$= 1.55$$

$$\text{dB} = 10 \log 1.55 = 1.9 \text{ dB loss}$$ *Answer*

Note: For $\beta l = 2.45$, power loss is calculated to be 1.37 dB.

Problem 7-16 Amplifier boosting of television signal on coaxial cable

A coaxial cable is to be used to transmit a television signal. The center frequency of signal bandwidth is 30 MHz. At this frequency, the parameters of the cable will be:

Series resistance: 50 ohms/loop mile
Series inductance: 500 μH/loop mile
Shunt capacitance: 0.2 μF/loop mile
Shunt conductance: 0.02 mho/loop mile

At the sending end of the line, the power input is to be from an amplifier that has a power output of 73 dB referred to 1 milliwatt. In order to maintain a satisfactory signal-to-noise ratio, the signal voltage on the cable must not be permitted to fall below 20 millivolts.

Amplifiers are available that will give 73 dB of power referred to 1 milliwatt with a 20-millivolt input. There will be complete matching of all components.

At what points along the cable should the amplifiers be placed?

Solution:

For very high frequencies, the characteristic impedance can be assumed equal to $\sqrt{L/C}$. First, the distance required for the attenuation to cause the voltage to drop 20 millivolts should be determined. Then, in this problem, an amplifier will restore the signal to its initial value.

For the high-frequency line,

$$Z_0 = R_0 = \sqrt{\frac{L}{C}} = \sqrt{\frac{500 \times 10^{-6}}{0.2 \times 10^{-6}}} = 50 \text{ ohms}$$

$$\alpha = \frac{R}{2R_0} + \frac{GR_0}{2} = 1 \text{ neper} = 8.7 \text{ dB (power)/mi}$$

$$= 4.35 \text{ dB (voltage)/mi}$$

Power input:

$$73 \text{ dB} = 10 \log x/1 \text{ mW}$$

$$x = 20{,}000 \text{ watts}$$

$$20{,}000 = E^2/R_0$$

$$E = 1000 \text{ volts input}$$

Distance for this to attenuate to 20 millivolts:

$$\text{dB loss} = 10 \log 1000/0.02 = 47 \text{ dB}$$

$$47/4.35 = 10.8 \text{ mi}$$

Therefore, install an amplifier every 10.8 mi *Answer*

chapter 8
ELECTRONIC CIRCUITS

In this chapter, some of the frequently used terms and concepts are presented to refresh the reader's memory; no attempt is made to explain electronic theory.

It is important to differentiate between *total* voltages and currents, and *alternating* components of these voltages and currents, when comparing the actual circuit diagrams with the equivalent (dynamic) circuits. Also note that the relationships used in small-signal applications cannot be used for large-signal applications, such as power amplifiers; in the latter, graphical methods must be used. These comments apply to both tube and transistor circuits.

Although the following relationships for the high-vacuum diode are not directly useful for solving problems, they do illustrate the fact that electron emission can be either temperature limited or space-charge limited.

Child's Equation:

$$i_b = Ke_b^{1.5}$$

where i_b and e_b = total values of plate current and plate potential, respectively, and K = constant based on electrode geometry. The cathode temperature is constant.

Dushman's Equation:

$$i_b = AT^2\epsilon^{-B/T}$$

where A and B = constants, i_b = maximum plate current obtainable by varying plate potential, T = absolute temperature in °K(°C + 273), ϵ = Naperian base. For small variations, r_p may be considered equal to $(1/K)e_b^{-1/2}$.

8-1 VACUUM TUBES AND CIRCUITS

The interrelationships among the variables of the grid-controlled, high-vacuum thermionic tube (basic triode) are shown in Fig. 8-1. As there are more than two variables, a composite of the individual curves is drawn and the dynamic characteristic, or load line, is obtained from which the condition for optimum performance, output power, and voltage can be determined.

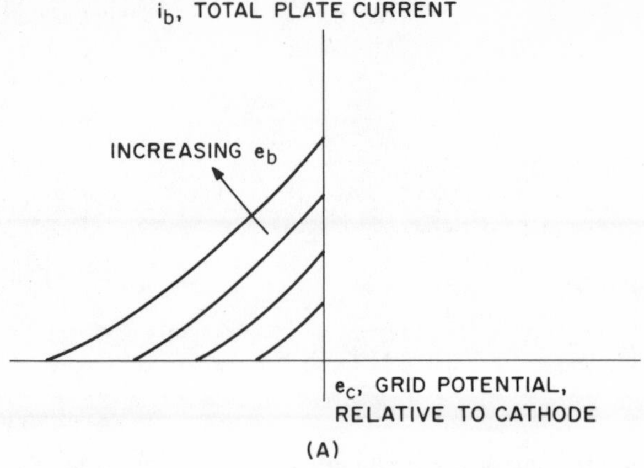

(A)

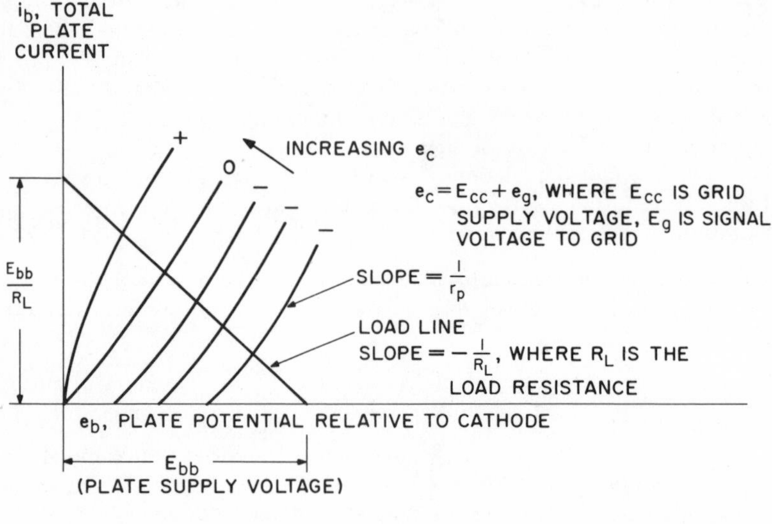

(B)

Figure 8-2 is for the idealized condition. Actually, the $e_c - e_b$ characteristic is not linear, and i_p does not oscillate about the $I_b = 0$ (quiescent value of total plate current) axis, but about an average (total) value $I_b = \frac{1}{2}[\frac{1}{2}(I_{max} + I_{min}) + (I_b)_0]$. It can also be shown that the rms fundamental of the a-c component is

$$I_p = \frac{1}{2\sqrt{2}}(I_{max} - I_{min})$$

and the second harmonic (rms) is

$$(I_p)_2 = \frac{1}{2\sqrt{2}}[\tfrac{1}{2}(I_{max} + I_{min}) - (I_b)_0]$$

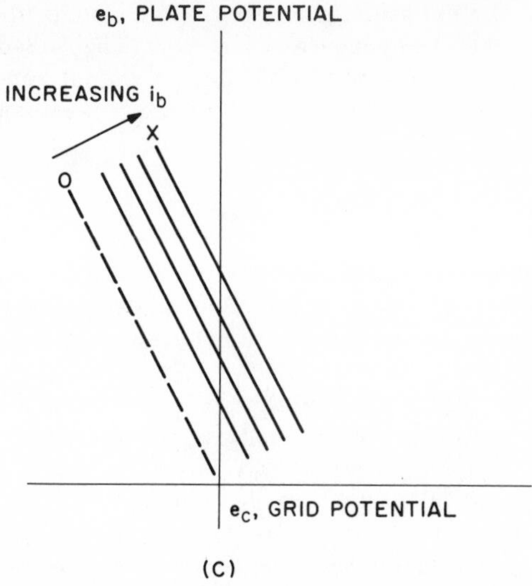

Figure 8-1. *Note:* i_b is the total plate current, e_b is the plate potential relative to the cathode, e_c is the grid potential relative to the cathode, E_{cc} is the grid supply voltage (negative), E_{bb} is the plate supply voltage, e_g is the signal voltage to the grid, and R_L is the load resistance.

The most commonly used configuration is the grounded (or common) cathode, characterized by a high input impedance and output impedance. The usual application is in power amplification. The circuit diagram is shown in Fig. 8-3, along with two equivalent circuits. In the latter circuit, only alternating currents and voltages are considered, and the relationships shown are for small signals where the parameters r_p and g_m are considered constant. C_c is a blocking capacitor of negligible reactance, and the interelectrode capacitances are omitted for simplicity.

Where the total plate current flows through the load resistor (such as R_c in Fig. 8-3, deleting C_c and R_{g1}), the total power supplied to the plate $P_{bb} = E_{bb}I_b$ can be divided into three components:

A-c output (considering only the fundamental): $P_{a\text{-}c} = I_p^2R_L$
D-c loss in load resistor: $P_{d\text{-}c} = I_b^2R_L$
Plate dissipation: $P_p = E_bI_b - P_{a\text{-}c}$

The plate efficiency is, therefore, $P_{a\text{-}c}/E_bI_b$. The overall circuit efficiency would be $P_{a\text{-}c}/P_{bb}$.

For a purely resistive load, the a-c load line is a straight line whose slope is $-1/R_L$. For optimum power transfer, because of the nonlinear characteristic of the triode, R_L should be about $2r_p$, and the optimum grid bias should be approximately $E_{cc} = -\frac{3}{4}(E_b)_0/\mu$. For pentodes, the optimum load resistance is from $0.2r_p$ to $0.3r_p$. For the beam power tube, the optimum R_L approximately equals r_p. When the load is not purely resistive, the load line is elliptical.

There are also the grounded (or common-) grid and the common-plate (cathode-follower) configurations, shown in Fig. 8-4. The former is used as an FM or video amplifier and as a voltage regulator in rectifier circuits; the input impedance is very low and the output impedance is very high. The cathode-follower, on the other hand, has a high input impedance and a low output impedance, and a gain of less than 1, making it useful as a direct coupling between an amplifier and the load in audio circuits.

Definitions

Before proceeding, the following definitions should be reviewed:

Mu-Factor (μ). The mu-factor is the relative effect of two electrode voltages on each other. Usually, μ signifies the amplification factor $= de_b/de_c$, with i_b constant.

Transconductance (g_m). Transconductance is the change of some current per unit change of an electrode potential. Usually, g_m signifies di_b/de_c, with e_b constant.

Driving Power. Driving power is the value of the radio- or audio-frequency power input required to obtain the specified output.

Grid Bias. Grid bias is the d-c potential of the grid with respect to the cathode.

Plate Resistance (r_p). Plate resistance is the apparent resistance of the tube to the flow of current (a-c component only is considered here). Basically, within the range of linearity, $\mu = g_m r_p$.

Tetrode. A tetrode is a triode to which a screen grid has been added to counteract the grid-plate capacitance and thus avoid oscillation otherwise brought about by resonance with the input circuit. The screen grid, maintained at a positive potential with respect to the cathode, increases the r_p and μ of the triode; the effects of secondary emission limit the applicability of the tube.

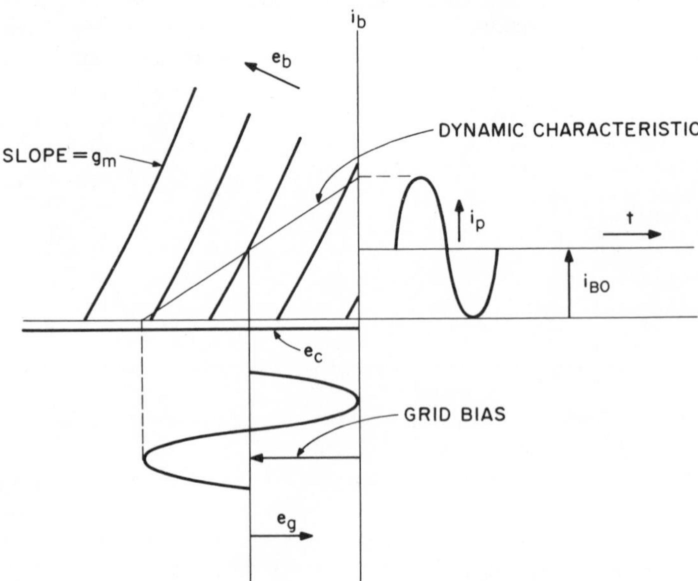

Figure 8-2

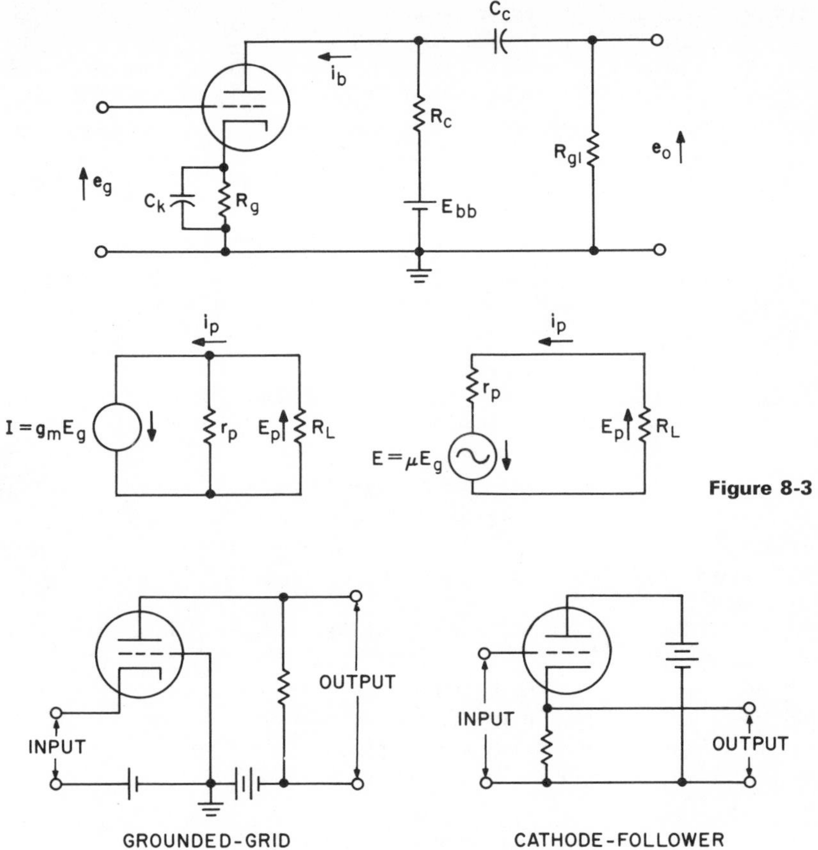

Figure 8-3

Figure 8-4

Pentode. A pentode is a tetrode to which a suppressor grid has been added that further increases r_p and μ. The suppressor grid, maintained at cathode potential, increases the range of linearity.

Phase-Inverter. The phase-inverter is used in lieu of a transformer because of size, weight, and cost. The single-tube inverter has a gain less than unity.

Push-Pull. Push-pull is a joint configuration of two tubes. No bypass capacitor is required across the cathode-bias resistor. It is used for power amplification, and as an economical method of avoiding distortion because of nonlinearity of the $e_c - i_b$ curve. Remember, impedances must be matched.

Interelectrode Capacitance. Interelectrode capacitance is the unavoidable capacitance between two electrodes. In the equivalent circuit, interelectrode capacitances are usually shown in dash-line fashion. Frequently, certain interelectrode capacitances can be ignored.

Equivalent Circuit. An equivalent circuit is the Thevenin or Norton equivalent that excludes the d-c supplies (and biasing components if they are not parts of the a-c circuit). The constant-current source concept should be used when R_L is negligible and there are numerous parallel circuits. For small-signal applications, linear operation is assumed, and the magnitude of the constant-current source is expressed as

$$I = g_m E_g \qquad \text{(rms values)}$$

For the constant-voltage source concept, use

$$E = \mu E_g$$

Response. Generally, response is the voltage gain of an amplifier. Frequently, the product of the midfrequency gain and the bandwidth between the −3-dB (half-power) points is used as a criterion of a tube or tube circuit.

Low- (High-) Frequency Compensation. Low- (high-) frequency compensation is the extension of the flat portion of the gain-vs.-frequency curve (usually a semilog plot) into the lower (higher) frequencies.

Class A Amplifier. A Class A amplifier is an amplifier operating on the linear portion of the e_c-i_b curve and whose plate current flows throughout a complete cycle. It has a low grid bias, used for small-signal (power) amplification.

Class B Amplifier. A Class B amplifier is an amplifier whose grid bias is near cutoff; plate current flows for about one-half cycle. The signal is larger and transconductance is larger than for Class A. A Class B amplifier is used as a power amplifier. A Class B_2 amplifier is one in which the grid potential is positive during part of the cycle.

Class C Amplifier. A Class C amplifier is one whose grid bias is about twice cutoff; plate current flows for less than a one-half cycle. A Class C amplifier is used only for radio frequencies (power amplification). A Class C_2 amplifier is one in which the grid potential is positive during part of the cycle.

Basic Amplifier Circuits

Two basic amplifier circuits are shown in Figs. 8-5 to 8-7. Formulas for gain and half-power frequencies follow.

Lowpass Amplifiers:

$$\text{Gain } K = \frac{-g_m R}{\left[1 + \left(\frac{f}{f_2}\right)^2\right]^{1/2}}$$

$$= \frac{-g_m R}{1 + j\omega CR}$$

where $R = \dfrac{r_p R_L}{r_p + R_L}$

$$f_2 = -3\text{-dB frequency} = 1/2\pi CR$$

If C_{gp} is to be considered,

$$K = \frac{-g_m + j\omega C_{gp}}{1/R + j\omega(C_{pk} + C_{gp})}$$

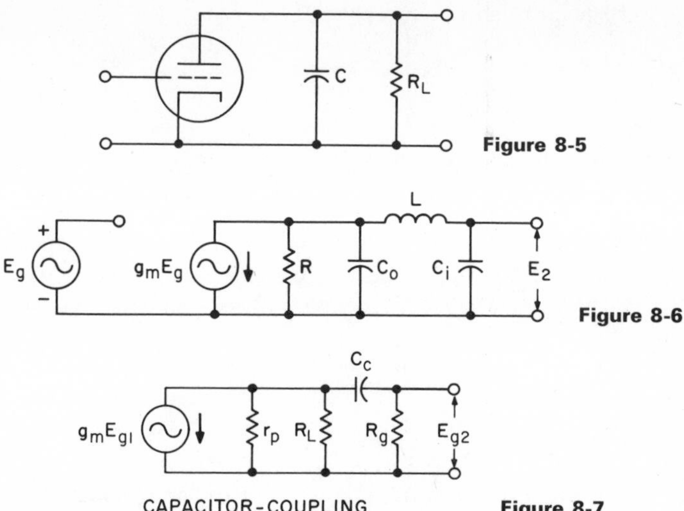

Figure 8-5

Figure 8-6

Figure 8-7

If inductance is added in series with R_L to resonate with C,

For maximal flatness, $Q_0 = 0.644 = \omega_0 L/R_L$

$$f_2' = -3\text{-dB frequency} = 1.71/2\pi CR$$

$$\omega_0 = 1/\sqrt{LC}$$

$$K = -g_m R\sqrt{\frac{1 + 0.414(\omega/\omega_0)^2}{1 + 0.414(\omega/\omega_0)^2 + (\omega/\omega_0)^4}}$$

This is one type of high-frequency compensation.

If series compensation is used:

For maximal flatness,

$$Q_0{}^2 = \tfrac{2}{3} = 1/\omega_0 CR$$

$$C_{in} = 3C_{out}$$

$$C = C_{in} + C_{out}$$

$$\omega_2 = 2/CR$$

$$\omega_0 = 1/\sqrt{LC}$$

Bandpass Amplifiers:

$$K = \frac{-g_m R}{\left[1 - j\left(\frac{f_1}{f}\right)\right]\left[1 + j\left(\frac{f}{f_2}\right)\right]}$$

$$f_1 = -3\text{-dB point (low frequency)}$$

$$= \frac{1}{2\pi C_c(R' + R_g)}$$

$$f_2 = -3\text{-dB point (high frequency)}$$
$$= 1/2\pi CR$$

$$\text{where } R' = \frac{r_p R_L}{r_p + R_L}$$

$$R = \frac{R'R_g}{R' + R_g}$$

A common means of improving the response at the lower frequencies is to insert a resistor in the plate supply circuit and a capacitor across the combination. (See Fig. 8-8.) It can be shown that optimum results are obtained when the following relationships hold:

$$C_b R_L = C_c R_g$$

$$R_g C_c = \frac{R_b R_L C_b}{R_L + R_b}$$

Other circuits can be derived from the above basic arrangements. The advantages of transformer-coupled interstages are so many, however, that they are more commonly used for bandpass amplifiers. It is recommended that the reader review the characteristics of circuits employing input, interstage and output transformers, as well as stagger-tuned interstages.

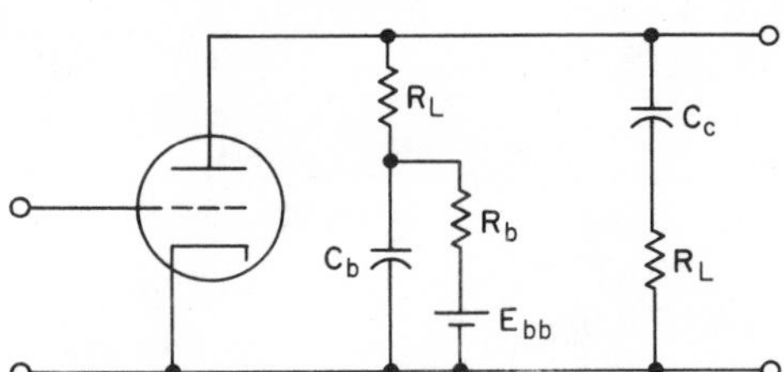

Figure 8-8

The Pentode

The actual pentode circuit and its equivalent diagram are shown in Fig. 8-9. A few hints on circuit design follow.

Note: For the pentode circuit of Fig. 8-9, ignore C_c for high frequencies and ignore C_p for low and intermediate frequencies.

$C_p = C_{pk}$ plus stray capacitance to left of C_c

$C_g =$ stray capacitance to right of C_c plus input capacitance of next stage

Input capacitance $= C_{gk} + C_{gp}(1 + G)$

where $G =$ gain per stage (about 15 for pentodes, 3 for triodes).

The total shunt capacitance per stage equals stray capacitance plus C_{gk} plus C_{pk} plus $C_{gp}(1 + G)$.

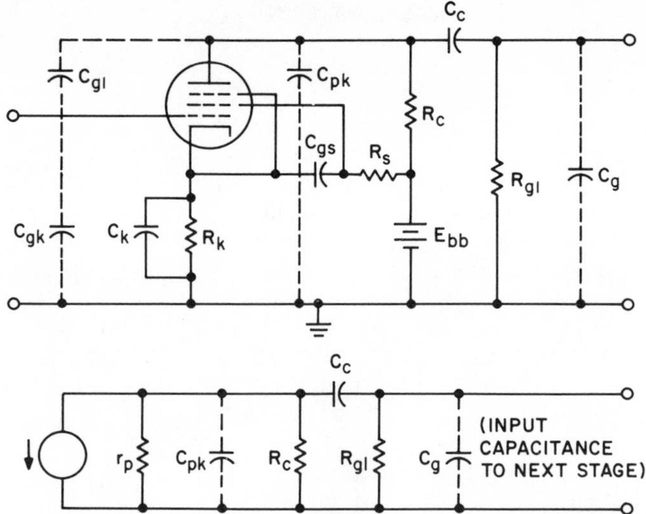

Figure 8-9

$$\text{Figure of merit of tube} = \frac{g_m}{C_{gk} + C_{pk} + C_{gp}(1 + G)}$$

For video amplifiers,

$$\text{Midfrequency gain} = g_m R_{eq}$$

where $R_{eq} = \dfrac{R_c}{1 + R_c/R_{g1} + R_c/R_p}$

$$\text{High-frequency response} = \frac{1}{1 + j(f/f_2)}$$

where f = high frequency

$f_2 = 1/2\pi C_s R_{eq}$

R_{eq} = parallel combination of R_p, R_{g1}, and R_c

$$\text{Low-frequency response} = \frac{1}{1 - j(f_1/f)}$$

where f = low frequency

$$f_1 = \frac{1}{2\pi C_c R}$$

$$R = R_{g1} + \frac{R_c}{1 + R_c/R_p}$$

For 70.7% response (−3 dB):

Low frequency: $X_{C_c} = R_{g1}$ plus parallel combination of R_c and R_p.

High frequency: X_{C_s} = parallel combination of R_c, R_{g1}, and R_p.

Feedback Amplifiers

It can be shown that the gain of a feedback amplifier can be expressed as

$$K' = \frac{K}{1 - \beta K}$$

where K = gain without feedback, and β = fraction of output added to the input. Consequently, when βK is negative, feedback reduces the gain. (See Fig. 8-10.)

As a criterion of stability, a plot of $-\beta K$ vs. frequency is usually made (Nyquist diagram) to show the effect of frequency. Should the plot enclose the point (-1), the amplifier will be unstable and will tend to oscillate.

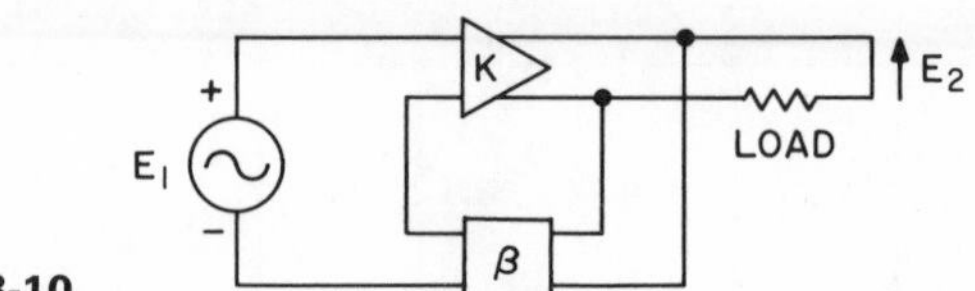

Figure 8-10

Large-Signal Applications (Power Amplifiers)

Untuned (audio) amplifiers usually operate within the linear portion of the i_b-e_b curve, or distortion is neutralized by operating in push-pull.

Tuned power amplifiers operate in Class B or C, and power transfer and efficiency are of great importance. Both maxima do not occur under the same conditions. Class C amplifiers are used only for constant-amplitude or on-off signals. Under Class A_1 operation, the grid bias varies, and for maximum power transfer with the simple triode amplifier, $R_L = 2r_p$.

Graphical solution of problems is employed. The examinee should review the construction of the d-c and a-c load lines to obtain the quiescent (Q) point, the adjustment of this Q point to account for asymmetry of the a-c wave, and the construction of the composite characteristics and load line for push-pull operation, and the construction of the $e_c = e_b$ line for Class C operation.

Oscillators

In a parallel resonant circuit, where I is the maximum value of a suddenly applied sinusoidal current,

$$e(t) = \frac{I}{\omega C} e^{-\alpha t} \sin \omega t$$

where $\alpha = 1/2RC$

$$\omega = \sqrt{\frac{1}{LC} - \frac{1}{4R^2C^2}}$$

For oscillation: $R \rightarrow \infty$, $\alpha = 0$, and $\omega = 1/\sqrt{LC}$. In the tuned-plate triode using positive feedback (see Fig. 8-11), for oscillations to begin:

$$\beta = -M/L_p$$
$$g_m \geqq L_p/MR$$
$$\omega = 1/\sqrt{L_pC}$$

Class A operation is valid to deduce the above relationships, even though operation proceeds into Class C_2 within a few cycles. See Fig. 8-12.

Given a particular circuit, the determination of the formulas for g_m and oscillating frequency in terms of circuit parameters is made by writing the mesh or nodal equations and setting the common determinant of the set of equations equal to zero.

The applicant should be familiar with the basic oscillating circuits, some of which are:

1. Tuned-grid (triode): Characteristics are similar to tuned-plate.
2. Tuned-grid tuned-plate (triode): Can be used at higher frequencies than the simpler type.
3. Colpitts (triode): Lowpass application. Oscillates at a frequency at which the filter sections have a 180° phase shift.
4. Hartley (triode): Highpass application. Oscillates at a frequency at which the filter sections have a 180° phase shift.
5. Clapp (triode): Bandpass application. Has improved frequency stability.
6. Electron-coupled (tetrode): The simplest master oscillator power amplifier. The load is isolated from the oscillating circuit.
7. Transitron (pentode): Resonant circuit is attached to the screen grid, with feedback to the suppressor grid. The suppressor potential rises as the oscillating current falls.
8. Franklin (triodes): A two-stage amplifier in which the resonant circuit is isolated by small coupling capacitors.
9. Crystal (piezoelectric): This type has a mechanically resonant element (crystal) coupled to the electric circuit.
10. RC: This is a relatively inexpensive oscillator that avoids large inductors that would otherwise be required at audio frequencies. A thermistor is used for amplitude stabilization. Variations of this type are the Wien bridge and the phase-shift oscillators.

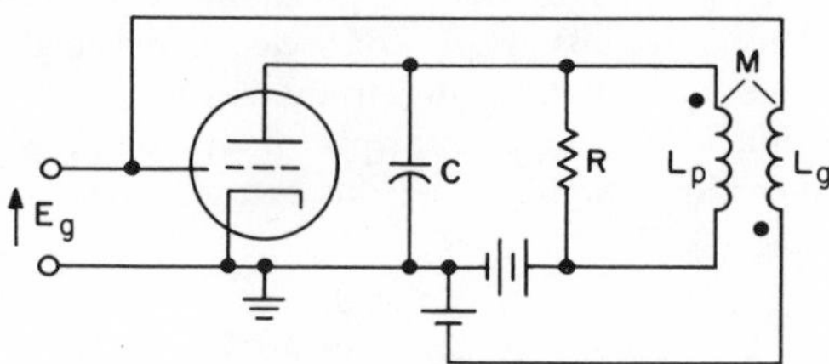

Figure 8-11

8-2 GAS-FILLED TUBES

Gas-filled tubes require much less plate-to-cathode potential for electron flow, and circuit efficiency is much higher than for thermionic vacuum tubes. The following comments apply to gas-filled tubes in common use:

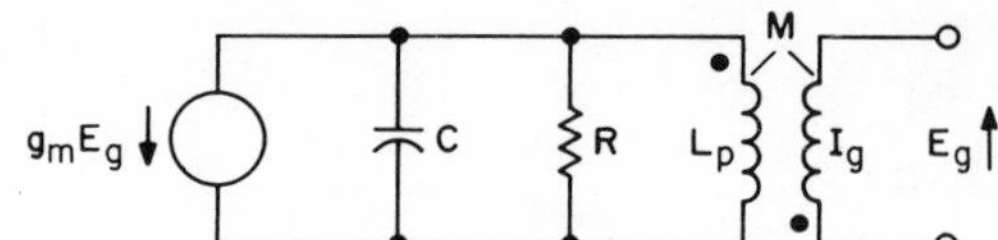

Figure 8-12

1. In the mercury-vapor thermionic diode, once the conductive voltage E_{cr} has been reached, the current flow is limited by the nature of the external circuit. Where the sinusoidal voltage input is E_i (rms) in the half-wave rectifier circuit shown in Fig. 8-13, the plate current flows only between the time angle $\theta_2 - \theta_1$ and not over the entire cycle.

$$\theta_1 = \sin^{-1}\frac{E_{cr} + E_o}{\sqrt{2}E_i} \text{ radians}$$

$$\theta_2 = \pi - \theta_1 \text{ radians}$$

The average (d-c) current is

$$I_{d\text{-}c} = \left(\frac{\sqrt{2}E_i}{\pi R_L}\right)\cos\theta_1 - \left(\frac{\pi - 2\theta_1}{2\pi}\right)\left(\frac{E_{cr} + E_o}{R_L}\right)$$

Compare this with the relationship for the high-vacuum thermionic diode having a constant rectifier resistance R_r,

$$I_{d\text{-}c} = \frac{\sqrt{2}E_i/\pi - E_o}{R_r + R_L}$$

2. The thyratron is a gas-filled discharge tube having a control grid that sets the firing angle but does not control the current once ionization has occurred. With an a-c supply, by varying the control-grid potential, the point of discharge (and, therefore, the voltage or current output magnitude) can be controlled over a wide range with an insignificant amount of control power. Types of control are (a) on-off, (b) phase-shift, and (c) combined a-c and adjustable d-c grid potential with fixed phase shift. A resistor must be inserted in the grid circuit to prevent flow of grid current when the grid potential swings positive after conduction has commenced. A capacitor is connected between the grid and cathode to limit the magnitude of transient current.
3. For cold-cathode gas filled tubes, the principle of operation is high field emission rather than thermionic emission. In this category are:

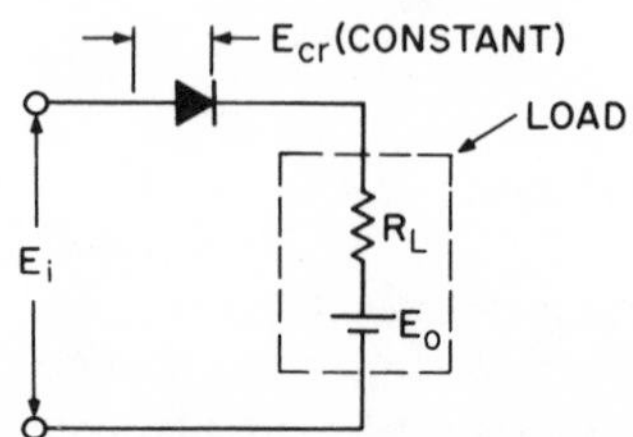

Figure 8-13

(a) Mercury-arc rectifiers, wherein the arc is self-sustaining, provided that the current is not allowed to fall to zero; an auxiliary electrode is used to prevent this. Voltage drop is somewhat higher than for the mercury-vapor thermionic rectifier; however, these tubes can handle thousands of amperes at appreciable voltages. Their output is limited primarily by heat transfer requirements.

(b) Ignitron rectifiers are similar to the mercury-arc rectifier except that the ignition technique used permits variation of the point in the cycle where ignition occurs.

8-3 BASIC THEORY AND APPLICATIONS OF SEMICONDUCTORS

There are some materials that, by reason of their monocrystalline structure and the energy distribution among the electrons within the atom, are neither insulators not conductors; in the pure state, their resistive characteristic varies with temperature. These materials, with the addition of certain impurities (doping), will have mobile electrons or holes (mobile electron absences) within the crystal, while at the same time adhering to the rule of charge neutrality considering the crystal as a whole. Such materials are known as semiconductors.

A semiconductor could be made from say germanium or silicon, using arsenic as a dopant, and it would have mostly mobile electrons and few holes within its crystals; it would be known as an *n-type* semiconductor. If indium were used as the dopant, then the majority charge carriers within the crystals would be holes and the minority charge carriers would be electrons; the doped crystal would be known as a *p-type* semiconductor.

If an n-type region were joined with a p-type region, some readjustment takes place, but without disturbing the law of charge neutrality. An equilibrium is reached when the degree of readjustment is limited by the resulting potential difference between the two regions—a potential barrier across the junction. Logic suggests that if an external potential were applied to overcome this barrier, more readjustment would occur. In fact, as long as electrons are supplied at one end and taken away (supplying holes) at the other end, an electric current would be established, the required energy coming from without the paired regions.

The above is intended to show that electron flow is demanded by logic. However, an adequate quantitative explanation of what occurs is not possible using circuit theory alone, and resort to quantum mechanics is made in the literature to completely reconcile observations with accepted hypotheses.

As we have accustomed ourselves to think of vacuum tubes as having electrodes that are voltage oriented (e.g., grid bias), so we usually think of semiconductor configurations as current oriented (e.g., base current bias).

When a p-type region is joined to an n-type region, the free electrons can flow across the p-n junction if other electrons are provided in the n-type region to replace them. The junction is then said to be under forward bias, as shown in Fig. 8-14.

Figure 8-14 contains a p-n junction that is basically a diode. If three semiconductor regions are assembled to form a sandwich, two p-n junctions are formed, and the resulting transistor is a current-oriented solid-state counterpart of the vacuum triode. This solid-state triode requires no heater power, has small weight

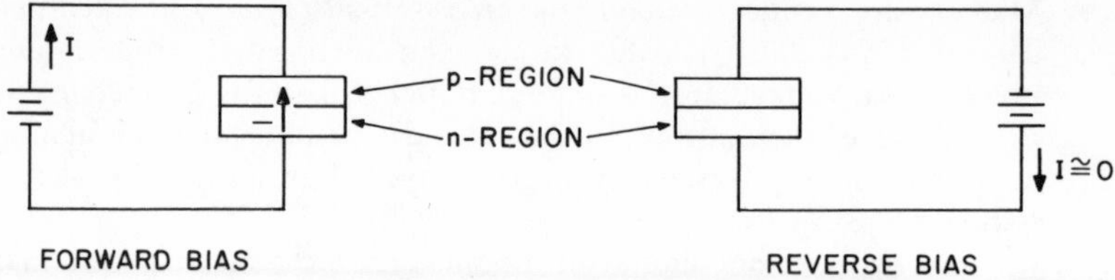

Figure 8-14

and space requirements, and has virtually unlimited life if not subjected to excessive voltages or temperatures. However, the transistor cannot be used where large signal voltages are involved, and its ability to withstand temperature (100 °C for germanium and 200 °C for silicon) is below that of the vacuum tube. An n-p-n transistor is shown in Fig. 8-15 with its accepted symbol. The line with the arrowhead represents the emitter (the symbol for the p-n-p transistor would have the arrow pointing inward). The center region is called the base, and the emitter current equals the sum of the collector and the base currents. The transistor, which is a single crystal, can be formed by several methods, the most common being the alloy junction method (an inexpensive p-n-p transistor for low-frequency applications) and the diffusion method (mesa and planar types) which is more expensive but yields transistors with higher breakdown voltages and improved parametric characteristics.

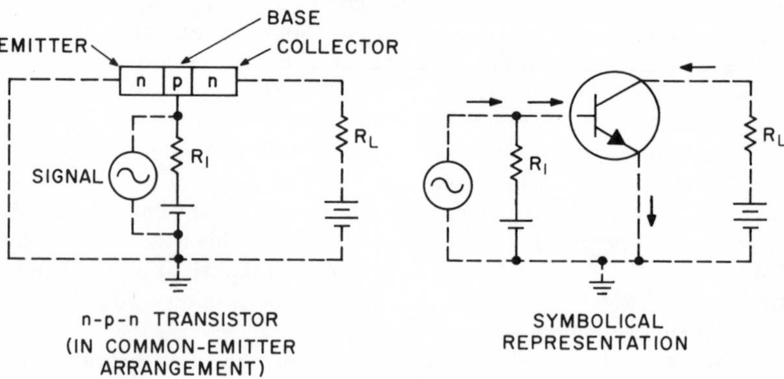

Figure 8-15

Just as there are common-cathode, common-grid, and cathode-follower configurations with vacuum triodes, there are common-emitter, common-base, and common-collector configurations, respectively, for the transistor. Regardless of the configuration used, the transistor can be approximated by the equivalent circuits shown in Fig. 8-16. The capital letter subscripts indicate *total* values of currents and voltages, which are pertinent in viewing quiescent conditions. For Fig. 8-16, I_{CO} is the leakage current flowing from collector to base with the emitter terminal disconnected. Sometimes it is designated as I_{CBO}. I_{CEO} is the leakage current flowing from collector to emitter with the base terminal disconnected. r_b' is the resistance of the base. e_{rbe} is the voltage drop across the emitter-base junction. This is about

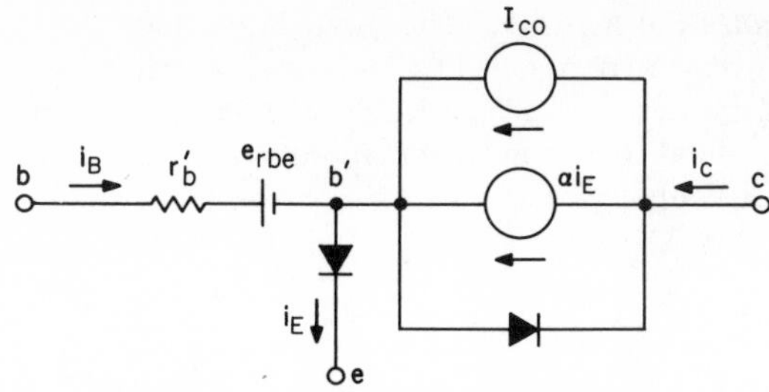

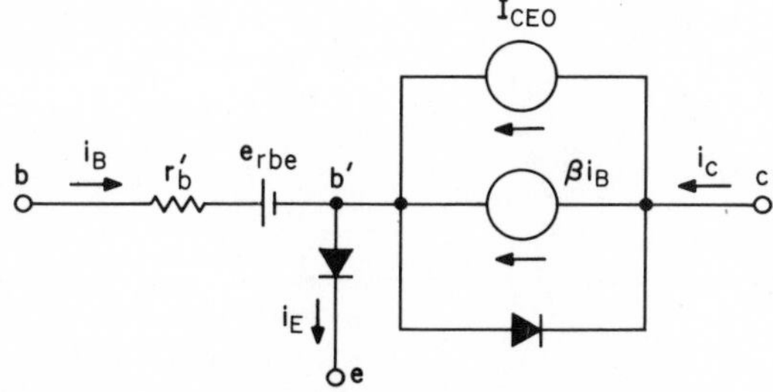

Figure 8-16. Linear circuit representations of the n-p-n transistor.

0.2 volts for germanium and about 0.6 volts for silicon. However, the voltage drop is nonlinear and varies with β and temperature.

$$\alpha = \left.\frac{\Delta i_C}{\Delta i_E}\right|_{v_{CB=constant}} \qquad \beta = \left.\frac{\Delta i_C}{\Delta i_B}\right|_{v_{CE=constant}}$$

Note that

$$\beta = \frac{\alpha}{1 - \alpha} \qquad 1 + \beta = \frac{1}{1 - \alpha}$$

$$I_{CEO} = (1 + \beta)I_{CO}$$

Assuming that the emitter-base junction remains forward biased and the collector-base junction remains reverse biased (as is normal), the collector diode may be omitted. Two dynamic, sometimes called incremental, equivalent circuits for the transistor are shown in Fig. 8-17. The symbol r_n represents both the base resistance r_b' and the effect of the a-c voltage drop across the emitter-base junction r_{be}. The latter is frequently observed to be negligible. (These circuits do not provide for a reverse-voltage effect, emitter to base, due to Δv_{ce}, which is frequently ignored).

As far as the a-c components are concerned, and regardless of the configuration used, the transistor can be represented by a four-terminal network, as shown in Fig. 8-18. Certain "hybrid" parameters have been developed. They are h_{11}, the input impedance with the output ac short circuited; h_{22}, the output admittance with the input ac open circuited; h_{12}, the reverse voltage ratio with the input ac open circuited; and h_{21}, the forward current ratio with the output ac short circuited.

The four-terminal network equations are

$$v_1 = h_{11}i_1 + h_{12}v_2$$
$$i_2 = h_{21}i_1 + h_{22}v_2$$

(The positive direction of i_2 is *into* the network.) The input impedance (h_{11}) for the common-base configuration would be designated h_{ib}, the output admittance (h_{22}) for the common emitter would be designated h_{oe}, etc. Remembering that these parameters are for use in small-signal theory only, the approximate relationships among them follow for the three configurations.

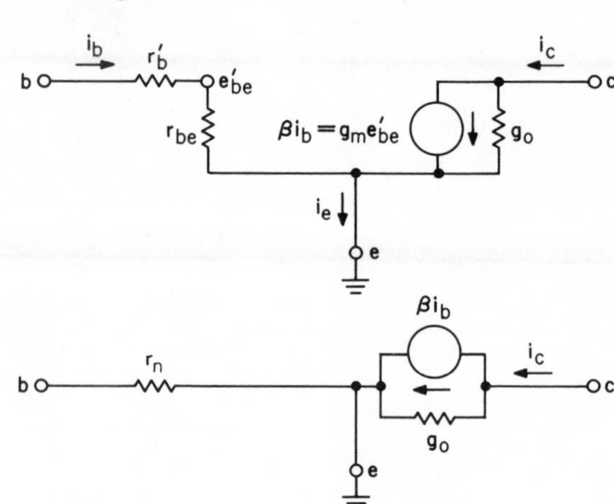

Figure 8-17. Incremental or dynamic circuit representation of the n-p-n transistor.

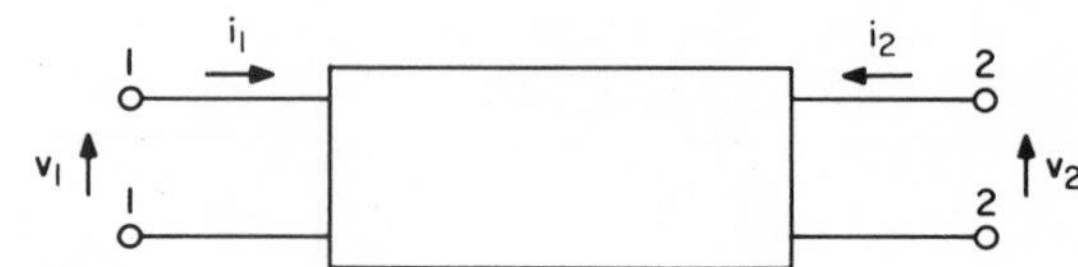

Figure 8-18

Common base. (See Fig. 8-19.)
Analogy: Common-grid triode.
Characteristics:

1. Low input impedance.
2. High output impedance.
3. Medium power gain, in the order of 25 dB.
4. Large voltage gain.
5. Low current gain (<1).
6. No phase inversion between input and output.

$$h_{11} = h_{ib} = \frac{h_{ie}}{1 + h_{fe}} = -\frac{h_{ic}}{h_{fc}}$$

$$h_{22} = h_{ob} = \frac{h_{oe}}{1 + h_{fe}} = -\frac{h_{oc}}{h_{fc}}$$

$$h_{12} = h_{rb} = \frac{h_{ie}h_{oe}}{1 + h_{fe}} - h_{re}$$

$$= h_{rc} - 1 - \frac{h_{ic}h_{oc}}{h_{fc}}$$

$$h_{21} = h_{fb} = -\frac{h_{fe}}{1 + h_{fe}} = -\frac{1 + h_{fb}}{h_{fb}}$$

Common emitter. (See Fig. 8-20.)
Analogy: Common-cathode triode.
Characteristics:

1. Moderate input impedance.
2. Moderate output impedance.
3. High power gain, in the order of 40 dB.
4. Moderate voltage gain.
5. Moderate current gain.
6. Can be used with one d-c supply.
7. Poor bias stability and frequency response.

$$h_{11} = h_{ie} = \frac{h_{ib}}{1 + h_{fb}} = h_{ic}$$

$$h_{22} = h_{oe} = \frac{h_{ob}}{1 + h_{fb}} = h_{oc}$$

$$h_{12} = h_{re} = \frac{h_{ib}h_{ob}}{1 + h_{fb}} - h_{rb}$$

$$= 1 - h_{rc}$$

$$h_{21} = h_{fe} = -\frac{h_{fb}}{1 + h_{fb}} = -(1 + h_{fc})$$

Common collector. (See Fig. 8-21.)
Analogy: Cathode-follower triode.
Characteristics:

1. High input impedance.
2. Low output impedance.
3. Low power gain, in the order of 15 dB.

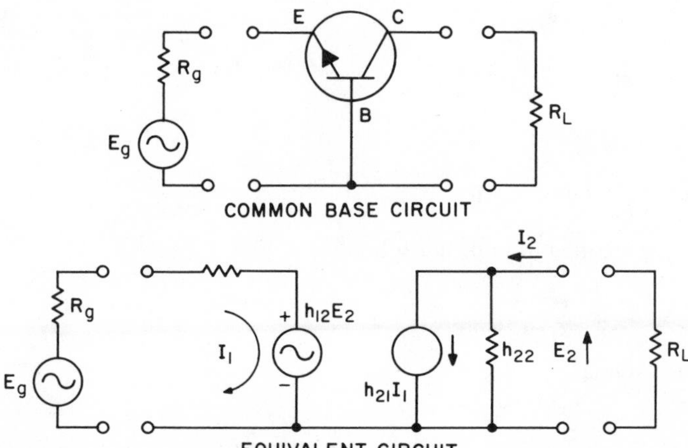

Figure 8-19

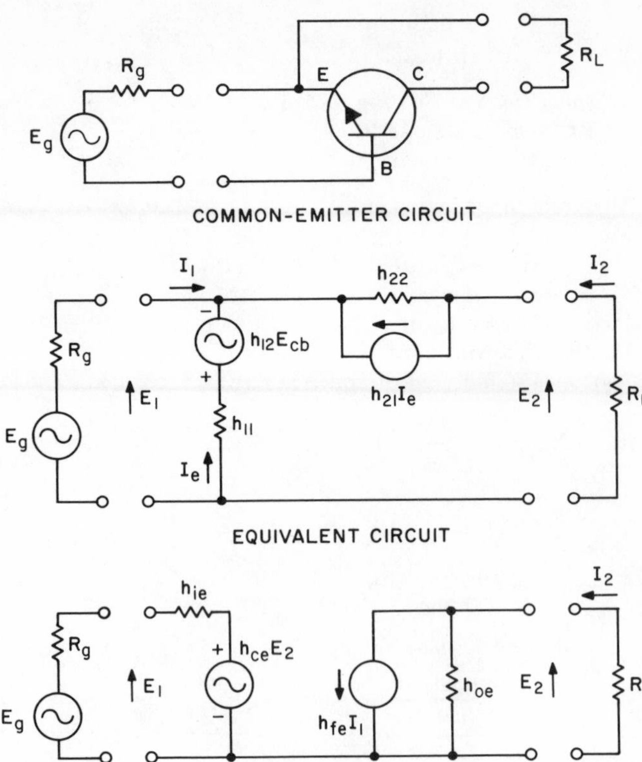

Figure 8-20

4. Small voltage gain (<1).
5. High current gain.

$$h_{11} = h_{ic} = h_{ie} = \frac{h_{ib}}{1 + h_{fb}}$$

$$h_{22} = h_{oc} = h_{oe} = \frac{h_{ob}}{1 + h_{fb}}$$

$$h_{12} = h_{rc} = 1 - h_{re}$$

$$h_{21} = h_{fc} = -(1 + h_{fe}) = -\frac{1}{1 + h_{fb}}$$

Regardless of the configuration, the following apply:

Input resistance $R_i = \dfrac{\Delta^h R_L + h_{11}}{h_{22}R_L + 1}$

where $\Delta^h = h_{11}h_{22} - h_{12}h_{21}$

Output resistance $R_o = \dfrac{h_{11} + R_g}{\Delta^h + h_{22}R_g}$

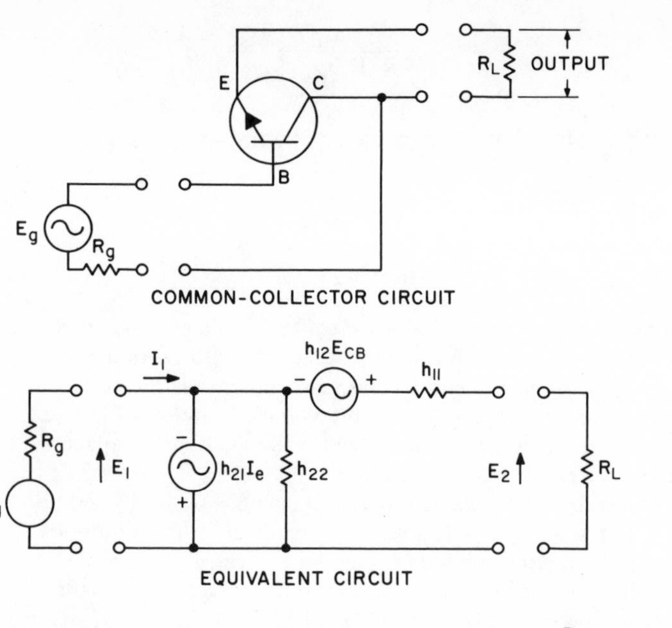

Figure 8-21

$$\text{Current gain } A_i = \frac{h_{21}}{h_{22}R_L + 1}$$

$$\text{Voltage gain } A_e = \frac{-h_{21}R_L}{h_{11} + \Delta^h R_L}$$

$$\text{Power gain } A_p = \frac{-h_{21}{}^2 R_L}{(h_{22}R_L + 1)(h_{11} + \Delta^h R_L)}$$

$$= A_i{}^2(R_L/R_i)$$

$$\text{Transducer gain} = \frac{\text{power out}}{\text{available generator power}}$$

$$= \frac{4h_{21}{}^2 R_L}{(R_g R_L h_{22} + R_g + \Delta^h R_L + h_{11})^2}$$

$$\text{Available power gain} = \frac{\text{available power at transistor output}}{\text{available generator power}}$$

$$= \frac{h_{21}{}^2 R_g}{(\Delta^h + R_g h_{22})(R_g + h_{11})}$$

$$\text{Maximum available gain MAG} = \frac{h_{21}{}^2}{[(\Delta^h)^{1/2} + (h_{11}h_{22})^{1/2}]^2}$$

where $R_g = \sqrt{\Delta^h h_{11}/h_{22}}$ and $R_L = \sqrt{h_{11}/\Delta^h h_{22}}$

Biasing

The operating point (quiescent values of collector voltage, base current, emitter current, etc.) of a transistor is established by biasing. Regardless of the configuration used, the current flowing in the emitter-base circuit controls the collector current. The biasing potentials are represented by d-c voltage sources in Fig. 8-22; arrows indicate conventional current flow (not electron flow). Bypass capacitors around the voltage sources are omitted for simplicity.

As in vacuum-tube circuits, single-battery biasing is desired for economy and space-saving purposes. Also, practical biasing circuits differ from those of Fig. 8-22 to avoid instability problems that would otherwise occur. For example, resistor R_1' in Fig. 8-23 would provide a forward bias for the emitter-base circuit. However, variable factors that would change the Q point are β, I_{CEO}, and e_{rbe} (the voltage across the emitter-base junction). I_{CEO} for germanium approximately doubles with each 10°C rise, and e_{rbe} for silicon decreases with a temperature increase at a rate

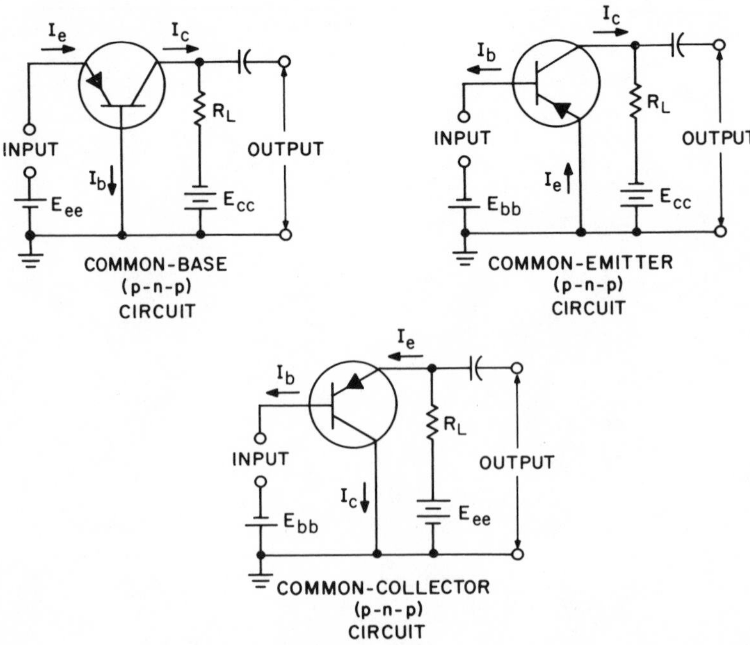

Figure 8-22

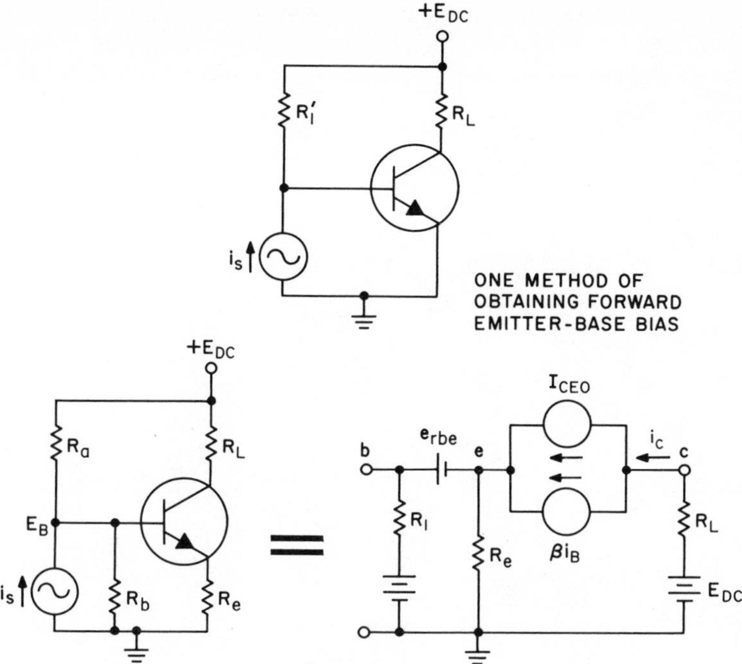

Figure 8-23

of about 2.5 mV/°C. β varies widely for transistors of the same type. Q point stabilization can be accomplished by inserting a resistor in the emitter lead (introducing a compensating feedback), and by using a voltage divider (R_a and R_b) in the base lead, as shown in Fig. 8-23.

Figure 8-23 shows a practical biasing scheme, where

$$E_B = \left(\frac{R_b}{R_a + R_b}\right)E_{DC}$$

$$R_1 = \frac{R_a R_b}{R_a + R_b}$$

Note: ΔI_{CEO} divides between R_1 and R_e, causing a negative $\Delta\beta i_B$. The net increase in Δi_C is less than ΔI_{CEO}. $\Delta\beta$ and Δe_{rbe} are compensated similarly.

Frequency Response; Pole-Zero Concept

Since gain and phase shift vary with frequency, it is necessary to select circuit parameters that will change these characteristics to meet the requirements. In many cases, uniform gain and linear phase shift are desired within the useful frequency band; sharpness of cutoff is another common requirement. Rather than calculating and plotting gain and phase angle for many frequencies, the more practical procedure is to use *pole-zero* analysis to rapidly determine the frequency response of a circuit or to design a circuit to give the desired response.

For the general case, pole-zero analysis is applied to the Laplace transform (see Chap. 10) expression for the excitation-response relationship. However for simplicity, the following discussion avoids use of the Laplace transform by assuming sinusoidal voltages and currents.

To evaluate the frequency response of a linear system, the following sequence is followed:

1. Draw the actual circuit.
2. Draw the equivalent incremental circuit.
3. Write the expression for gain in terms of angular frequency and the circuit constants.
4. Rearrange this expression as a function of $j\omega$

$$A_v(j\omega) = K\frac{(j\omega + \omega_1)(j\omega + \omega_2)(\cdots)}{(j\omega + \omega_3)(j\omega + \omega_4)(\cdots)}$$

where $A_v(j\omega)$ = voltage gain for any angular frequency ω
K = real number, determined by the circuit constants, and is proportional to maximum gain
$\omega_1, \omega_2, \omega_3, \ldots$ = constants determined by circuit parameters

5. Express this as a function of m

$$A_v(m) = K\frac{(m - m_1)(m - m_2)(\cdots)}{(m - m_3)(m - m_4)(\cdots)}$$

where $m = j\omega$, $m_1 = -\omega_1$, $m_2 = -\omega_2, \ldots$

Any value of m that will make $A_v(m)$ equal zero is called a *zero;* any value of m that will make $A_v(m)$ infinity is called a *pole.*

6. Plot the poles and zeros against $j\omega$. From this pole-zero pattern can be determined the shape of the gain characteristic curve (decibel gain vs. logarithmic frequency), phase shift, peaking frequencies, etc. The following examples will illustrate the use of this valuable tool:

Example

One stage of a tuned amplifier with its equivalent (high voltage) incremental circuit is shown in Fig. 8-24. The applicable expression for the gain of this circuit is

$$A_v(m) = -\frac{\mu}{LC}\left(\frac{1}{m^2 + (R/L)m + 1/LC}\right)$$

where R = plate resistance and the transformer winding resistance
L = leakage reactance of transformer
C = shunt (stray) capacitance plus shunt capacitance of following stage.

Rewriting the expression, using symbols of convenience,

$$A_v(m) = -\mu\omega_0{}^2\frac{1}{(m - m_1)(m - m_2)}$$

and the poles are

$$m = -\alpha \pm j\beta$$

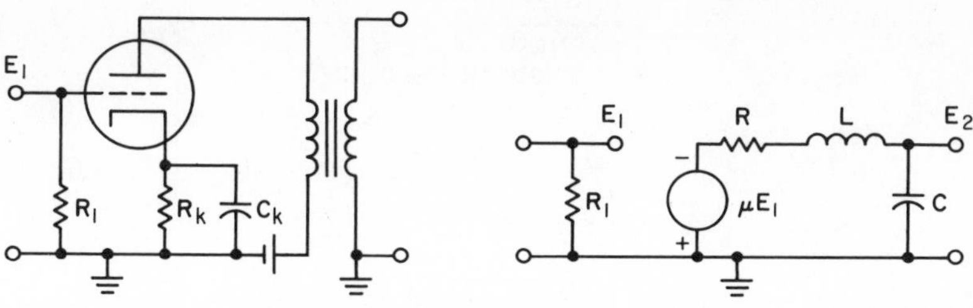

Figure 8-24

where $\omega_0 = 1/LC$, $\alpha = R/2L$, and $\beta = j\sqrt{\omega_0^2 - \alpha^2}$

The pole-zero plot of Fig. 8-25 shows the significance of the symbols. In Fig. 8-25(A), for any value of $j\omega$,

$$A_v = A_{max} \sin \phi$$

$$|A_v| = \frac{\mu\omega_0^2}{2\alpha\beta} = \frac{\mu\omega_0^2}{\rho_1\rho_2}$$

The particular values of $j\omega$ and $-j\omega$ shown, happen to be the intersections of the *peaking* circle with the axis of imaginaries, and represent the amplitude peaks. If the circle were made tangent to the imaginary axis (in this case, by decreasing R), this would give the maximum bandwidth obtainable without peaking. If the circle does not touch the $j\omega$ axis at all, then there are no resonant peaks and the maximum gain occurs at zero frequency. It is obvious that the location of the poles can be manipulated by varying α and β (i.e., R, L, and C).

Figure 8-25(B) shows the phase angle for any value of $j\omega$.

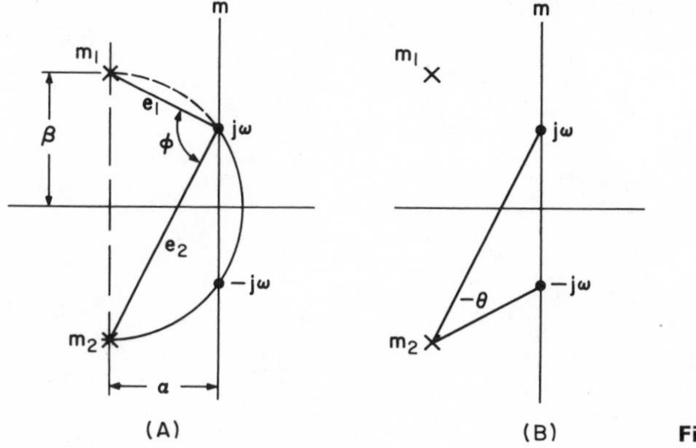

Figure 8-25

Example

To illustrate the significance of poles and zeros in establishing *break-point* frequencies (i.e., the intersections of the asymptotes of the decibel gain vs. log frequency characteristic), assume that the poles and zeros of a particular amplifier are as shown in Fig. 8-26 (not to scale).

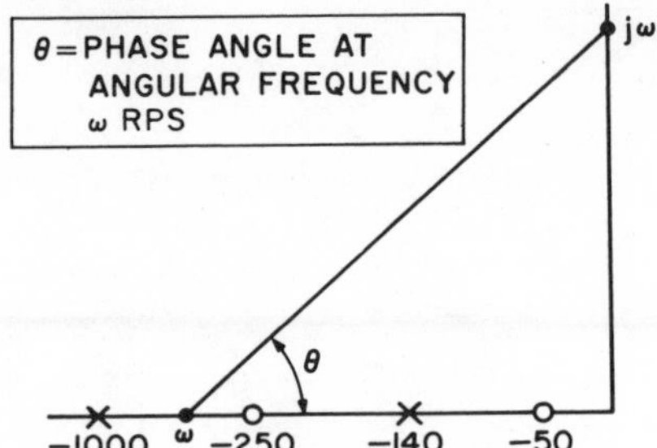

Figure 8-26

The gain equation would be

$$A_v = K\frac{(j\omega + 50)(j\omega + 250)}{(j\omega + 140)(j\omega + 1000)}$$

Observing that a pole introduces a change of slope of an asymptote of −6 dB per octave and that a zero introduces a change of slope of +6 dB per octave, the asymptotic structure would appear as shown in Fig. 8-27. Assume that $K = 630$ (i.e., $20 \log K = 56$ dB). The actual gain characteristic is shown, using the asymptotes as guides.

Note: Since $j\omega + \omega_1 = \omega_1(1 + j\omega/\omega_1)$, the gain equation can be expressed as

$$A_v = \frac{12.5}{140}K\frac{(1 + j\omega/50)(1 + j\omega/250)}{(1 + j\omega/140)(1 + j\omega/1000)}$$

where $(12.5/140)K$ is A_{max} (assumed to be 630 in this example).

Example of small-signal analysis (neglecting biasing and frequency response)

To illustrate the use of h parameters in analyzing transistor circuits consider the following two-stage amplifier circuit.

The parameters for transistor No. 1:

$h_{ie} = 890$
$h_{re} = 6 \times 10^{-4}$
$h_{fe} = 21.0$
$h_{oe} = 2 \times 10^{-5}$
$\Delta^h = 5.2 \times 10^{-3}$

The parameters for transistor No. 2:

$h_{ie} = 2000$
$h_{re} = 16 \times 10^{-4}$
$h_{fe} = 49.0$
$h_{oe} = 5 \times 10^{-5}$
$\Delta^h = 2.16 \times 10^{-2}$

For the second stage:

$$(A_i)_2 = \frac{h_{fe}}{h_{oe}R_L + 1} = 42.6$$

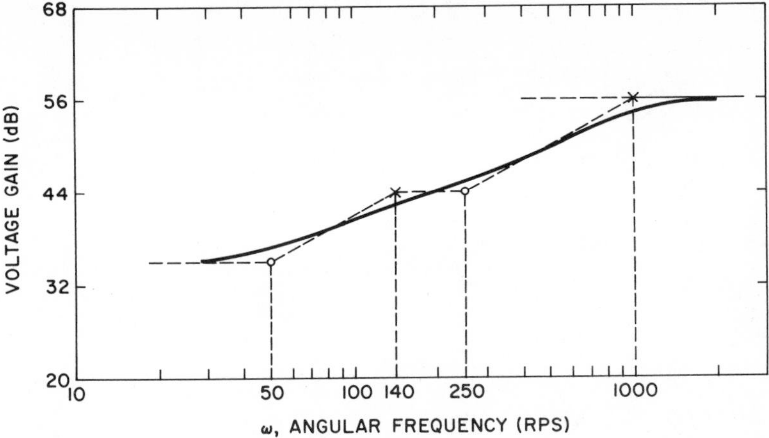

Figure 8-27

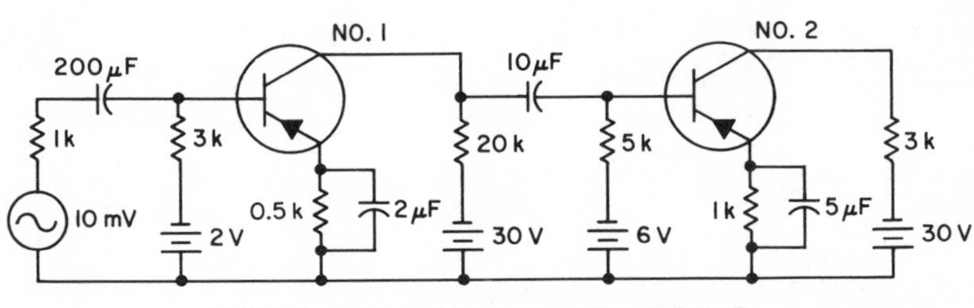

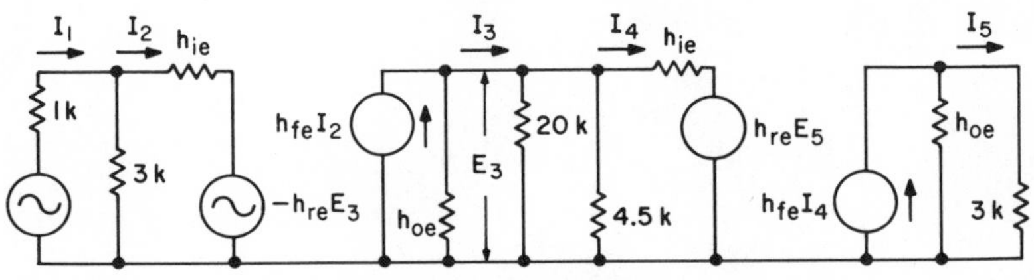

Figure 8-28

$$(R_i)_2 = \frac{\Delta^h R_L + h_{ie}}{h_{oe} R_L + 1} = 1800 \text{ ohms}$$

Interstage current gain (see Fig. 8-29):

$$\frac{I_4}{I_3} = \frac{20k \times 4.5k/24.5k}{(20k \times 4.5k/24.5k) + 1.8k}$$

$$= 0.670$$

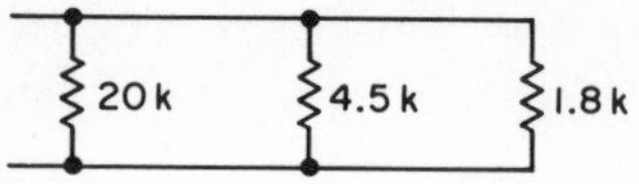

Figure 8-29

$$1/R_{eq} = 1/1.8k + 1/4.5k + 1/20k$$

$$R_{eq} = 1.21k$$

For the first stage,

$$R_{eq} = R_{L1}$$

Therefore,

$$(A_i)_1 = \frac{I_3}{I_2} = \frac{h_{fe}}{h_{oe}R_{L1} + 1} = 20.6$$

$$R_i = \frac{\Delta^h R_{L1} + h_{ie}}{h_{oe}R_{L1} + 1}$$

$$= 880 \text{ ohms}$$

For the resistance network prior to the first stage (see Fig. 8-30),

$$A_i = I_2/I_1 = 3/3.88 = 0.773$$

$$R_i = \frac{(0.88k)(3k)}{3.88k} = 680 \text{ ohms}$$

Total current gain:

$$(A_i)_T = 0.773 \times 20.6 \times 0.670 \times 42.6 = 454$$

Total power gain:

$$A_p = \frac{A_i^2 R_L}{R_i} = 454^2 \times 3000/680 = 0.910 \times 10^6 \text{ or } 53.8 \text{ dB}$$

$$P_{in} = \frac{E_g^2 R_i}{(R_g + R_i)^2} = \frac{(1.5 \times 10^{-2})^2(680)}{(1.68 \times 10^3)^2} = 5.97 \times 10^{-8}$$

$$P_{out} = P_{in}A_p = (5.97 \times 10^{-8})(0.910 \times 10^6) = 54.4 \text{ mW}$$

$$P_{g(avail)} = \frac{E_g^2}{4R_g} = \frac{(1.5 \times 10^{-2})^2}{4k} = 5.63\ \mu\text{W}$$

$$\text{Transducer gain} = \frac{54.4 \times 10^{-3}}{5.63 \times 10^{-6}} = 0.965 \times 10^6 \text{ or } 59.8 \text{ dB}$$

Large-Signal Applications (Power Amplifiers)

For power amplifiers, the h parameters cannot be used, and recourse must be made to graphical analysis. Although maximum power output is the main criterion, it is necessary to consider collector efficiency, distortion, and power dissipation. The collector efficiency is used as the criterion of amplifier performance:

$$\text{Collector efficiency} = \frac{\text{a-c output power}}{\text{battery input power}}$$

A common measure of distortion is the second harmonic distortion:

$$\text{Percent distortion} = \frac{\frac{1}{4}(I_{max} + I_{min}) - \frac{1}{2}I_c}{\frac{1}{2}(I_{max} - I_{min})} \times 100$$

where I_{max} and I_{min} refer to the collector current, and I_c is the quiescent value of collector current.

As with vacuum-tube circuits, amplifiers are classified as Class A, B, AB, and C, depending on the placement of the bias point and the intended usage.

To determine the operating characteristics of a power amplifier, the graph of collector current vs. collector voltage (in the common-base and the common-emitter configurations) must be used. Power amplifiers are usually shunt fed; hence, it is necessary to plot both the a-c and d-c load lines on the characteristic curve.

The quiescent point is located at the intersection of the a-c and d-c load lines and is usually placed about half way between the saturation region and the collector dissipation curve. The latter is determined by plotting the rated collector dissipation power against collector voltage. The allowable dissipation is derated if the ambient temperature is above normal.

$$T_{der} = K(T_{ambient} - 25\,^\circ\text{C})$$

where K is the degradation factor in watts/°C, and T_{der} is the amount that the rated dissipation should be reduced.

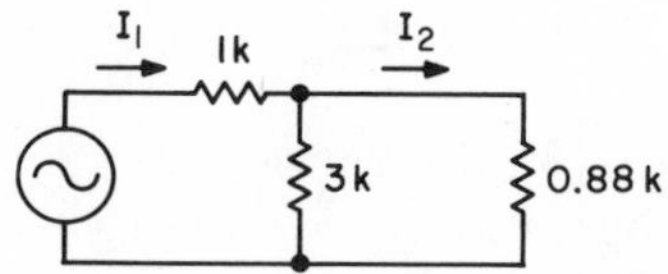

Figure 8-30

Example of power amplifier design

The following is an example of a design of a power amplifier for Class A operation. In this case, a power output of 2 watts is desired over the audio spectrum. The manufacturer's specifications for this transistor are

$P_{dis} = 6$ watts $\quad (V_c)_{max} = 25$ volts

$K = 3$ mW/°C $\quad R_i = 1.75$ ohms

Assume no derating is necessary.

Solution:

For a shunt-fed amplifier (see Fig. 8-31),

Ideal $P_{out} = \frac{1}{2}P_{bat}$

Ideal $P_{dis} = 2P_{out}$

Hence, Ideal $P_{dis} = 2 \times 2$ watts. A 6-watt transistor is satisfactory.

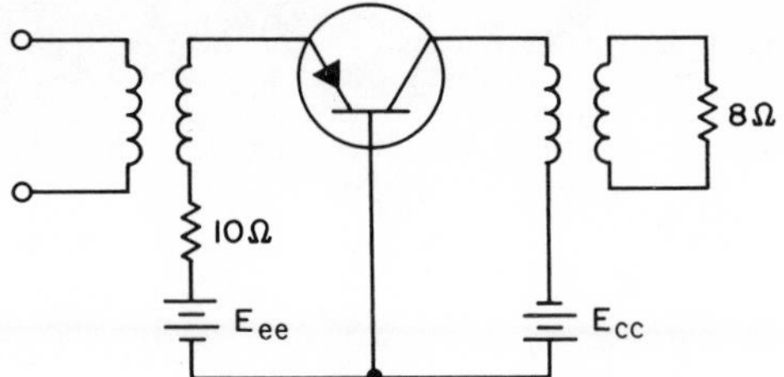

Figure 8-31

For a transformer-coupled Class A amplifier, the voltage swing is about twice the supply voltage. To keep within the 25 volts $(V_c)_{max}$, select a value of 9 volts for E_{cc}. To get 2 watts output power with an efficiency of less than 50%, the quiescent point must be so chosen that $P_Q = 4$ watts. If I_E is chosen to be 0.6 amps, then

$$P_Q = 9 \times 0.56 = 5.05 \text{ watts}$$

The d-c load line is drawn almost vertically, since the output transformer presents negligible resistance. The slope of the a-c load line is chosen so that the voltage swings on either side of the operating point are approximately equal. A load of about 16 ohms will give the proper load line (see Fig. 8-32). Therefore, the output transformer should have a 2:1 turns ratio.

With these load lines, the maximum swings in voltage and current are

$$E_{max} \cong 18 \text{ volts} \qquad I_{max} \cong 1.1 \text{ amp}$$

$$E_{min} \cong 0 \text{ volts} \qquad I_{min} \cong 0.04 \text{ amp}$$

$$\text{Output power} = (18 - 0)(1.1 - 0.04) = 2.38 \text{ watts}$$

$$\text{Collector efficiency} = \frac{(E_{max} - E_{min})(I_{max} - I_{min})}{8E_{cc}I_{cc}} = 47.1\%$$

For the desired bias conditions, $I_E = 0.6$ amp. Therefore, $E_{ee} = 0.6 \times 10 = 6$ volts.

From the curves, it is seen that the emitter current swing is 1.16/2 or 0.58 amp. The second harmonic distortion is

$$100 \times \frac{\frac{1}{4}(1.1 + 0.04) - \frac{1}{2}(0.58)}{\frac{1}{2}(1.1 - 0.04)} = -0.945\%$$

Required input power:

$$P_{in} = I^2(\text{rms})R_{in} = 0.58^2/2 \times 1.75 = 0.294 \text{ watts}$$

Power gain:

$$A_p = 10 \log 2.38/0.294 = 9.08 \text{ dB}$$

PROBLEMS

Problem 8-1 Vacuum-tube, low-frequency amplifier impedance and gain

Calculate the input and output impedances and voltage gain of the low-frequency amplifier shown in Fig. 8-33. State the approximate limits on input voltage within which linear operation of the amplifier is possible.

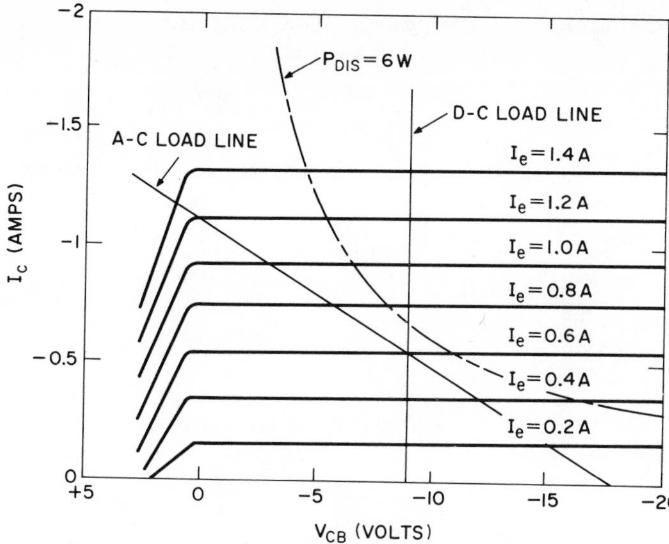

Figure 8-32

Solution:

From Fig. 8-33, the stages of the amplifier are (a) first stage: grounded grid; and (b) second stage: cathode-follower.

The first stage matches the amplifier to the low-impedance source and the high-input impedance of the second stage. The first stage performs the necessary amplification. The second stage matches the first stage output to the load. As far as the second stage is concerned, the input and the output are in phase and its grid cannot go positive with higher input voltage and cause nonlinearity. Actually, the amplification of the cathode follower is less than unity.

From the tube manual,

$$g_m = 1600\ \mu\text{mhos} \qquad C_{pk} = 1.2\ \text{pF}$$
$$r_p = 62{,}500\ \text{ohms} \qquad C_{gp} = 1.7\ \text{pF}$$
$$\mu = 100 \qquad C_{gk} = 1.8\ \text{pF}$$

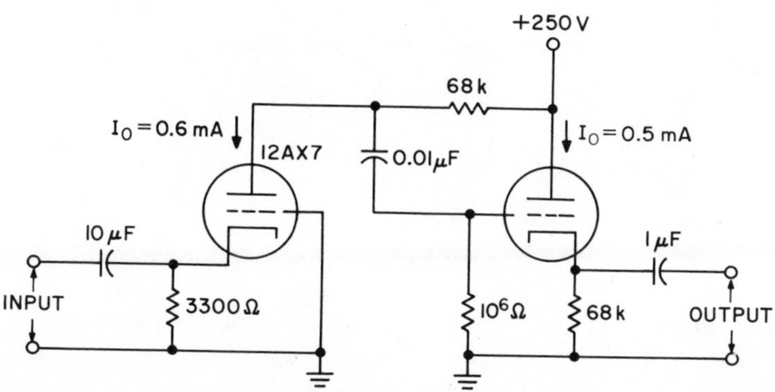

Figure 8-33

Observing the equivalent circuits of each portion of the network, as shown in Fig. 8-34, the reduction in signal strength in the preamplifier portion is

$$\sqrt{\frac{3300^2}{3300^2 + 1/\omega^2C^2}}$$

Assuming a frequency of 5000 Hz, $1/\omega^2C^2 = 10.15$; the reduction is negligible.

The gain of the first stage is

$$\begin{aligned} A &= (1 + \mu)\left(\frac{R_L}{r_p + R_L}\right) \\ &= (1 + 100)\left(\frac{10^6}{1{,}062{,}500}\right) \\ &= 95 \end{aligned}$$

(Calculation will show that the interelectrode capacitances may be ignored.)

The gain in the second stage is

$$\begin{aligned} A &= \frac{\mu R}{r_p + (1 + \mu)R} \\ &= \frac{100 \times 68{,}000}{62{,}500 + (1 + 100)(68{,}000)} \\ &= 0.98 \end{aligned}$$

Therefore, the overall gain is $95 \times 0.98 = 93$. *Answer*

Output impedance. The load "sees" only the equivalent voltage of the last stage, $[\mu/(1 + \mu)]E$, and its series impedance, $r_p/(1 + u)$. The output impedance is equal to $62{,}500/(1 + 100) = 618$ ohms. *Answer*

Input impedance. The source "sees" only the grounded grid first stage, or

$$Z_{in} = \frac{r_p + Z}{\mu + 1} = \frac{62{,}500 + 68{,}000}{101} = 1290 \text{ ohms} \qquad \textit{Answer}$$

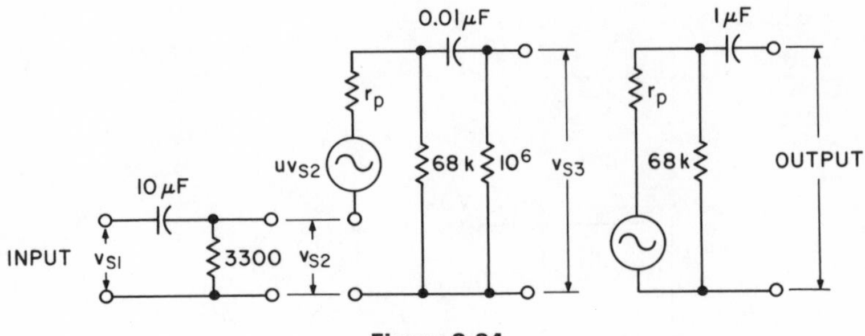

Figure 8-34

Input voltage limitations. As long as g_m and r_p remain constant, the operation will be linear. Assuming that this will hold if the grid voltage does not become positive, then the input voltage can be as high as the bias voltage:

$i_aR_k = 0.0006 \times 3300 = -1.98$ volts (peak)

$= 1.4$ volts rms *Answer*

Problem 8-2 Resistor-capacitor (RC) coupled amplifier stages

A chain of simple resistor-capacitor coupled amplifier stages are to be built to give an overall voltage gain in the order of 90 dB. At 40 Hz, the overall gain should not be more than 3 dB down from the midfrequency overall gain; and at 700 kHz, the overall gain should not be more than 3 dB down from the midfrequency overall gain. Type 6AC7 pentodes are easily obtained and their use is preferred. Manufacturer's data pertaining to this tube:

With −2.0 volts control-grid bias and 150 volts on the screen,

Plate current = 10 milliamps
Screen current = 3 milliamps
Plate-to-control grid $g_m = 9000\ \mu$mhos
Plate resistance = infinite
Input capacitance = 11 pF
Output capacitance = 6 pF
Grid resistor should not exceed 0.5 Meg
Stray capacitance of each stage coupling $\cong$ 20 pF

Compute and specify for each stage: (a) load resistor, (b) coupling capacitor, (c) self-bias components, (d) plate supply voltage, and (e) screen dropping resistor.

Solution:

Draw the basic circuit, showing one stage. See Fig. 8-35. Assume a reasonable gain per stage, and apply the gain formulas for low and high frequencies. Note that the response at high frequencies depends on R_c, R_{g1}, and the shunt capacitances, and that the latter are beyond our control. It is recommended that R_c be calculated to satisfy the required high-frequency response, rather than to satisfy the simple relationship for midfrequency gain.

Assume three stages and 30 dB per stage.

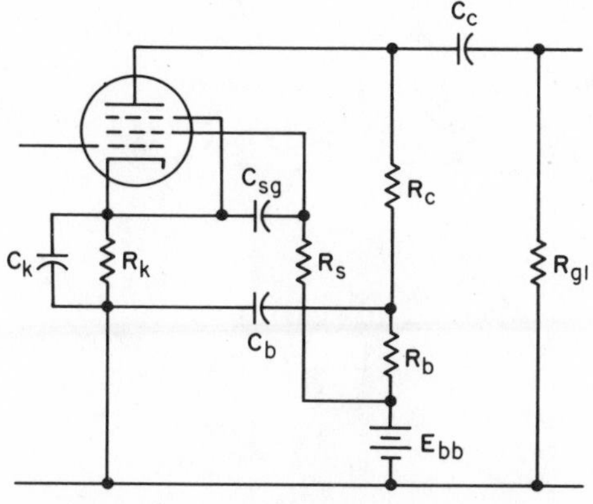

Figure 8-35

$R_{g1} = 0.5 \times 10^6$ ohms

At high frequencies,

$$\text{Gain (K)} = \frac{-g_m R}{1 + j(f/f_2)}$$

where $f_2 = \dfrac{1}{2\pi C_s R}$

$$C_s = (11 + 6 + 20) \times 10^{-12}$$

$$R = \frac{R_c R_{g1}}{R_c + R_{g1}} \qquad \text{since } r_p = \infty$$

At midfrequency,

$$K_m = -g_m R$$

At low frequencies,

$$K = \frac{-g_m R}{1 - j(f_1/f)}$$

where $f_1 = \dfrac{1}{2\pi C_c(R_c + R_{g1})}$

At 40 Hz and 700 kHz,

$$-1 \text{ dB (per stage)} = 20 \log X$$

$$X = \text{response} = K/K_m$$

$$= 0.89$$

From the above relationships, it is seen that for f = 700,000,

$$0.89 = \frac{1}{1 + j(700{,}000/f_2)}$$

$R = 3180$ ohms

$R_c = 3200$ ohms *Answer*

For f = 40,

$$0.89 = \frac{1}{1 - j(f_1/40)}$$

$C_c = 0.0153\ \mu F$ *Answer*

At midfrequency,

$$K_m = -g_m R = -(9000 \times 10^{-6})(3180)$$

$$= -28.6 \quad \text{which is equal to 29.1 dB}$$

Overall gain = (3)(29.1) = 87.3 dB

Assume this is satisfactory.

If it is desired, R_c could be increased, since high-frequency compensation could be applied. Low-frequency compensation will be applied here by selecting proper values for C_b and R_b.

Grid bias resistor:

$$R_k = \frac{2 \text{ volts}}{i_b + i_s}$$

$$= \frac{2}{13 \times 10^{-3}}$$

$$= 153 \text{ ohms}$$

(Tube manual states 160 ohms, *minimum.*)

At low frequencies, R_k appreciably reduces the gain. It is recommended that

$1/C_kR_k \gtreqless 0\ 1 \times 2\pi \times$ (lowest frequency to be amplified)

or $\quad C_k = 0.026\ \mu F$

For sharp cutoff, $f = \frac{1}{2}C_kR_k$; however, a larger value for C_k is recommended if phase shift at low frequency is to be avoided.

Plate supply voltage (E_{bb}): Before we can determine E_{bb}, we must know the value of R_b that is desired for low-frequency compensation. It can be shown that for best performance,

$$C_bR_c = C_cR_g$$

or in this problem, $C_b = 2.45\ \mu F$ *Answer*

$$\text{Ideally, } R_gC_c = \frac{R_cR_bC_b}{R_c + R_b}$$

or in this problem, $R_b = 122{,}500$ ohms. However, this value requires a rather high supply voltage.

Let $R_b \gtreqless 10\ X_{C_b} = 16{,}300$, using C_b as obtained above. *Answer*

Then,

$$I_b(R_c + R_b) = 10 \times 10^{-3} \times 19{,}500 = 195 \text{ volts.}$$

Again, we may assume that the lowest plate potential at which plate current is independent of plate voltage when plate current is twice its d-c value equals 20% plate supply voltage, or

$$e_p = 0.20(195 + e_p)$$

$$= 46 \text{ volts}$$

$$E_{bb} = 240 \text{ volts}$$

Tube manual specifies 300 volts. *Answer*

Screen bias resistor (dropping resistor) R_s and capacitor C_{sg}:

C_{sg} and R_{sg} must be properly related for low-frequency response, since at low frequencies the amplification factor is reduced. It is recommended that

$$\omega C_{sg}R_s = 1$$

where $\omega \ll$ lowest angular frequency to be amplified.

$E_{bb} - 150 \text{ volts} = i_s R_s$

$$R_s = \frac{240 - 150}{3 \times 10^{-3}} = 30{,}000 \text{ ohms} \qquad \textit{Answer}$$

If $\omega = 0.10 \times 2\pi \times 40$, $C_{sg} = 1.33\ \mu F$ *Answer*

For sharp cutoff,

$$f = \frac{1 + K}{2\pi C_{sg} R_{sg}}$$

where R_{sg} = dynamic resistance of screen circuit (not given)

$K = R_{sg}/R$

If phase distortion is to be minimized, use a larger value of C_{sg}.

Problem 8-3 Cascaded amplifiers with feedback

An amplifier is composed of five identical stages in cascade. The gain of each stage is given by $A = K/(1 + j\omega/\omega_1)$.

If feedback is used around this amplifier, determine the value of K at which this system becomes unstable and the corresponding frequency of oscillation. The feedback network has the following transfer function:

$$\beta = \frac{0.001}{1 + j\omega/2\omega_1}$$

Solution:

The condition under which oscillations will start will be $\beta A' = 1$, where A' is the overall gain (without feedback).

$$0.001K^5 = (1 + j\omega/2\omega_1)(1 + j\omega/\omega_1)^5$$

Since K is a real number, the imaginaries = zero. Solving, K = 9.9 (say 10). *Answer*

Problem 8-4 Amplifier designed from tube characteristics

An amplifier uses a tube whose plate characteristic curves are shown in Fig. 8-36. The tube is operated Class C at 300 volts plate voltage and −50 volts grid bias. The effective a-c load is resistive with a value of 4000 ohms. The d-c load resistance is substantially zero.

(a) Draw the a-c load line on Fig. 8-36.

(b) Show, by a graph drawn on Fig. 8-36, the shape of the plate current that would flow if potential $e_c = -50 - 54 \sin \omega t$ is applied to the grid. (Plot points at 30° intervals.)

(c) Determine approximately the conduction angle.

(d) Determine the approximate average plate current.

(e) If the tank circuit capacitance is 100 pF, what is the Q of the plate load at the resonance frequency of 1.5 MHz?

Solution:

The load-line construction on the i_b–e_b curves for small-signal application cannot be used for Class C operation because the relationship is not linear over the large

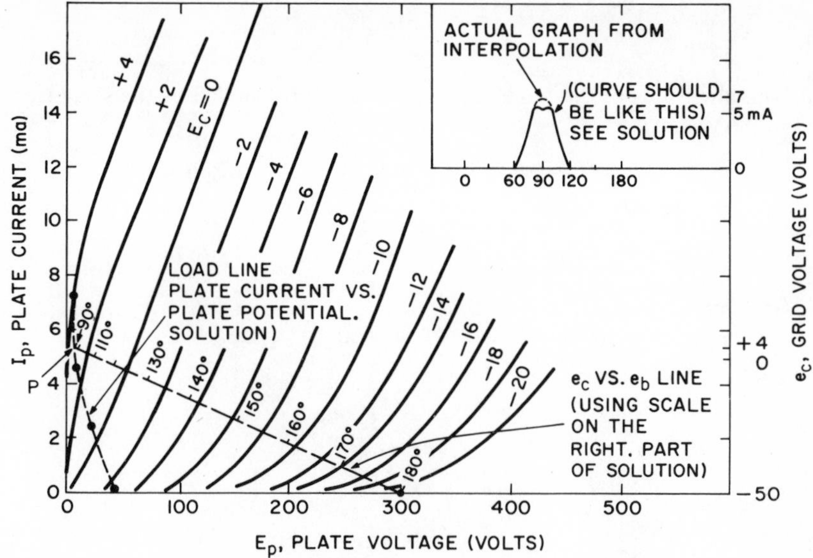

Figure 8-36

range of grid potential values. Recourse is made to the constant (plate) current family of curves superimposed on the e_c–e_b graph. However, the information here must be deduced from the plate characteristics. Because the positive values of grid potential are so small, the usual dip in the i_b–ωt plot is lacking. The set of curves in Fig. 8-37 show the relative variation of e_c and e_b with time.

First, to find the grid potentials corresponding to values of e_b, plot the operating line PQ (the 90° and 180° points on the e_c vs. e_b graph). *Note:* Figure 8-36 does not use the symbols adopted as standard by the IEEE. It is assumed that i_b and e_b are intended. The e_c scale on the right is part of this solution.

Observe that the values of grid potential e_c and total instantaneous plate current i_b are

ωt	e_c (volts)	e_b (volts)	i_b (mA)
90°	+4.0	4	7.1
100°	+3.3	8	4.5
110°	+0.6	23	2.4
120°	−2.4	41	0.2

(a) The plate current is plotted on the graph as the load line.

(b) The plate current variation with time is shown on the graph.

(c) The conduction angle is approximately 60° (from 60° to 120°). *Answer*

(d) The average total plate current over a complete cycle is the steady-state (d-c) component or offset, which is

$$I_{bs} = (1/18)(0.5 \times 7 + 4.5 + 2.4 + 0.2)$$
$$= 0.588 \text{ mA} \qquad \textit{Answer}$$

Note: The amplitude of the fundamental can be approximated by the same (modified Fourier) analysis:

$$I_{1(max)} = (1/9)(0.5 \times 7 + 0.985 \times 4.5 + 0.94 \times 2.4 + 0.866 \times 0.2)$$
$$= 1.15 \text{ mA}$$

(e) Q of the plate load:

$$Q = \omega CR$$
$$= 2\pi \times 1.5 \times 10^6 \times 100 \times 10^{-12} \times 4000$$
$$= 3.77 \qquad \textit{Answer}$$

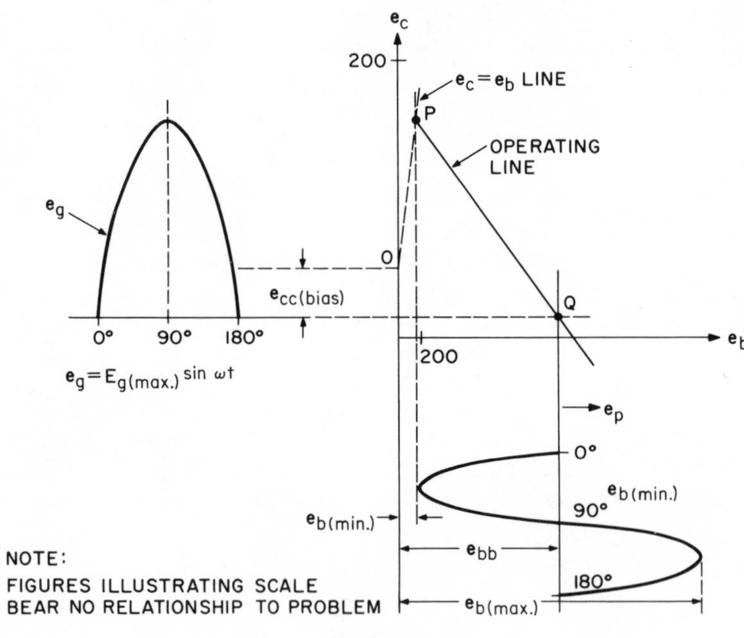

Figure 8-37

Problem 8-5 Vacuum-tube characteristics and applications

Give the information required in part (a) for each of the tubes listed in part (b).

(a) 1. Type of tube (vacuum or gas filled). 2. Type of emission (thermionic, photoelectric, etc.). 3. Kind of discharge (Townsend, glow, arc, etc.). 4. Unit of anode current (ampere, milliampere, microampere). 5. Principal application (radio receiver, radar transmitter, etc.).

(b)
1. Receiving-type triode
2. Receiving-type pentode
3. Magnetron
4. Klystron
5. Kinescope
6. Thyratron
7. Ignitron
8. Rectigon or Tungar
9. Iconoscope
10. Voltage regulator
11. Cathode ray
12. Strobotron
13. Ballast lamp

Solution:

See Table 8-1.

Problem 8-6 Design of a variable-frequency oscillator

The plan for an oscillator circuit is shown in Fig. 8-38. The amplifier input impedance is very much greater than the impedance of R_1 and C_1, and the output impedance is very much smaller than the impedance of R_2 and C_2.

(a) Specify the magnitude and phase of amplifier gain K.

(b) A ganged variable capacitor with two identical sections is available, which can vary from 50 to 5000 pF per section. It is desired to have the oscillator operate at 5000 Hz when the capacitor is in its middle position. Select the values of the resistors.

(c) Determine the frequency range of the oscillator.

Solution:

For an oscillator with RC regenerative coupling, frequency can be shown to be

$$f = \frac{1}{2\pi(R_1R_2C_1C_2)^{1/2}}$$

If the resistances are made equal and the capacitors made equal, the solution is simple. Then determine K from its definition $E_{out} = KE_{in}$.

For acceptable performance, the amplifier should have negligible phase shift. Let $R_1 = R_2$ and $C_1 = C_2$. Then,

$$f = 5000 = \frac{1}{2\pi R(2525 \times 10^{-12})}$$

$R = 12{,}600$ ohms *Answer, part (b)*

For $C_1 = C_2 = 50$ pF, $f = 252{,}500$ Hz

For $C_1 = C_2 = 5000$ pF, $f = 2525$ Hz *Answer, part (c)*

From Fig. 8-38, it will be seen that the input to the amplifier is the voltage across the R_1C_1 section. Hence,

$$E_{out} = KE_{in}$$

$$E_{in} = \left(\frac{Z_{R1\text{-}C1}}{Z_{R1\text{-}C1} + Z_{R2\text{-}C2}}\right)E_{out}$$

Expressing the impedances of each branch in complex form and simplifying, it will be seen that

Table 8-1

Tube	*Type*	*Emission*	*Discharge*	*Anode Current*	*Application*
Receiving-type triode	Vacuum	Thermionic	Space charge	mA	Radio receivers
Receiving-type pentode	Vacuum	Thermionic	Space charge	mA	Radio and video receivers
Magnetron	Vacuum	Thermionic	Space charge	mA	High-frequency oscillators
Klystron	Vacuum	Thermionic	Space charge	mA	VHF oscillators and amplifiers
Kinescope	Vacuum	Thermionic	Space charge	mA	Television picture tube (projection)
Thyratron	Gas	Thermionic	Arc	mA	Control amplifiers
Ignitron	Gas	High Field	Arc	A	Power rectifiers
Rectigon or Tungar	Gas	Thermionic	Arc	A	Battery charger
Iconoscope	Vacuum	Photo	Space charge	μA	Motion picture transmission
Voltage regulator	Gas	High Field	Glow	mA	Voltage regulation
Cathode ray	Vacuum	Thermionic or High Field	Space charge	μA	Visual wave analysis
Strobotron	Gas	High Field (Cold Cathode)	Space charge	mA	Control tube for high-speed flash lamp
Ballast lamp	Gas	High Field (Cold Cathode)	Arc	A	Current limiter

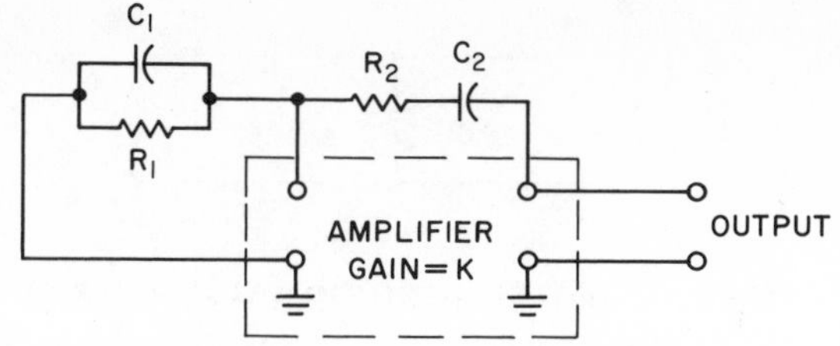

Figure 8-38

$$K = \frac{18900 - j18800}{6300 - j6300} = 2.97 \qquad \textit{Answer, part (a)}$$

with negligible phase shift.

Problem 8-7 Design of an oscillating system

An oscillating system is to be arranged as shown in Fig. 8-39. The resistors are 50 kilohms each and the capacitors are 0.01 μF each.

(a) For sustained oscillation, what must be the value of the gain K?

(b) What will be the frequency of oscillation?

Solution:

Since $e_1 = e_0$, this can be solved as a simple mesh network with source voltage of Ke_0. (See Fig. 8-40.)

$$Ke_0 = I_1(R - jX_C) + jI_2X_C$$

$$0 = I_1(jX_C) + I_2(R - j2X_C)$$

$$I_2 = \frac{\begin{vmatrix} R - jX_C & Ke_0 \\ jX_C & 0 \end{vmatrix}}{\begin{vmatrix} R - jX_C & jX_C \\ jX_C & R - 2jX_C \end{vmatrix}}$$

Substituting $e_0 = I_2R$,

$$K = 3 + j(R/X_C - X_C/R)$$

For I_2R to be in phase with e_1, the imaginaries must cancel or

$$RC = \frac{1}{\omega^2 CR}$$

$$\omega = 2000$$

$$f = 318 \text{ Hz} \qquad \textit{Answer, part (b)}$$

$$K = 3 \qquad \textit{Answer, part (a)}$$

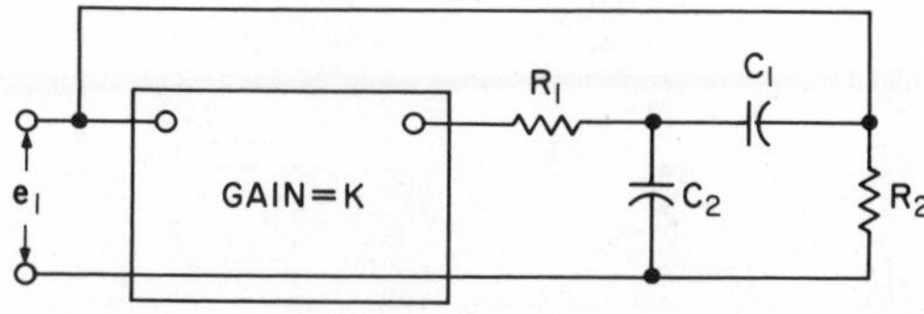

Figure 8-39

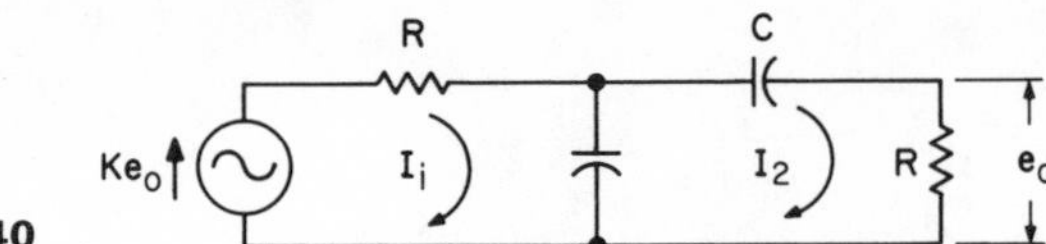

Figure 8-40

Problem 8-8 Design of a free-running multivibrator

Design a free-running multivibrator that will give a peak-to-peak output of 200 volts at 2000 Hz. Show the complete circuit diagram with all circuit elements and voltage supplies.

Solution:

The free-running multivibrator is a nonsinusoidal waveform oscillator in which neither of the two stages attains a stable state, and therefore is capable of self-excitation. See Fig. 8-41. Design proceeds on the basis of using time delay of charge and discharge of a capacitor through a resistor.

(a) Plate-supply voltage = 200 volts to give 200 peak plate potential.

(b) Select a high-g_m tube (6SN7 twin triode or 6K5 triodes). The tube manual specifies 200 volts as the minimum plate supply voltage E_b.

(c) For simplicity, let

$$R_{p1} = R_{p2}$$
$$R_{g1} = R_{g2}$$
$$C_1 = C_2$$

(d) Select trial $R_g = 10^6$ ohms. (A resistor is required in the grid circuit to prevent a charge from accumulating on the grid, due to the input (signal) voltage. Also, in this case, it determines the discharge and charge time of the capacitor, and therefore frequency.)

(e) Observe the I_p–E_g curves for the 6J5 tube. Draw a load line to give a reasonable value of plate current, say 6.8 mA for $E_g = 0$. This line cuts the Y-axis at $I_p = 10$ mA.

(f) Then

$$R_p = \frac{200}{10 \times 10^{-3}} = 20{,}000 \text{ ohms}$$

When $I_p = 0$, plate potential $E_p = 200$ V. When I_p is maximum (i.e., $e_g = 0$), $E_p = 200 - (6.8 \times 10^{-3} R_p) = 64$. Therefore, the plate voltage swing during the period C is discharging = 200 − 64 = 136 volts.

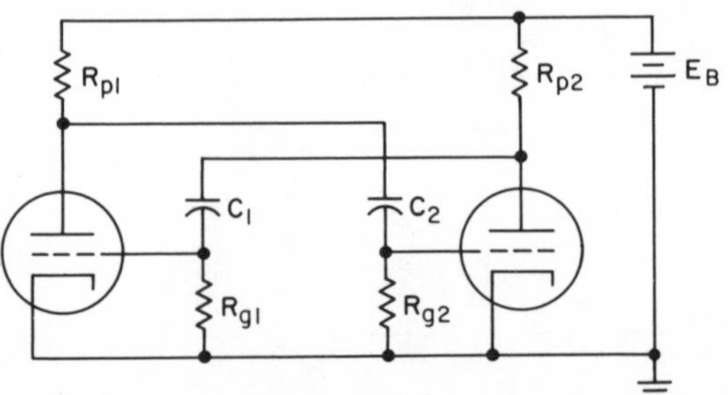

Figure 8-41

The swing of e_g during discharge is from −136 to −12 volts (cutoff) or 124 volts. (The −12-volt cutoff is observed from the grid volts–plate amps curve and is the e_g curve that crosses the X-axis at $E_p = E_b = 200$ volts.)

(g) The discharge, therefore, is 91.5% of total charge, since $124/136 = 0.915$. The period of discharge is approximately equal to $1/(2f) = 0.25 \times 10^{-3}$ sec. From the universal time constants charts this requires 2.4 time constants. One time constant = RC. Therefore, $2.4RC = 0.25 \times 10^{-3}$ or $C = 104$ pF.

Problem 8-9 Design of a phototube relay circuit

For the circuit shown in Fig. 8-42, the phototube current is given in microamperes as $i_{\mu A} = 1.0 + 10.0L$, where L is the light flux in lumens striking the phototube cathode. The pentode current is given in milliamperes as $i_{mA} = 25 + 2e_c$, where e_c is the grid voltage in volts. The relay closes at a current of 15 mA and opens at a current of 9 mA. Neglect any transient effects.

(a) Determine the minimum light flux necessary to close the relay contacts.

(b) Determine the maximum light flux to open the relay contacts.

(c) Determine the minimum value of resistance that can be placed in parallel with the relay coil such that the relay contact can be closed without requiring grid current in the pentode.

(d) Repeat parts (a) and (b) using the resistor found in part (c).

Solution:

This solution consists solely of using the relationships given in the problem to apply Kirchhoff's laws.

(a) For relay closure,

$$i_p = 15 \times 10^{-3} = 25 + 2e_c$$

$$e_c = -5 \text{ volts}$$

$$= e_g - 10$$

where e_g is the voltage across the 1-Meg resistor.

Therefore,

$$e_g = +5 \text{ volts}$$

$$i_{\mu A} = 5/10^6 = 5\ \mu A = 1 + 10\ L$$

$$L = 0.40 \text{ lumens (minimum)}$$ *Answer*

(b) To open contacts,

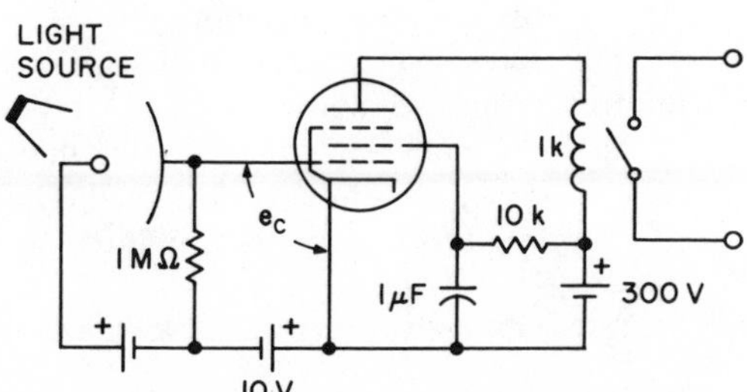

Figure 8-42

$i_p = 9 \times 10^{-3} = 25 + 2e_c$

$e_c = -8$ volts

$e_g = 2$ volts

$i_{\mu A} = 2\ \mu A = 1 + 10\ L$

$L = 0.1$ lumen (maximum) *Answer*

(c) For $e_c = 0$,

$i_{mA} = 25$

$$\frac{R}{1000} = \frac{15 \times 10^{-3}}{(25 - 15) \times 10^{-3}}$$

$R = 1.5$ k *Answer*

(d) $e_c = 0 \qquad e_g = 10 \qquad i_{\mu A} = 10\ \mu A$

$L = 0.9$ lumens for closure *Answer*

To open,

$(i_p)_{coil} = 9$ mA

$E_R = 9$ volts

$$(I_p)_R = \frac{9}{1.5} \times 10^{-3} = 6 \text{ mA}$$

$$(I_p)_{total} = 15 \text{ mA};\ e_c = \frac{i_p - 25}{2} = -5.$$

$E_g = 5$ volts

$i_{\mu A} = 5\ \mu A$

$L = 0.4$ lumens *Answer*

Problem 8-10 D-c power supply with a transistor as a series regulating element

A d-c power supply employs a transistor as a series regulating element as shown in Fig. 8-43. The output of the power supply is 24 volts dc at currents from 0 to 1 amp. Line voltage input is 115 volts ± 10 volts rms at 60Hz. Leakage reactance and winding resistance of the transformer are such that voltage regulation of the transformer is 10% when the power supply delivers full output current.

(a) Assuming that during rectifier conduction the filter capacitor charges to the peak value of the transformer secondary terminal voltage, calculate the maximum peak-to-peak ripple voltage across the filter capacitor.

(b) If the instantaneous voltage across the transistor collector junction is not to fall below 1 volt, specify the transformer winding ratio.

(c) Calculate the range of the d-c component of i_b neglecting thermal effects.

(d) Under the most adverse operating conditions calculate the peak-to-peak value of the a-c component of i_b required to remove the ripple voltage from the output.

(e) Does the transistor operate within its rating under all normal operating conditions?

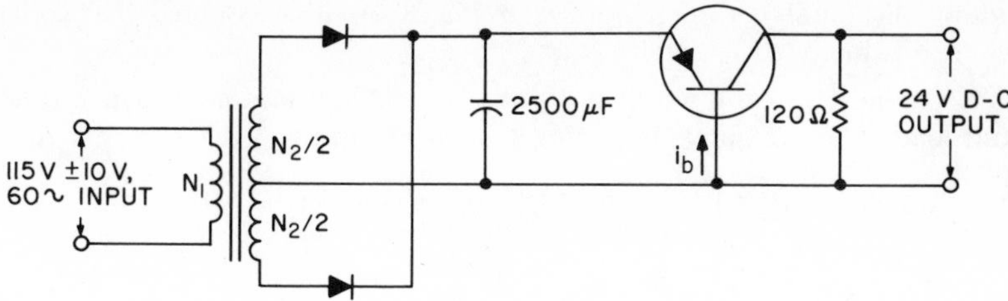

Figure 8-43

(f) For the currents determined in part (c), what is the greatest correction that must be applied to i_b to take into account temperature change of the collector junction? What is the direction of this correction?

Transistor data follows:

$\beta = h_{fe} = 20$

h_{oe} = open-circuit output admittance = 0.004 mho

$(V_{ce})_{max} = 25$ volts

$(P_{collector})_{max} = 15$ watts

Thermal resistance of collector junction = 2.3°C/watt.

$I_{co} = 0.1$ mA at $V_{ce} = -10$ volts and $T = 25°C$.

See Fig. 8-44.

Solution:

Fundamental principles governing this solution are:

1. During rectifier conduction, the rectifier supplies energy to the load (including transistor losses) and charges the capacitor. On discharge, the capacitor supplies energy to the load. The rate of energy supply is proportional to the square of the voltage across the capacitor. The energy stored in the capacitor is also proportional to the square of the voltage.
2. For all conditions of supply voltage and load, the operating points must fall

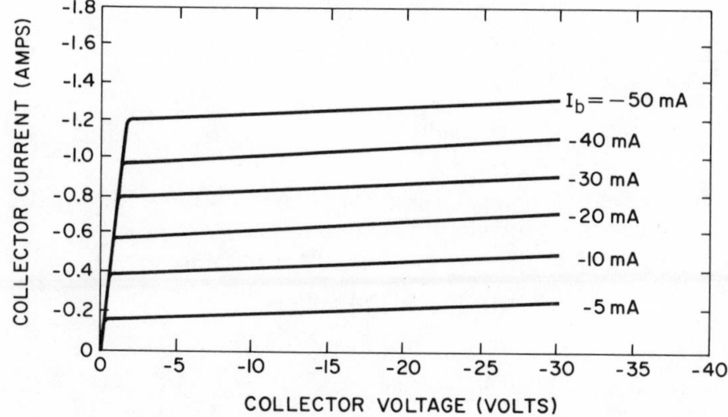

Figure 8-44

within the family of curves given in Fig. 8-44; it is assumed that collector voltage is intended to signify V_{CE}.

(a) Assume V_{CE} (minimum) is 1 volt, occurring at minimum supply voltage and full load. I_C is 1.2 amps, including the current through the 120-ohm resistor.

Change in stored energy per cycle $= \frac{1}{2}C(v_2^2 - v_1^2)$

where $v_1 = 25$ volts

$v_2 - v_1 =$ peak-to-peak ripple

Ripple frequency = 120 Hz.

Then

$$\tfrac{1}{2} \times 2500 \times 10^{-6} \times 120(v_2^2 - 625) = 25 \times 1.2 = 30 \text{ watts}$$

$$v_2 = 28.6 \text{ volts}$$

$$v_2 - v_1 = 3.6 \text{ volts} \qquad \textit{Answer}$$

(b) Turns ratio should not be greater than

$$\frac{N_1}{N_2} = \frac{105\sqrt{2}}{1.10 \times 2 \times 28.6} = 2.37 \qquad \textit{Answer}$$

Use 2.25; explained in part (c).

(c) From the curves, the minimum V_{CE} to stay within the curves at full-load amperes is 2 volts. Therefore, the turns ratio should not be more than

$$\frac{N_1}{N_2} = \frac{105\sqrt{2}}{1.10 \times 2 \times 29.6} = 2.28 \cong 2.25$$

Average values of V_{CE} can now be calculated and values of I_b observed:

	$I_C = 1.2$		$I_C = 0.2$	
	V_{CE}	I_b	V_{CE}	I_b
105-volt supply	4.2 (1)	−50 mA	8.7 (3)	−6.5 mA
125-volt supply	9.9 (2)	−48.5	15.0 (4)	−5.0

$$\frac{105\sqrt{2}}{1.10 \times 2 \times 2.25} - \frac{3.6}{2} - 24 = 4.2 \text{ volts} \tag{1}$$

$$\frac{125\sqrt{2}}{1.10 \times 2 \times 2.25} - \frac{3.6}{2} - 24 = 9.9 \text{ volts} \tag{2}$$

$$\frac{105\sqrt{2}}{2 \times 2.25} = 33.2 \text{ volts} = v_2 \qquad \text{[as in part (a)]}$$

$$\tfrac{1}{2} \times 2500 \times 10^{-6} \times 120[(33.2)^2 - v_1^2] = 33 \times 0.2 = 6.6 \text{ watts}$$

$$v_1 = 32.4 \text{ volts}$$

$$v_2 - v_1 = 0.8 \text{ volt (ripple)}$$

$$\text{Average } V_{CE} = 33.2 - 0.45 - 24 = 8.7 \text{ volts} \tag{3}$$

$$\frac{125\sqrt{2}}{2 \times 2.25} - 0.45 - 24 = 15 \text{ volts} \tag{4}$$

Hence, the range of the d-c component of I_b is approximately from -5 to -50 mA, the greatest change being necessitated by load variation. *Answer*

(d) The maximum ripple occurs at full load, and the maximum bias is required at low supply voltage. To overcome the 3.6-volt ripple, the peak-to-peak value of the a-c component of I_b is about 2 mA (from the curves). *Answer* This answer applies only if the turns ratio is low enough to permit the 2 volts V_{CE} required at full load and still permit an output of 24 volts.

(e) Not if turns ratio is selected to give a minimum V_{CE} of 1 volt, since the curves indicate a minimum value of 2 volts at full load.

With the turns ratio selected (2.25), and assuming that greater bias is permissible, the transistor will operate within its rating.

(f) The largest transistor loss is

$$(V_{CE})_{max} \times (I_C)_{max} = 9.9 \times 1.2 = 11.9 \text{ watts}$$

$$\Delta T = 11.9 \times 2.3 = 27.5°\text{C}$$

Both h_{fe} and I_{CO} increase with temperature; assume I_{CO} doubles with each 10°C rise. The leakage current now becomes $0.1 \times 2^{2.75} = 0.67$ mA. I_b should be increased by this amount.

An increase of h_{fe} with temperature will decrease h_{ob} since $h_{ob} = h_{oe}/(1 + h_{fe})$. In this case, the a-c component of I_b should be increased by the percentage increase in h_{ob} to maintain load current. Estimate 30% or 0.6 mA peak to peak.

Problem 8-11 Transistorized voltage comparator

In the voltage comparator circuit shown in Fig. 8-45, A and B are inputs and C is the output. T_1, T_2, and T_3 are silicon transistors, each with $\beta = 100$. T_4 and T_5 are germanium transistors, each with $\beta = 20$. In the circuit shown, make the following simplifying assumptions:

1. I_{co} is negligible for all transistors.
2. r_b and r_e of all transistors can be disregarded by assuming a base-emitter potential of 0.2 volt for germanium and 0.6 volt for silicon, when a transistor is conducting.
3. The saturated collector-emitter potential of the germanium transistors is 0.1 volt and for the silicon transistors is 0.5 volt.

With the input voltage at B = 0.0 volts, as shown:

(a) What change of base current is required at the base of T_1, input A, in order to swing the output level at C from +5.9 volts to 0.0 volts?

(b) What is the approximate output level at C when the voltage at A is -1.0 volt? Explain.

Solution:

This circuit is a network of directly-coupled amplifiers. It is helpful to identify each transistor type and indicate the conventional direction of current flow at each terminal, as shown in Fig. 8-46. It should be noted that a transistor at cutoff and

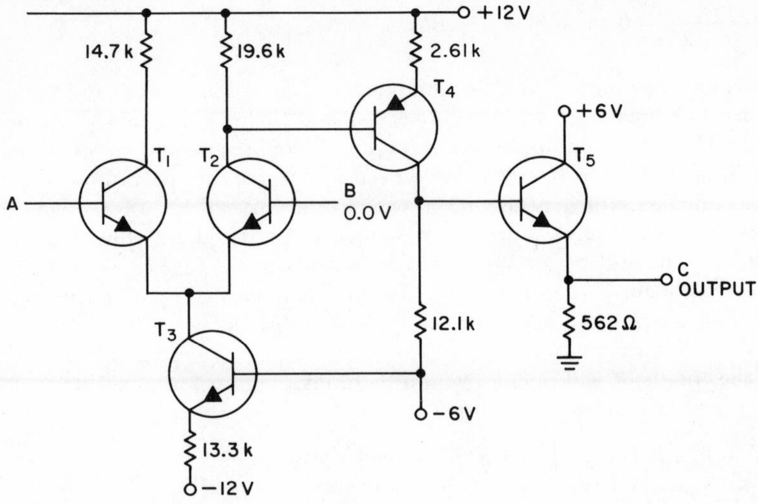

Figure 8-45

at saturation resembles the circuits of Fig. 8-47(A) and (B), respectively (voltage drops V_{BE} and V_{CE} are omitted for simplicity, but they could be represented by d-c voltage sources).

(a) When voltage at C = +5.9 volts:

For T_5,

$$V_{CE} = 0.1 \text{ volt (saturation)}$$

$$V_B = 5.9 + 0.2 = 6.1 \text{ volts}$$

$$I_E = 5.9/562 = 10.5 \text{ mA}$$

$$I_B = I_E/(1 + \beta) = 0.5 \text{ mA}$$

For T_4,

$$V_C = 6.1 \text{ volts}$$

$$I_C = 0.5 + 12.1/12.1 = 1.5 \text{ mA}$$

$$I_B = 1.5/20 = 0.075 \text{ mA}$$

$$I_E = 1.575 \text{ mA}$$

$$V_B = 12 - (1.575)(2.61) - 0.2 = 7.68 \text{ volts}$$

For T_2,

$$I_C = \frac{12 - 7.68}{19.6 \text{ K}} + 0.075 = 0.295 \text{ mA}$$

$$I_E = \left(\frac{1 + \beta}{\beta}\right) I_C = 0.298 \text{ mA}$$

For T_3,

$$I_E = \frac{6 - 0.6}{13.3\ K} = 0.406\ mA$$

$$I_C = \left(\frac{\beta}{1 + \beta}\right) I_E = 0.402\ mA$$

For T_1,

$$I_E = 0.402 - 0.298 = 0.104\ mA$$

$$I_B = \left(\frac{1}{1 + \beta}\right) I_E = 1.03\ \mu A$$

When voltage at C is 0.0 volts:

For T_5, assume it has just reached cutoff (since it is nonconducting).

$$V_B = 0.2\ volt$$

For T_4,

$$V_C = 0.2\ volt$$

$$I_C = 6.2/12.1\ K = 0.512\ mA$$

$$I_E = \left(\frac{1 + \beta}{\beta}\right) I_C = 0.538\ mA$$

$$V_E = 12 - (2.61)(0.538) = 10.8\ volts$$

$$V_B = 10.8 - 0.2 = 10.6\ volts$$

$$I_B = 0.512/20 = 0.0256\ mA$$

For T_3,

$$I_C = 0.402\ mA\ (as\ before)$$

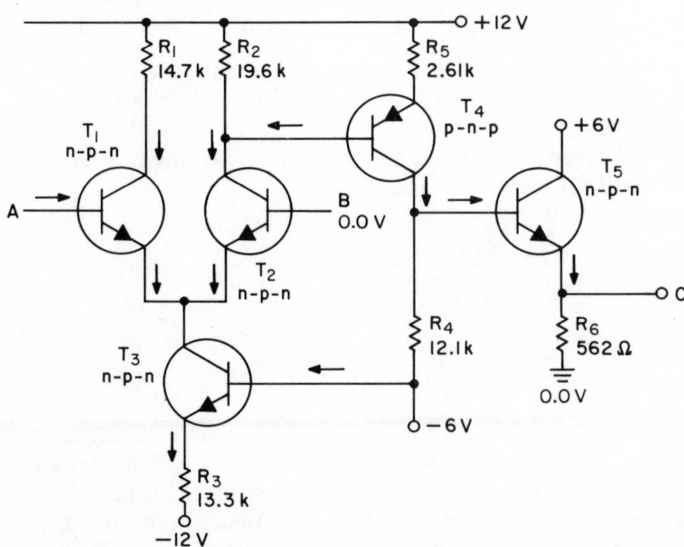

Figure 8-46

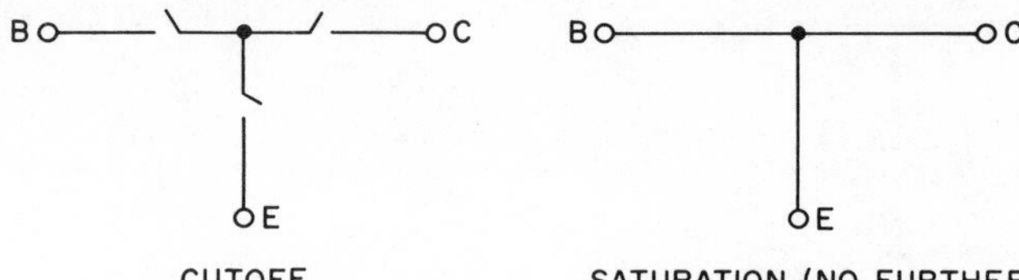

Figure 8-47

For T_2,

$$I_C = \frac{12 - 10.6}{19.6\ K} + 0.0256 = 0.0971\ mA$$

$$I_E = 0.0981\ mA$$

For T_1,

$$I_E = 0.402 - 0.0981 = 0.304\ mA$$

$$I_B = \frac{I_E}{1 + \beta} = 3.0\ \mu A$$

Therefore, the change in I_B is $3.00 - 1.03 = 1.97\ \mu A$. *Answer*

(b) When voltage at A is -1.0 volt:

For T_2,

$$V_E = -0.6 \text{ volt}$$

For T_1,

$$V_E = -0.6 \text{ volt}$$

$V_B = -1.0$ volt, and T_1 is reverse biased and therefore is not conducting.

From part (a) it was shown that as T_1 becomes less conducting, T_5 becomes saturated. Therefore, the voltage at point C is $+5.9$ volts. *Answer*

Problem 8-12 Insertion power gain of transistor circuit calculated from h parameters

The grounded-base h parameters for the transistor of Fig. 8-48 are

$$h_{ib} = 50 \text{ ohms} \qquad h_{rb} = 5 \times 10^{-4}$$

$$h_{fb} = -0.97 \qquad h_{ob} = 1.0\ \mu\text{mho}$$

What is the insertion power gain?

Solution:

Here, the common-emitter configuration is used. It is necessary to calculate the hybrid parameters for the common-emitter circuit, and then calculate the ratio of a-c power delivered to the load resistor R_L to the a-c power input to the circuit. Care must be taken to add resistance R_g to the input resistance, since the diagram indicates that the signal current flows through this resistance.

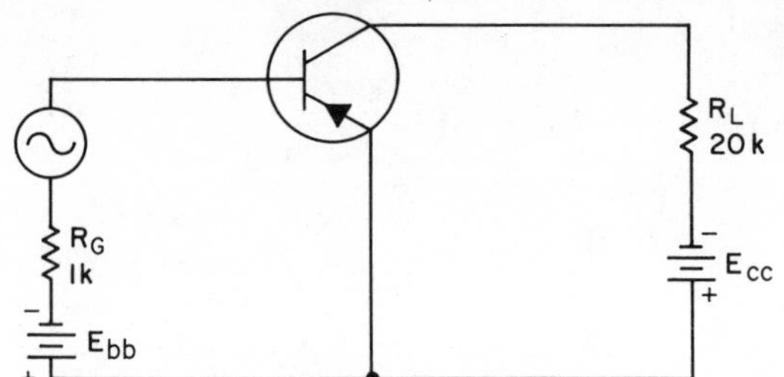

Figure 8-48

$$h_{11} = R_g + \frac{h_{ib}}{1 + h_{fb}} = 1000 + \frac{50}{1 + (-0.97)} = 2670 \text{ ohms}$$

$$h_{22} = \frac{h_{ob}}{1 + h_{fb}} = \frac{10^{-6}}{0.03} = 33.3 \times 10^{-6} \text{ mho}$$

$$h_{12} = \frac{h_{ib}h_{ob}}{1 + h_{fb}} - h_{rb} = \frac{50 \times 10^{-6}}{0.03} - (5 \times 10^{-4}) = 11.7 \times 10^{-4}$$

$$h_{21} = -\frac{h_{fb}}{1 + h_{fb}} = \frac{0.97}{0.03} = 32.3$$

$$\begin{aligned} \Delta^h &= h_{11}h_{22} - h_{12}h_{21} \\ &= (2670 \times 33.3 \times 10^{-6}) - (11.7 \times 32.3 \times 10^{-4}) \\ &= 0.0512 \end{aligned}$$

$$\begin{aligned} \text{Gain } (A_p) &= \frac{-(h_{21})^2 R_L}{(h_{22}R_L + 1)(h_{11} + \Delta^h R_L)} \\ &= \frac{-20.8 \times 10^6}{1.67 \times 3694} = 3370 \qquad \textit{Answer} \end{aligned}$$

chapter 9
WAVE ANALYSIS

By the simple method of addition of phasors, it can be demonstrated that a sinusoidal waveform is the sum of *n* sinusoidal waves having the same frequency as the original frequency; *n* is any integer. It can also be shown that any periodic, single-valued function is the sum of a number of sinusoidal waves whose frequencies are *n* multiples of the original frequency. The number of such components may be infinite, but in many cases the lower order harmonics are the only ones of significance. This statement is expressed mathematically as follows:

$$y = f(t) = a_0 + a_1 \cos \omega t + a_2 \cos 2\omega t + a_3 \cos 3\omega t + \cdots + a_n \cos n\omega t$$
$$+ b_1 \sin \omega t + b_2 \sin 2\omega t + b_3 \sin 3\omega t + \cdots + b_n \sin n\omega t \quad (9\text{-}1)$$

$$y = f(t) = a_0 + c_1 \cos(\omega t + \alpha_1) + c_2 \cos(2\omega t + \alpha_2) + \cdots \quad (9\text{-}2)$$

For the waveform in question and with a few rules, the general expressions given above can be simplified in many cases. The values of the constant coefficients a_0, a_1, b_1, etc. can be found by rapid graphical methods (which are really integration processes), and the values of the phase angles α_1, α_2, etc. can be found from the coefficients.

9-1 BASIC RULES

1. If the curve is symmetrical about the abscissa, or if the areas above and below the abscissa are equal, a_0 is zero.
2. If $f(t) = f(-t)$, the wave contains cosine terms only in Eq. (9-1). It is called an even function.
3. If $f(t) = -f(-t)$, the wave contains sine terms only in Eq. (9-1). It is called an odd function.
4. If $f(t + T/2) = -f(t)$, the wave contains odd harmonics only. Using this rule it will be seen that the wave in the right-hand portion of Fig. 9-1 contains only odd harmonics, while the wave on the left contains both odd and even harmonics.

9-2 GRAPHICAL ANALYSIS

In Eqs. (9-1) and (9-2), a_0 equals the average value of f(t). It is necessary only to algebraically add all the ordinates arbitrarily but uniformly spaced throughout the entire wave and calculate the average value.

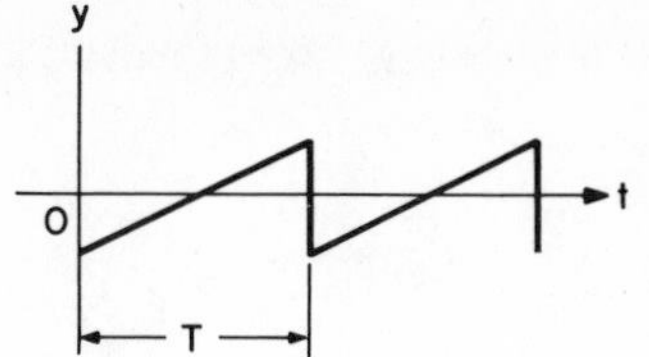

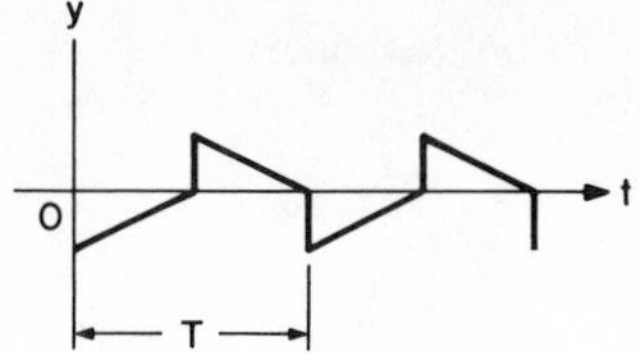

Figure 9-1

The coefficient a_n equals twice the average value of f(t) cos nωt.
The coefficient b_n equals twice the average value of f(t) sin nωt.
The coefficient c_n is obtained from a_n and b_n:

$$c_n = \sqrt{a_n^2 + b_n^2}$$

$$\alpha_n = -\tan^{-1} b_n/a_n$$

To illustrate the foregoing, the coefficients a_0 and b_3 will be determined for the waveform shown in Fig. 9-2. For simplicity, 30° increments have been selected; smaller increments would give more accurate results.

Interpolating the values of the ordinates of the curve, we can tabulate them in a column headed f(t), and then enter calculated values of f(t) sin 3ωt:

ωt	*f(t)*	*sin 3ωt*	*f(t)sin 3ωt*
30°	4.5	sin 90° = 1.0	4.5
60°	7.0	sin 180° = 0.0	0.0
90°	8.5	sin 270° = −1.0	−8.5
120°	9.8	sin 360° = 0.0	0.0
150°	9.5	sin 90° = 1.0	9.5
180°	5.6	sin 180° = 0.0	0.0
210°	4.4	sin 270° = −1.0	−4.4
240°	0.0	sin 360° = 0.0	0.0
270°	−1.8	sin 90° = 1.0	−1.8
300°	−4.0	sin 180° = 0.0	0.0
330°	−3.5	sin 270° = −1.0	3.5
360°	0.0	sin 360° = 0.0	0.0
Average:	3.33		0.233

Therefore,

$a_0 = 3.33 \qquad b_3 = 0.466$

9-3 RECTILINEAR WAVES

Straight-line waveforms do not require graphical methods such as those described in the preceding section, since the average ordinates are obvious by inspection. Take for example the square wave shown in Fig. 9-3. By inspection, a_0 equals 0, and the waveform contains cosine terms only. Coefficient a_1 is determined by

$$a_1 = \frac{1}{\pi}\left[5\int_0^{\pi/2} \cos(\omega t)\, d(\omega t) - 5\int_{\pi/2}^{3\pi/2} \cos(\omega t)\, d(\omega t) + 5\int_{3\pi/2}^{2\pi} \cos(\omega t)\, d(\omega t)\right]$$

$$= 20/\pi$$

The complete solution is

$$f(t) = \frac{20}{\pi}\cos\omega t - \frac{20}{3\pi}\cos 3\omega t + \frac{20}{5\pi}\cos 5\omega t - \cdots$$

In many problems, only the average and effective values of the function are to be determined. These values are readily found in handbooks for the common waveforms; however, the following examples indicate the basic approach:

Example 1

Determine the effective value of the triangular waveform shown in Fig. 9-4.

Solution:

$$\text{Average square} = \frac{1}{D}\int_0^D y^2\, dt$$

Since $y = At/D$,

$$Y(\text{rms}) = \left[\frac{1}{D}\int_0^D \frac{A^2}{D^2} t^2\, dt\right]^{1/2}$$

$$= [A^2/3]^{1/2} \qquad \textit{Answer}$$

Example 2

Determine the effective value of the triangular waveform shown in Fig. 9-5.

$$\text{Average square} = \frac{1}{T}\left[\int_0^D \frac{A^2t^2}{D^2} dt - 0\right]$$

$$Y(\text{rms}) = A[D/3T]^{1/2}$$

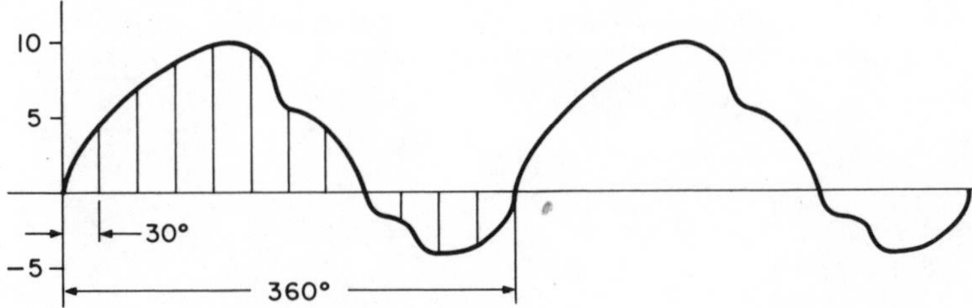

Figure 9-2

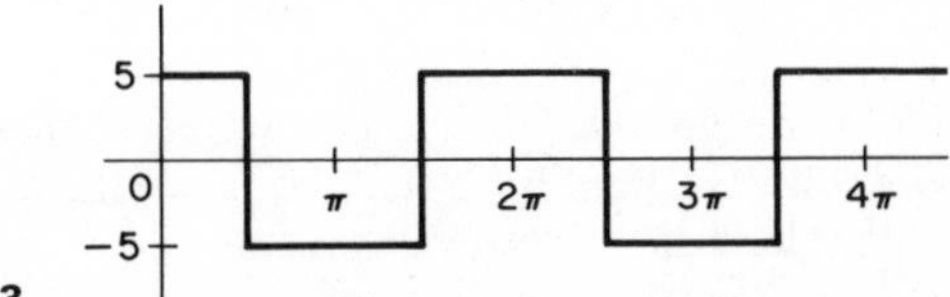

Figure 9-3

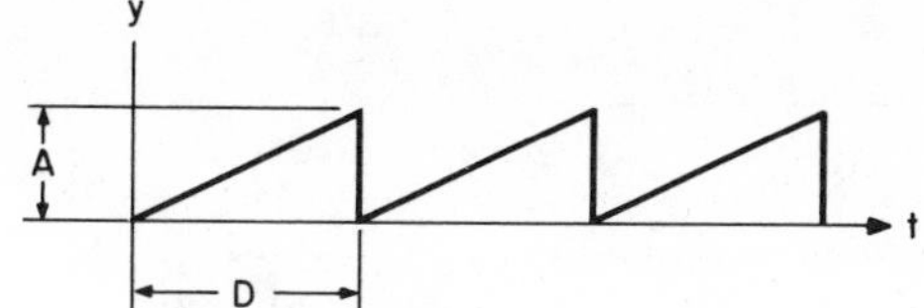

Figure 9-4

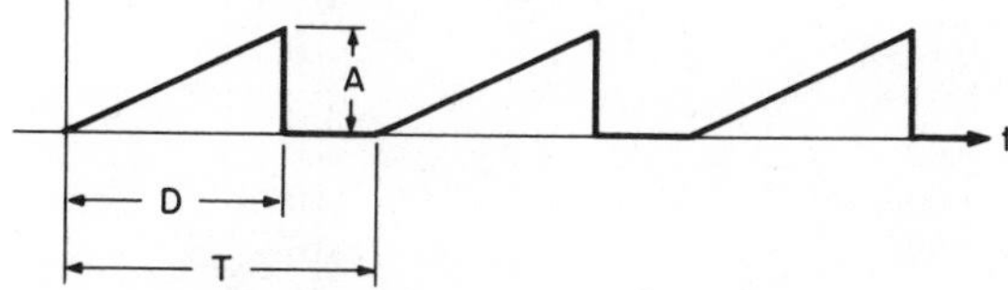

Figure 9-5

PROBLEMS

Problem 9-1 Solution for Fourier coefficients of a waveform

The following data are the coordinates of the waveform of the positive halfcycle of the current in a coil with a magnetic core that is supplied from a sinusoidal voltage source:

Degrees	*Amperes*	*Degrees*	*Amperes*
0	0.000	100	1.37
10	0.250	110	1.57
20	0.450	120	2.00
30	0.550	130	2.27
40	0.675	140	2.35
50	0.755	150	2.30
60	0.826	160	1.35
70	0.875	170	0.65
80	1.000	180	0.00
90	1.120		

Determine the amplitudes of the first and third harmonics.

Solution:

When a sinusoidal voltage is impressed across a coil having a magnetic core, the flux waveform is also (approximately) a sinusoid, and the negative half cycle of the current waveform is a mirror image of the positive half cycle. In other words, f(t) does *not* equal $\pm f(-t)$, but $f(t) = -f(t + T/2)$. The waveform contains both sine and cosine terms (referred to the original axes), and the waveform contains odd harmonics only. Although we could apply a "short-cut" method, such as the Fischer-Hinnen method described in handbooks, the following solution adheres to that discussed in Sec. 9-2.

Solve for the Fourier coefficients a_1, b_1, a_3, and b_3.

ωt	$f(\omega t)$	$f(\omega t)$ cos (ωt)	$f(\omega t)$ sin (ωt)	$f(\omega t)$ cos $(3\omega t)$	$f(\omega t)$ sin $(3\omega t)$
30°	0.550	0.475	0.275	0.0	0.550
60°	0.826	0.413	0.716	−0.826	0.0
90°	1.12	0.0	1.12	0.0	−1.12
120°	2.00	−1.0	1.73	2.00	0.0
150°	2.30	−1.99	1.15	0.0	2.30
180°	0.0	0.0	0.0	0.0	0.0
210°	−0.550	0.475	0.275	0.0	0.550
240°	−0.826	0.413	0.716	−0.826	0.0
270°	−1.12	0.0	1.12	0.0	−1.12
300°	−2.00	−1.00	1.73	2.00	0.0
330°	−2.30	−1.99	1.15	0.0	2.30
360°	0.0	0.0	0.0	0.0	0.0
a_0	0.0				
a_1		-0.35×2			
b_1			0.832×2		
a_3				0.196×2	
b_3					0.288×2

Amplitude of fundamental:

$$\sqrt{a_1^2 + b_1^2} = 1.80 \qquad \textit{Answer}$$

Amplitude of third harmonic:

$$\sqrt{a_3^2 + b_3^2} = 0.696 \qquad \textit{Answer}$$

Problem 9-2 Solution for rms value and Fourier coefficients

For the waveform shown in Fig. 9-6, determine: (a) the rms value, (b) the amplitude of the fundamental, and (c) the amplitude of the third harmonic.

Solution:

By inspection of the waveform, it will be seen that the steady-state component of the waveform (a_0) is zero, that both sine and cosine waves are involved, and that no even harmonics are present. If the harmonics higher than the third are considered insignificant, the effective value of the function is equal to the square root of the sum of the squares of the rms values of the fundamental and third harmonic components.

Solve for the Fourier coefficients:

Between 0° and 30°, average f(t) = 1
Between 30° and 90°, average f(t) = 2
Between 90° and 120°, average f(t) = 6
Between 120° and 180°, average f(t) = 5
Between 180° and 210°, average f(t) = −1
Between 210° and 270°, average f(t) = −2

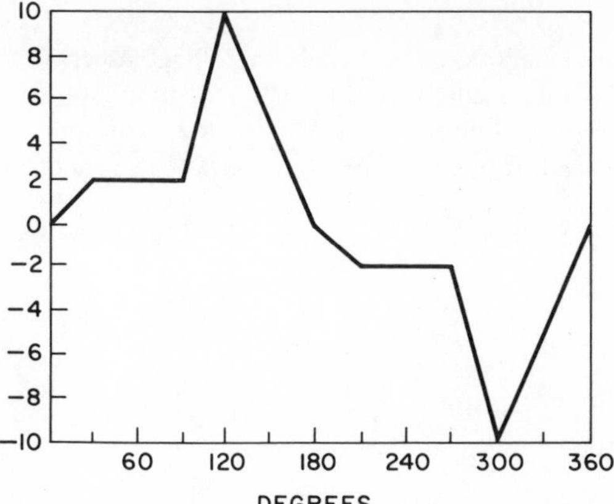

Figure 9-6

Between 270° and 300°, average f(t) = −6
Between 300° and 360°, average f(t) = −5

$$\text{Average value of f(t) cos } \omega t = \frac{1}{360°}\int_{0°}^{360°} f(t) \cos\theta \, d\theta$$

$$= \frac{1}{360°}\Big[1 \times 30° \sin\theta\Big|_{0°}^{30°} + 2 \times 60° \sin\theta\Big|_{30°}^{90°} + 6 \times 30° \sin\theta\Big|_{90°}^{120°}$$

$$+ 5 \times 60° \sin\theta\Big|_{120°}^{180°} - 1 \times 30° \sin\theta\Big|_{180°}^{210°} - 2 \times 60° \sin\theta\Big|_{210°}^{270°}$$

$$- 6 \times 30° \sin\theta\Big|_{270°}^{300°} - 5 \times 60° \sin\theta\Big|_{300°}^{360°}\Big]$$

$$= -1.16$$

$$a_1 = -2.32$$

Similarly, $b_1 = 3.84$ $\quad a_3 = -0.111$ $\quad b_3 = 1.56$

$$\text{Amplitude of fundamental} = \sqrt{a_1^2 + b_1^2}$$

$= 4.48$ *Answer, part (b)*

$$\text{Amplitude of 3rd harmonic} = \sqrt{a_3^2 + b_3^2}$$

$= 1.56$ *Answer, part (c)*

$$\text{Rms value of wave} = 0.707\sqrt{4.48^2 + 1.56^2}$$

$= 3.33$ *Answer, part (a)*

Problem 9-3 Magnitude and angular displacement of second harmonic of a waveform

Figure 9-7 shows the graph of a signal voltage. Calculate the magnitude and angular displacement from the origin of the second harmonic in this signal.

Solution:

This is a periodic, single-valued function and is therefore susceptible to Fourier analysis. We could resort to a specific formula for rectangular pulses, and to such devices as shifting the origin to eliminate sine (or cosine) components. However, it is best to learn one procedure well; this solution uses the general approach of Problems 9-1 and 9-2.

Solve for the Fourier coefficients a_2, b_2, and then c_2 and the phase angle in

$$f(\omega t)_2 = c_2 \cos (2\omega t + \alpha_2)$$

Average value of $f(\omega t) \cos (2\omega t)$

$$= \frac{1}{4\pi}\left[\frac{50\pi}{2} \sin 2\omega t\Big|_{\omega t=0}^{\omega t=\pi/2} + \frac{100\pi}{2} \sin 2\pi t\Big|_{\pi/2}^{\pi} + .0\right] = 0$$

Therefore, $a_2 = 0$.

Average value of $f(\omega t) \sin (2\omega t)$

$$= \frac{1}{4\pi}\left[-\frac{50\pi}{2} \cos 2\omega t\Big|_{\omega t=0}^{\omega t=\pi/2} - \frac{100\pi}{2} \cos 2\omega t\Big|_{\omega t=\pi/2}^{\omega t=\pi} + 0\right] = -\frac{100}{8}$$

Therefore $b_2 = -25$ $(=c_2)$.

The second harmonic $= -25 \sin 2\omega t$

$= 25 \sin (2\omega t - 90°)$ *Answer*

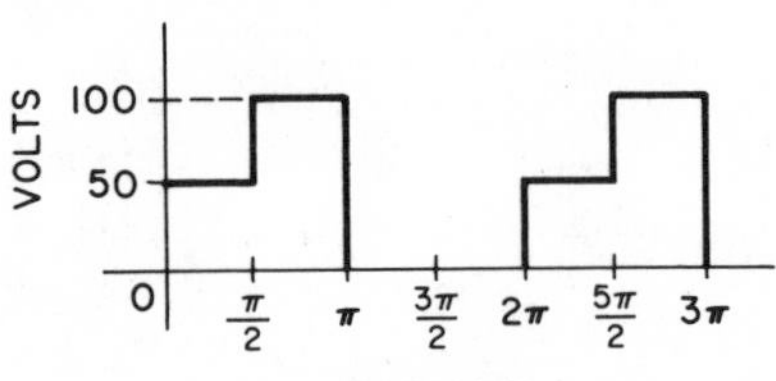

Figure 9-7

Problem 9-4 Meter reading and average power developed by a triangular waveform

A repetitive triangular voltage waveform viewed on an oscilloscope is shown in Fig. 9-8.

(a) What value would a D'Arsonval voltmeter indicate?
(b) What is the rms value of this voltage?
(c) What is the average power if this voltage is connected to a 2-ohm resistor?
(d) Calculate the amplitude of the fundamental component of this wave.

Solution:

An ideal D'Arsonval galvanometer would give a variable reading proportional to the instantaneous voltage. Actually, it will give an indication proportional to the average value.

For variety, instead of applying the general equation, this solution makes use of formulas already derived by Fourier analysis, and makes use of some devices.

(a) By inspection, the average value is 2.5 volts; this would be indicated by a D'Arsonval voltmeter *Answer*

(b) Since rms $= \sqrt{(1/D)(A^2d/3)}$ for a waveform such as Fig. 9-9(A), and since we have the sum of two waveforms shown in Fig. 9-9, then

$$\text{rms} = \sqrt{\frac{100 \times 2T}{3 \times 3T} + \frac{25T}{3 \times 3T}} = 5 \text{ amps} \qquad \textit{Answer}$$

(c) $V^2/R = 25/2 = 12.5$ watts *Answer*

(d) A sawtooth wave is expressed as

$$y(t) = 2A_{avg}\left(\frac{1}{2} - \frac{1}{\pi}\sin\theta - \frac{1}{2\pi}\sin 2\theta - \cdots - \frac{1}{n\pi}\sin n\theta\right)$$

where the amplitude of the function is $2A_{avg}/\pi$ and where the abscissa is chosen to give all positive values.

Therefore, move the X-axis to conform. See Fig. 9-10.

$$y(t) = 2 \times \frac{15}{2} \times \left(\frac{1}{2} - \frac{1}{\pi}\sin\theta\right)$$

or amplitude of the fundamental $= 15/\pi$ or 4.77 amps *Answer*

Note: for the X-axis given in the problem, the steady component would change, but the amplitude of the fundamental would not change.

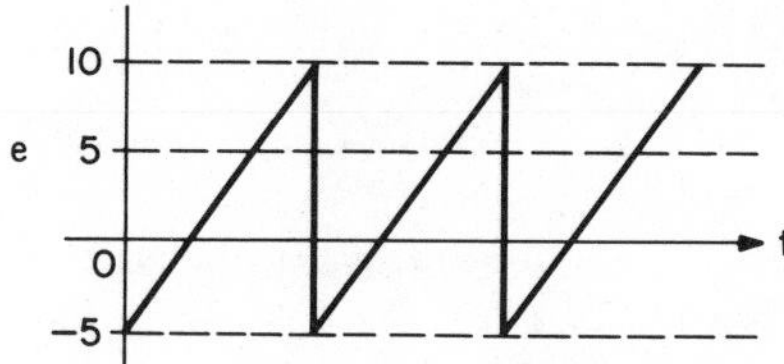

Figure 9-8

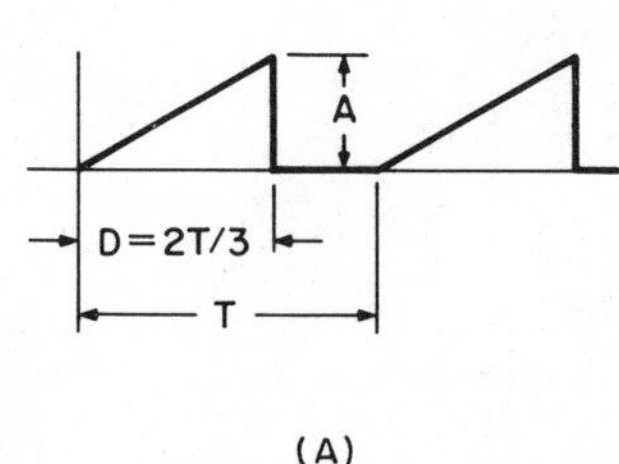

Figure 9-9

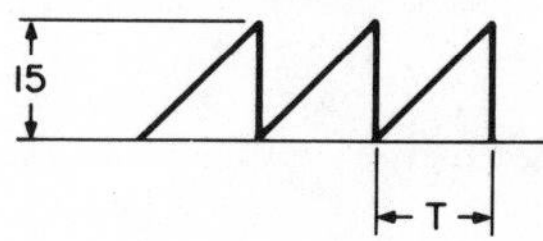

Figure 9-10

Problem 9-5 Components and effects of a trapezoidal waveform

For the current waveform shown in Fig. 9-11:

(a) What is the maximum value of the resulting voltage if the current flows through a 3.0-ohm resistor?

(b) What is the d-c component of the current waveform?

(c) What is the rms or effective value of the current waveform?

(d) If the current flows through a 0.4-henry inductor having negligible resistance, what is the voltage across the inductor during the time from t = 4 to t = 5?

(e) If the current passes through a 0.5-farad capacitor, what is the voltage change during the time interval from t = 4 to t = 5?

Solution:

(a) The maximum value of current is 2.0 amps; therefore, the maximum voltage across the resistor is 6 volts. *Answer*

(b) The average value of current is

$$\frac{(1 \times 1) + (2 \times 1)}{2} = 1.5 \text{ amps} \qquad \textit{Answer}$$

(c) The rms value of the waveform is, by definition,

$$\frac{1}{T}\int_0^T i^2\,dt = \frac{1}{2}\left(\int_0^1 t^2\,dt + 2\right) = 1\tfrac{1}{6} \text{ amps} \qquad \textit{Answer}$$

(d) $e = L\,di/dt$

$= 0.4 \times 2 = 0.8$ volt *Answer*

(e) $i = C\,de/dt$

During the interval t = 3 to t = 4, the current is 2 amps, and the voltage change is therefore 4 volts/sec. Between the values t = 4 and t = 5, the *rate of change* of voltage varies from zero to 4 volts/second. *Answer*

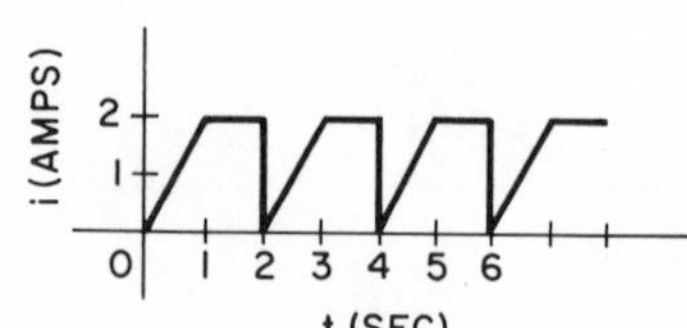

Figure 9-11

Problem 9-6 Analysis of rectangular pulse applied to an antenna

A radar antenna has a radiation resistance of 45 ohms. It is excited with rectangular pulses at a rate of 600 pulses/sec and a pulse duration of 2 μsec. The amplitude of the pulse is 15 kilovolts.

Determine: (a) The rms value of the antenna voltage, (b) the peak power delivered to the antenna, and (c) the average value of the power supplied to the antenna.

Solution:

Power = V^2/R, taking care that the proper value is used for V. The average value of any waveform over a full cycle is the area under the curve divided by the abscissa (in this case, time, in sec). The rms value of any waveform is the area under the curve constructed by the original waveform values squared, divided by the abscissa.

$$V_{rms} = V_{max}\sqrt{\frac{d}{T}} = 15\sqrt{\frac{2 \times 10^{-6}}{(600)^{-1}}} = 0.518 \text{ kV} \qquad \textit{Answer, part (a)}$$

$$V_{avg} = \frac{V_{max}}{T} = \frac{15 \times 2 \times 10^{-6}}{(600)^{-1}} = 0.018 \text{ kV}$$

$$\text{Average power} = V_{rms}^2/R = (518)^2/45 = 6.0 \text{ kW} \qquad \textit{Answer, part (c)}$$

$$\text{Peak power} = V_{max}^2/R = (15{,}000)^2/45 = 5000.0 \text{ kW} \qquad \textit{Answer, part (b)}$$

Problem 9-7 Carrier deviation of a frequency-modulated wave

A frequency-modulated wave is given by the expression

$$e = 500 \cos(\omega t + 0.1 \sin at)$$

(a) What is the carrier deviation in hertz if a is 12,560?

(b) If this voltage is applied to a pure resistance of 600 ohms, what power in watts is dissipated in the resistance?

Solution:

(a) In this problem, the modulating signal is a simple sinusoid.

Let the modulating signal be $e_2 = E_2 \cos 2\pi f't$, and let the effect of this signal on the carrier frequency be Be_2.

Then the instantaneous frequency of the total wave will be

$$f'' = f + BE_2 \cos 2\pi f't$$

where f is the carrier frequency in the expression $e_1 = 500 \cos 2\pi ft$.

The instantaneous phase angle of the total wave at time t can be found by integrating the instantaneous frequency between 0 and t. The total wave equation is then

$$e = E_1 \cos\left(2\pi ft + \frac{BE_2}{f'} \sin 2\pi f't\right)$$

The maximum frequency deviation is BE_2.

The waveform represented by the above expression can be expanded into a series of waveforms each with a constant frequency. The amplitude of each wave is obtained from tables of Bessel functions. When the modulation index (BE_2/f') is small, as in this problem, all of the energy is usually assumed to be contained in the carrier and first-order sideband components. (Further treatment of this theory is too extensive for this book. The reader is referred to *Radio Engineers' Handbook,* by F. E. Terman. New York: McGraw-Hill Book Co., Inc.)

By observing the expression for the sinusoidally frequency-modulated wave, it is seen that

$$a = 12{,}560 = 2\pi f'$$

$$f' = 2000$$

$$0.1 = BE_2/2000$$

$$BE_2 = 200 \text{ Hz} \qquad \textit{Answer}$$

(b) Expanding the wave:

$$e = 500\{J_0 \cos \omega t + J_1[\sin (\omega + f')t - \sin (\omega - f')t]\}$$

where J_0 and J_1 are Bessel functions of the first kind with argument 0.1 (the modulation index).

From tables of Bessel functions,

$$J_0 = 0.9975 \qquad J_1 = 0.0499$$

The rms values of the three component waves are therefore 352, 17.5, and 17.5, respectively. The effective value of the voltage is $[(352)^2 + (17.5)^2 + (17.5)^2]^{1/2} =$ 355 volts.

The power absorbed by the resistor is

$$E^2_{rms}/R = 125{,}600/600 = 209 \text{ watts} \qquad \textit{Answer}$$

chapter 10
TRANSIENTS

By definition, a linear dynamic system is one for which the relationship between excitation and response can be expressed by an equation containing nothing higher than first-order derivatives and integrals. The parameters of the system are independent of excitation and response.

For example, the relationship between voltage and current in Fig. 10-1 is

$$E = L\frac{di}{dt} + Ri + \frac{1}{C}\int i\,dt \tag{10-1}$$

Equation (10-1) is an elementary expression, but its solution is arduous. For the more complicated circuits, which are the ones most frequently encountered, the classical solution does not lend itself to rapid (and therefore economical) calculations. Further, when the initial value of the excitation or response is not zero (in this case, if the potential across the capacitor is not zero before the switch is thrown), the solution becomes more ponderous. For these reasons, operational calculus was developed to permit one to treat derivatives and integrals somewhat as we treat algebraic quantities. To emphasize this, the classical solution to Eq. (10-1) follows, and in Sec. 10-2 the use of the Laplace transform is briefly explained.

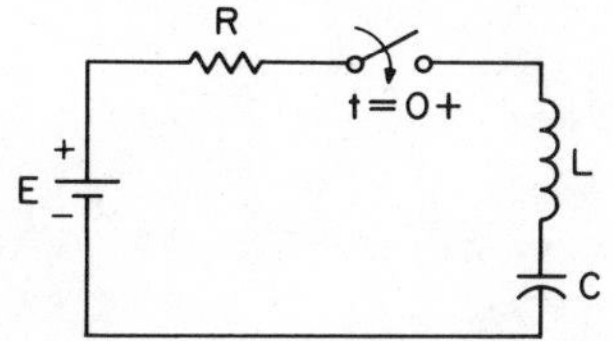

Figure 10-1

Differentiating Eq. (10-1) with respect to t and using accepted symbols for first and second derivatives,

$$Li'' + Ri' + i/C = 0$$

$$i'' + \frac{R}{L}i' + \frac{i}{LC} = 0 \tag{10-2}$$

By trial, it has been found that the solution for an equation of this form is obtained by the valid substitution $i = \epsilon^{mt}$. Then, $di/dt = m\epsilon^{mt}$ and $d^2i/dt^2 = m^2\epsilon^{mt}$. Therefore, when $t = 0$, Eq. (10-2) becomes

$$m^2 + \frac{R}{L}m + \frac{1}{LC} = 0 \tag{10-3}$$

Solving Eq. (10-3),

$$m = \frac{R}{L} \pm \sqrt{\frac{CR^2 - 4L}{L^2C}}$$

or $$m = -\frac{R}{L} \pm j\sqrt{\frac{4L - CR^2}{L^2C}}$$

Substituting in Eq. (10-2) and integrating to revert to Eq. (10-1), we can obtain the general solution for i:

$$i = (\epsilon^{-Rt/2L})\left[\frac{2(E - E_0) - RI_0}{R\sqrt{1 - \dfrac{4L}{R^2C}}} \sinh \frac{Rt}{2L}\sqrt{1 - \frac{4L}{R^2C}} + I_0 \cosh \frac{Rt}{2L}\sqrt{1 - \frac{4L}{R^2C}}\right]$$

where E_0 is the potential across C just before the switch is closed, and I_0 is the current through L just before the switch is closed (which in this example would be zero).

Expressing the hyperbolic functions in exponential form,

$$i = (\epsilon^{-Rt/2L})\left\{\left[\frac{2(E - E_0) - RI_0}{2R\sqrt{D}}\right](\epsilon^{R\sqrt{D}t/2L} - \epsilon^{-R\sqrt{D}t/2L}) + \frac{I_0}{2}(\epsilon^{R\sqrt{D}t/2L} + \epsilon^{-R\sqrt{D}t/2L})\right.$$

$$= (\epsilon^{-Rt/2L})\,\{K_1\epsilon^{R\sqrt{D}t/2L} + K_2\epsilon^{-R\sqrt{D}t/2L}\}$$

where $$D = 1 - \frac{4L}{R^2C}$$

K_1, K_2 = convenient constants

Three cases are possible:
Case 1: D is positive (overdamped case).
Case 2: D is zero (critically damped case).
Case 3: D is negative (underdamped or oscillatory case).
For the over-damped case, when $L/R^2C < 0.01$,

$$i \cong \left(\frac{E - E_0}{R}\right)(\epsilon^{-t/RC}) + \left(I_0 - \frac{E - E_0}{R}\right)(\epsilon^{-Rt/L})$$

For the critically damped case,

$$i = (\epsilon^{-Rt/2L})\left[\left(\frac{E - E_0}{L}\right)t + I_0\left(1 - \frac{R}{2L}t\right)\right]$$

For the oscillatory case,

$$i = I_m(\epsilon^{-Rt/2L}) \sin(\omega_0 t + \psi)$$

where $\omega_0 = \sqrt{1/LC - R^2/4L^2}$

$$I_m = \frac{1}{\omega_0 L}\sqrt{(E - E_0 - RI_0/2)^2 + \omega_0{}^2L^2I_0{}^2}$$

$$\psi = \tan^{-1}\frac{\omega_0 LI_0}{E - I_0 - RI_0/2}$$

When the applied voltage is sinusoidal, $e = E \sin(\omega t + \alpha)$, the total current may be found by adding the steady-state value $(E/Z) \sin(\omega t + \alpha - \phi)$ to the transient value. The latter is found by determining the value I_0 and the capacitor voltage E_0 that would exist due to a voltage $-e_t = 0$. This transient current i is

$$i = I_0 = -\frac{E}{Z}\sin(\alpha - \phi)$$

and $\quad e_c = E_0 = \dfrac{E}{\omega CZ}\cos(\alpha - \phi)$

where $\phi = \tan^{-1}\dfrac{\omega^2 LC - 1}{\omega CR}$

For the circuit shown Fig. 10-2, similar expressions can be formed by observing the similarity of the applicable differential equation to Eq. (10-1).

$$I = C\frac{de}{dt} + Ge + \frac{1}{L}\int e\, dt$$

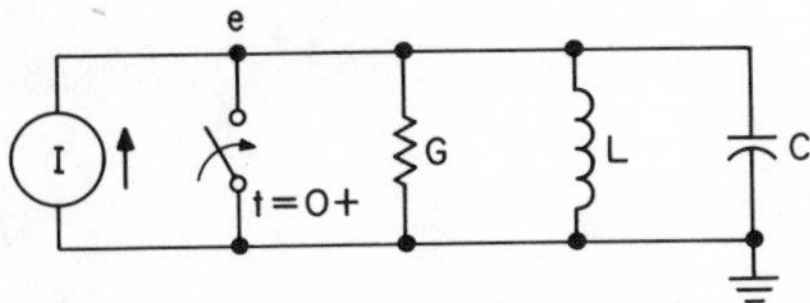

Figure 10-2

10-1 ELEMENTARY TRANSIENT EXPRESSIONS

Sometimes the solution of a problem can be written by observation, using an elementary expression for the charge or discharge of a magnetic or electrostatic field. A frequently used characteristic is the time constant (T).

The time constant is the time in seconds required for a variable to accomplish $1/\epsilon(= 0.3679)$ of its total transient change in value (A). The transient is expressed by $f(t) = A\epsilon^{-at}$, where $a = 1/T$. The following are useful expressions:

For the capacitor $(T = RC)$. (See Fig. 10-3.)

On charge,

$$i = I_0(\epsilon^{-t/RC})$$

$$e_c = E_0(\epsilon^{-t/RC}) + \{E[1 - \epsilon^{-t/RC}]\}$$

On discharge,

$$i = I_0(\epsilon^{-t/RC})$$

$$e_c = E_0(\epsilon^{-t/RC})$$

where I_0 and E_0 are values at t = 0 and E = 0.

For the inductor $(T = L/R)$.

On charge:

$$i = I(1 - \epsilon^{-Rt/L})$$

On discharge,

$$i = I(\epsilon^{-Rt/L})$$

where I = E/R.

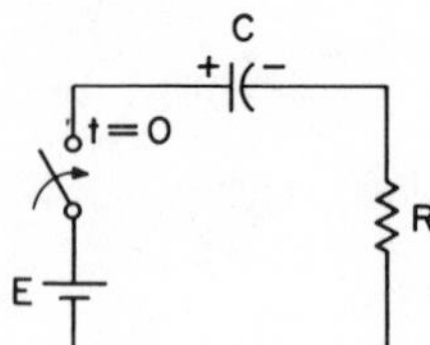

Figure 10-3

10-2 THE LAPLACE TRANSFORM

Just as logarithms and antilogarithms facilitates the multiplication and division of numbers, the Laplace transform and its inverse function facilitates the solution of differential equations.

The Laplace transform of a function is defined in mathematical language as

$$\mathcal{L}\, f(t) = \int_0^\infty f(t)(\epsilon^{-st})\, dt = F(s)$$

where $s = \sigma + j\omega$.

The inverse transformation would be

$$\mathcal{L}^{-1}F(s) = \frac{1}{2\pi j}\int_{c-j\infty}^{c+j\infty} F(s)(\epsilon^{st})\, ds = f(t)$$

Actually, recourse is made to tables of f(t) and F(s) for many cases, just as recourse is made to tables of logarithms. Some common transform pairs are

$$\mathcal{L}\, u_{-1}(t) = 1/s$$

$$\mathcal{L}\, kf(t) = k\mathcal{L}f(t)$$

$$\mathcal{L}\sin\omega t = \frac{\omega}{s^2 + \omega^2}$$

$$\mathcal{L}\cos\omega t = \frac{s}{s^2 + \omega^2}$$

$$\mathcal{L}\,\epsilon^{\alpha t} = \frac{1}{s - \alpha}$$

$$\mathcal{L}\,\epsilon^{-\alpha t} = \frac{1}{s + \alpha}$$

$$\mathcal{L}\,\frac{\omega_0}{\alpha}\,\epsilon^{-\alpha t} = \frac{\omega_0}{\alpha}\left(\frac{1}{s + \alpha}\right)$$

$$\mathcal{L}\,\frac{d}{dt}\,f(t) = s\,\mathcal{L}\,f(t) - f(0^+)$$

$$\mathcal{L}\int f(t)\,dt = \frac{\mathcal{L}\,f(t) + f^{-1}(0^+)}{s}$$

where the exponent -1 signifies integration and $f(0^+)$ = initial value of f(t) from positive side of $t = 0$.

Note: If $f(t) = v(t)$,

$$\mathcal{L}\int v(t)\,dt = V(s)/s + \lambda(0^+)/s$$

where λ = flux linkages.
If $f(t) = i(t)$,

$$\mathcal{L}\int i(t)\,dt = I(s)/s + Q(0^+)/s$$

Usually, the function F(s) that is first obtained does not resemble the simple expressions given but must be broken into parts that do resemble them. If this cannot be done by observation, the recommended procedure is to arrange F(s) in the following form:

$$F(s) = F_1(s) + F_2(s) + \cdots + K\,\frac{s^n + a_1 s^{n-1} + \cdots + a_n}{s^m + b_1 s^{m-1} + \cdots + b_m}$$

where $m > n$.

The polynomial denominator is then factored, and the ratio of polynomials broken up by partial fraction expansion.

10-3 SINGULARITY FUNCTIONS

Three frequently used time functions (*singularity functions*) are the *step function,* the *impulse function,* and the *ramp function,* illustrated graphically and symbolically in Fig. 10-4.

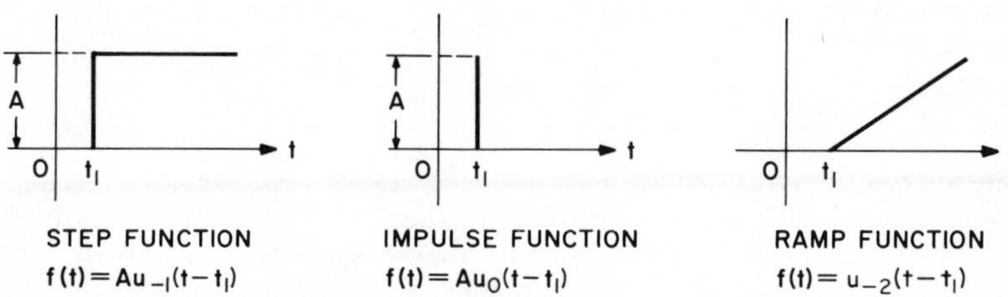

Figure 10-4

The derivative of a ramp function is a step function.

The integral of a step function is a ramp function.

The derivative of a step function is an impulse function.

The integral of an impulse function is a step function.

From Fig. 10-4, where the magnitude A is unity, we have the *unit step* or the *unit impulse*. When the slope of the ramp function is unity, we have the *unit ramp*.

The Laplace transforms of these singularity functions should be noted:

$$\mathcal{L}\, u_0(t) = 1$$

$$\mathcal{L}\, u_{-1}(t) = 1/s$$

$$\mathcal{L}\, u_{-2}(t) = 1/s^2$$

Note also that

$$\mathcal{L}\, f(t - a) = (\epsilon^{-as})\, \mathcal{L}\, f(t)$$

10-4 THE TRANSFORM IMPEDANCE DIAGRAM

To further facilitate transient analysis, an electrical circuit diagram can be readily redrawn, showing both the parameters and initial conditions as functions of s. The corresponding Kirchhoff's laws equations, mesh, or nodal equations are the actual transform expression for the differential equations that would have been written for the original circuit. This is best illustrated in Fig. 10-5, where I_0 and V_0 signify the initial conditions.

10-5 STEADY-STATE ANALYSIS

In some problems involving transient conditions, we may be more interested in the final or steady-state values than we are in the transient values. Methods of determining the steady-state values will be treated briefly.

Method 1. Method 1 determines the steady-state value by logical deduction upon observation. In the circuit shown in Fig. 10-6, it is obvious that the inductance will oppose a *change* in current; that is, it will delay the attainment of the final value of current. As the current approaches the final value, the change in current decreases and the inductance offers little opposition. The final value is, therefore, E/R.

Method 2. Method 2 determines the limit of f(t) as t approaches ∞. In the circuit of Fig. 10-6, the transform expression for F(s) is

$$I(s) = \frac{E/s}{R + sL}$$

$$i(t) = \frac{E}{R}[1 - \epsilon^{-Rt/L}]$$

As t approaches ∞, i approaches E/R.

Method 3. Method 3 applies the final value theorem. This consists in multiplying F(s) by s and finding the limit of sF(s) as s approaches zero. This will give the final value of the response in the time domain. This theorem is not applicable when the polynomial denominator (see Sec. 10-2) has roots whose real parts are positive.

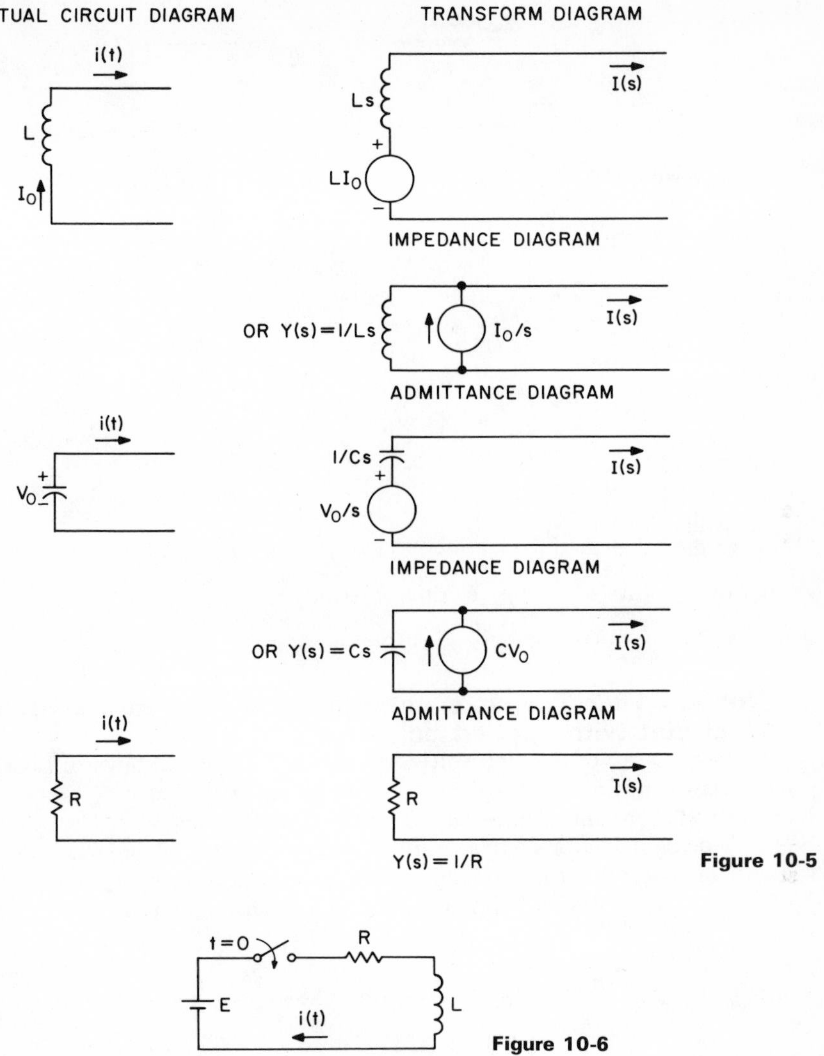

Figure 10-5

Figure 10-6

PROBLEMS

Problem 10-1 Triangular voltage applied to an RC circuit

The voltage E impressed on the circuit shown in Fig. 10-7 varies as indicated. Calculate the value of the steady-state or forced current I.

Solution:

In this problem, all that is necessary is to write the differential equation of the circuit and observe that $di/dt = 0$ when $i = I$.

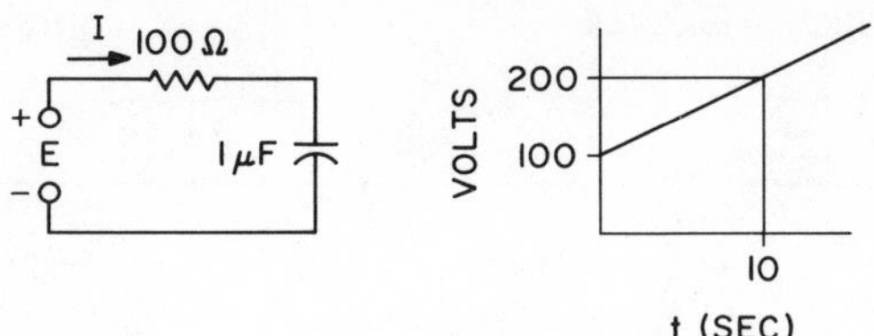

Figure 10-7

From the graph,

$$e = 100 + 10t$$

$$= iR + \frac{1}{C}\int i\,dt$$

$$i = C\frac{d(e - iR)}{dt}$$

$$= C\left(\frac{de}{dt} - R\frac{di}{dt}\right)$$

$$i + R\frac{di}{dt} - C\frac{de}{dt} = 0;$$

but $de/dt = 10$ and $di/dt = 0$ (steady state)

Therefore, $I = 10$ microamperes. *Answer*

Problem 10-2 Transient voltage calculation in a switched RL circuit with applied dc

A d-c voltage source of $E = 100$ volts is applied to the circuit shown in Fig. 10-8 by closing switch S_1 at $t = 0$, switch S_2 remaining open.

(a) At what instant of time will current i reach 15 amps?

(b) When $i = 15$ amps, a relay starts to pull in to close S_2. This switch actually closes 0.1 sec later. What is the value of current i when S_2 closes?

(c) What is the value of current i after S_2 has been closed for 2 sec?

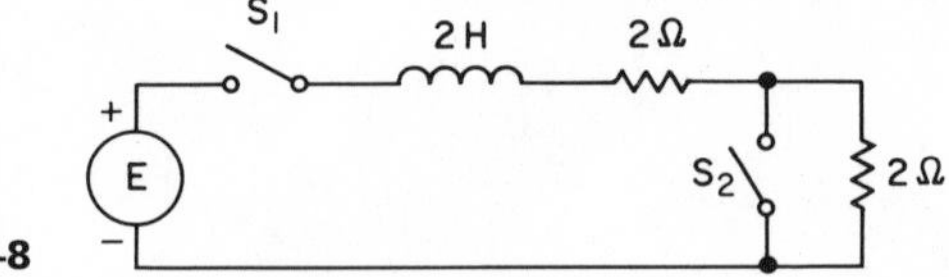

Figure 10-8

Solution:

Current buildup in an RL circuit is expressed by

$$i = I(1 - \epsilon^{-Rt/L})$$

where I = final (steady-state) value.

(a) $I = 100/4 = 25$ amps

$$i = I(1 - \epsilon^{-2t}) = 15$$

$t = 0.46$ sec *Answer*

(b) When $t = 0.56$ sec,

$i = 25(1 - \epsilon^{-1.12}) = 25 - (25 \times 0.3263) = 16.84$ amps *Answer*

(c) If the initial value is 16.84, $t_0 = 0$, and $t = 2$,

$i = I(1 - \epsilon^{-2t/2}) + 16.84 \exp(-2t/2)$
$= 50 - (50 \times 0.1353) + (16.84 \times 0.1353)$ or 45.3 amps *Answer*

Problem 10-3 Transient voltage calculation in a switched RLC circuit with applied dc

A d-c voltage source of $E = 100$ volts is applied to the circuit shown in Fig. 10-9 by closing switch S_1 at $t = 0$, switch S_2 remaining open.

(a) What is the time constant T of the circuit with switch S_2 open?

(b) What will be the current in R_1 when $t = 1$ sec?

(c) What will be the voltage across the capacitor when $t = 1$ sec?

(d) When $t = 1$ sec, switch S_2 closes. Switch S_1 remains closed. What is the value of the time constant now?

(e) What is the value of the current through R_1 an instant after switch S_2 is closed?

(f) What is the value of the current through R_2 an instant after switch S_2 is closed?

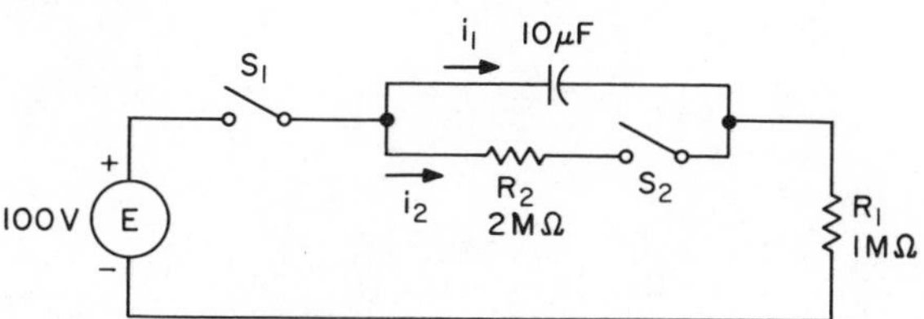

Figure 10-9

Solution:

The solution demonstrates the ease of applying the Laplace transform technique to a circuit in which a transient condition exists with zero initial condition and a succeeding transient condition with an initial potential across the capacitor.

(a) $T = RC = 10^6 \times 10^{-5} = 10$ *Answer*

(b) $i_1 = I_0(\epsilon^{-t/RC})$
$= 10^{-4}(\epsilon^{-0.1})$
$= 90.5\ \mu A$ *Answer*

(c) $v_c = 100 - i_1R_1 = 9.5$ volts *Answer*

(d) Write Kirchhoff's law equations:

$$100 = \frac{1}{C}\int i_1\,dt + (i_1 + i_2) \times 10^6$$

$$100 = (i_1 + i_2) \times 10^6 + 2i_2 \times 10^6$$

Eliminating i_2,

$$200 = 0.3 \times 10^6 \int i_1 \, dt + 2 \times 10^6 i_1$$

Write the Laplace transform:

$$\frac{200}{s} = \frac{0.3 \times 10^6}{s}\left[I_1(s) + Q(0)\right] + 2 \times 10^6 I_1(s)$$

$$Q(0) = e_c C \qquad \text{where } e_c = 9.5 \text{ volts}$$
$$= 95 \times 10^{-6}$$

$$\frac{200}{s} = \frac{0.3 \times 10^6}{s} I_1(s) + \frac{0.3 \times 10^6 \times 95 \times 10^{-6}}{s} + 2 \times 10^6 I_1(s)$$

Rearranging:

$$I_1(s) = \frac{85.75 \times 10^{-6}}{s - (-0.15)}$$

Note that this is in the form $1/(s - \alpha)$, where the inverse transform is $\epsilon^{\alpha t}$. Therefore, the inverse transform is

$$\mathcal{L}^{-1} I_1(s) = \mathcal{L}^{-1} 85.75 \times 10^{-6} \times \frac{1}{s - (-0.15)}$$

$$i_1 = 85.75 \times 10^{-6} \epsilon^{-0.15t}$$

$$T = 1/0.15 = 6.67 \text{ sec}$$ *Answer*

(e and f) Let t = zero when switch S_2 is closed. From part (d),

$i_1 = 85.75\ \mu A$ *Answer, part (e)*

$i_2 = 4.7\ \mu A$ [from the voltage equation in the solution to part (d)]

Current through $R_1 = i_1 + i_2 = 90.5\ \mu A$ *Answer, part (f)*

Problem 10-4 Transient voltage calculation in a switched RLC circuit with applied dc

In the circuit shown in Fig. 10-10, the switch S is closed after the circuit has reached a steady-state condition.

(a) What is the initial steady-state current through resistor R_2 prior to the closing of the switch?

(b) What is the equation for current through resistor R_2 after the switch is closed?

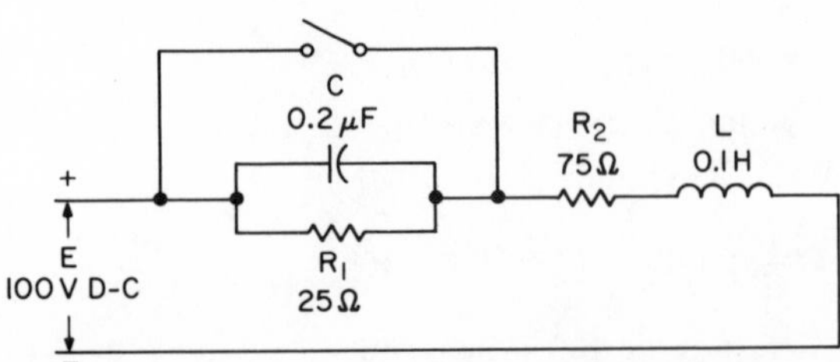

Figure 10-10

(c) Give an expression or sketch of the current through the switch after it is closed.

Solution:

Prior to the closing of the switch, the total circuit resistance is $R_1 + R_2$. After the switch is closed, the total circuit resistance is R_2. These circuit resistors, together with the circuit voltage E, determine the respective steady-state current values for the two conditions. The inductor can only affect the *change* in current. The capacitor, charged to a potential equal to the voltage drop across R_1 (25 volts) is discharged in zero time through zero switch resistance. Although this current would be infinite (from the circuit given in problem), it would be limited by the switch and capacitor resistance and the speed of closing of the switch. It would not be affected by R_1.

(a) $I_0 = E/R = 100/100 = 1$ amp *Answer*

(b) $i = I_0 + (I - I_0)(1 - \epsilon^{-R_2t/L})$

where $I = E/R_2 = 1.333$ amps.

$i = 1 + 0.3(1 - \epsilon^{-750t})$ *Answer*

(c) $i_{switch} = i + C\, de_c/dt$

where de_c/dt = speed of closing of the switch.

$$i_{switch} = i + \frac{25}{R_s}\epsilon^{-t/R_sC} \qquad \textit{Answer}$$

where the switch is assumed to close in zero time as in part (b), but where R_s is the resistance of the switch and capacitor.

Problem 10-5 Laplace transform analysis of an RLC oscillatory circuit

In the circuit of Fig. 10-11, specify conductance g in mhos so that the circuit will oscillate with an angular velocity of 1000 radians/sec. The amplitude of node voltage a relative to node b will be attenuated. Explain your answer.

Solution:

The Laplace transform equation for the current (a unit step function) for the circuit in Fig. 10-11 is

$$\frac{1}{s} = gE(s) + CsE(s) + \frac{1}{Ls}E(s)$$

$$E(s) = \frac{1}{s(g + Cs + 1/Ls)}$$

$$= \frac{L}{gLs + LCs^2 + 1}$$

$$= \frac{1}{C}\left(\frac{1}{s^2 + gs/C + 1/LC}\right)$$

$$= \frac{1}{C}\left[\frac{1}{(s + g/2C)^2 + (\omega_0\sqrt{1 - \zeta^2})^2}\right]$$

where $\zeta = \frac{g}{2}\sqrt{\frac{L}{C}}$ = damping constant

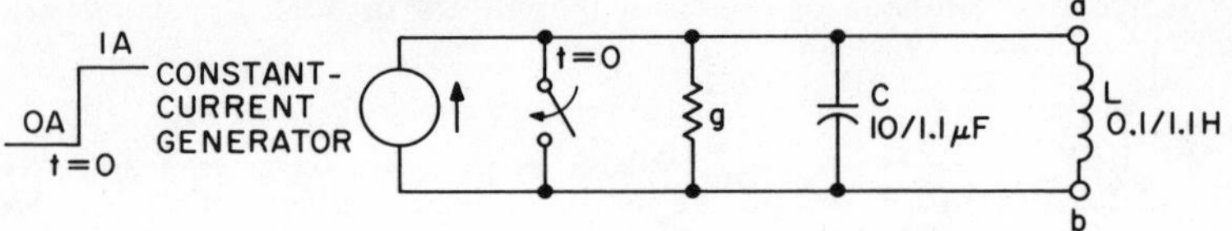

Figure 10-11

$$\omega_0 = \sqrt{1/LC} = \text{natural angular frequency}$$

$$E(s) = \frac{1}{C}\left[\frac{1}{(s + g/2C)^2 + (\omega_0\sqrt{1 - \zeta^2})^2}\right]$$

$$e(t) = \frac{1}{\omega_0 C\sqrt{1 - \zeta^2}}(\epsilon^{-gt/2C}) \sin(\omega_0\sqrt{1 - \zeta^2})t$$

The expression $\omega = \omega_0\sqrt{1 - \zeta^2}$ signifies the actual oscillating frequency.

The natural frequency $\omega_0 = 1/\sqrt{LC}$ radians/sec

$$= \frac{1}{\sqrt{0.091 \times 9.1 \times 10^{-6}}} = 1100$$

The frequency of oscillation $= \omega = \omega_0\sqrt{1 - \zeta^2}$

where ζ = the damping constant $= \frac{g}{2}\sqrt{\frac{L}{C}}$.

$$1000 = 1100\sqrt{1 - \zeta^2}$$

$$\zeta = 0.414 = \frac{g}{2}\sqrt{\frac{0.091 \times 10^6}{9.1}}$$

$g = 0.00828$ mho *Answer*

chapter 11
THE ELECTRICAL CIRCUIT ANALOG

The solution of engineering problems usually involves the determination of an *output* corresponding to a given *input*. In many cases, the mathematical expression describing the *excitation–response* relationship is a linear integrodifferential equation, and the solution is the same whether the dynamic system is electrical, mechanical, thermal, acoustical, or chemical. The electrical engineer should have no difficulty in calculating the rate of oxygen uptake in a liquid waste effluent entering a surface water system or lake when he understands the similarity of the relationships among the variables used by the sanitary engineer to those used in the equations of the linear electrical network. In mechanical translational or rotational problems, as long as the proportional limit is not exceeded, the velocity resulting from a given force can be calculated in the same manner as one would calculate the potentials in a linear network caused by a current being injected somewhere in the system.

The similarity permits an electrical circuit model to be constructed that represents the actual system. With a compatible system of units, the performance of a mechanical system can be studied without setting up an awkward, expensive, or impractical model. Before considering a compatible system of units, two thoughts justify discussion:

1. By observation, the engineer recognizes the laws of conservation of charge, energy, momentum, etc. The variables of these laws cannot change in zero time. For example, the energy stored in a capacitor is $\frac{1}{2}Ce^2$ joules, where C is the capacitance in farads and e is the potential across the capacitor in volts. Voltage e, therefore, cannot change in zero time as this would require an infinite current, since $i = C\, de/dt$. Similarly, the energy stored in a magnetic field of an inductor is $\frac{1}{2}Li^2$. The current through the coil cannot change in zero time as this would require an infinite voltage, since $e = L\, di/dt$. This reasoning can be extended to other systems by using the corresponding (analogous) variables for that system.
2. The engineer does not necessarily think of the excitation as being a potential variable. For example, although the voltage source of an electrical circuit can be considered the excitation and the current as the response, there is justification for considering the potential in a circuit as the response and the current as the excitation. This flexibility frequently simplifies the solution of a problem. Also, this reasoning can be extended to other non-electrical systems.

11-1 ANALOGOUS ELECTRICAL, MECHANICAL, ACOUSTICAL, AND THERMAL LINEAR SYSTEMS

First, compatible systems of units must be selected. Satisfactory systems are shown in Table 11-1.

To illustrate the ease with which analogous expressions can be written, various relationships are shown in Table 11-2. Note that mass in the mechanical system is analogous to capacitance in the electrical system, *if* the velocity is considered analogous to voltage. If force were taken as the potential variable, then mass would be analogous to inductance. In the problems at the end of the chapter, velocity is used as the potential variable.

A rule to follow in the electrical analog circuit is to connect the capacitance directly to ground. This will be demonstrated in the problems.

Table 11-1 Compatible Systems of Units

Variable	*Symbol*	*Unit*
Electrical		
Voltage	e	volt
Current	i	ampere
Resistance	R	ohm
Inductance	L	henry
Capacitance	C	farad
Mechanical (Translational)		
Velocity	v	meter/sec
Force	f	newton
Damping constant	B_t	newton-sec/meter
Spring constant	K_t	newton/meter
Mass	M	kilogram
Mechanical (Rotational)		
Angular velocity	ω	radian/sec
Torque	τ	newton-meter
Damping constant	B_r	newton-meter-sec/radian
Spring constant	K_r	newton-meter/radian
Angular moment	J	newton-meter/radian/sec^2
Acoustical		
Differential pressure	p	newton/meter^2
Flow	vS	cu meter/sec
Resistance	R_a	newton-sec^2/meter^5
Inertial constant	M_a	newton-sec^2/meter^5
Capacitance	C_a	meter^5/newton
Thermal		
Differential temperature	t°	degree (°F)
Heat flow	Q	Btu/hr
Resistance	R_t	degree/Btu/hr
Capacitance	C_t	Btu/degree

PROBLEMS

Problem 11-1 Laplace transform analysis of force applied to mass

If a constant force F newtons is suddenly applied as shown in the Fig. 11-1, write the Laplace transform expression that would lead to a solution giving the instantaneous value of velocity of the 2-kilogram mass. Assume rolling friction is negligible.

Solution:

First draw the electrical circuit analog and then draw the corresponding transform network, including the excitation, which is a step function (see Fig. 11-2), and finally write the algebraic expression for the velocity, which is represented by a nodal voltage in the electrical circuit.

Nodal equations:

Node a:

$$\frac{F}{s} = (3s + 250)E_a \qquad - 250\ E_b$$

Node b:

$$0 = \qquad -250\ E_a + (2s + 250 + 1000/s)\ E_b \qquad - \frac{1000}{s} E_c$$

Node c:

$$0 = \qquad - \frac{1000}{s} E_b + (s + 500 + 1000/s)\ E_c$$

The capital letters represent the transforms of the nodal voltages.

$$E_b = \frac{\begin{vmatrix} 3s + 250 & F/s & 0 \\ -250 & 0 & -1000/s \\ 0 & 0 & s + 500 + 1000/s \end{vmatrix}}{\begin{vmatrix} 3s + 250 & -250 & 0 \\ -250 & 2s + 250 + 1000/s & -1000/s \\ 0 & -1000/s & s + 500 + 1000/s \end{vmatrix}}$$

$$= 41.7F \frac{s^2 + 500s + 1000}{s^5 + 708s^4 + 105{,}000s^3 + 500{,}000s^2 + 20.6 \times 10^6 s - 5.28 \times 10^6}$$

Using this expression and after factoring the denominator, resolving into partial fractions, and finding the inverse transform of the function E_b, the velocity of the 2-kilogram mass is known as a function of time. There would be insufficient time in an examination to perform the mathematics; however, the suggestion is obvious

Table 11-2 Analogous Expressions

	I	*II*	*III*	*IV*	*V*
Electrical	$e = Ri$	$e = R\frac{dq}{dt}$	$q = \frac{1}{R}\int e\,dt$		
		$e = L\frac{di}{dt}$	$i = \frac{1}{L}\int e\,dt$	$e = L\frac{d^2q}{dt^2}$	$q = \frac{1}{L}\int\left[\int e\,dt\right]dt$
	$q = Ce$	$i = C\frac{de}{dt}$	$e = \frac{1}{C}\int i\,dt$		
Mechanical[1] (Translation)	$f = Ma$	$f = M\frac{dv}{dt}$	$v = \frac{1}{M}\int f\,dt$	$f = M\frac{d^2x}{dt^2}$	$x = \frac{1}{M}\int\left[\int f\,dt\right]dt$
	$f = K_t x$	$v = \frac{1}{K_t}\frac{df}{dt}$	$f = K_t\int v\,dt$	$a = \frac{1}{K_t}\frac{d^2f}{dt^2}$	$f = K_t\int\left[\int a\,dt\right]dt$
	$f = B_t v$	$f = B_t\frac{dx}{dt}$	$x = \frac{1}{B_t}\int f\,dt$		
		$a = \frac{1}{B_t}\frac{df}{dt}$	$f = B_t\int a\,dt$		
Mechanical[2] (Rotation)	$\tau = J\alpha$	$\tau = J\frac{d\omega}{dt}$	$\omega = \frac{1}{J}\int \tau\,dt$	$\tau = J\frac{d^2\theta}{dt^2}$	$\theta = \frac{1}{J}\int\left[\int \tau\,dt\right]dt$
	$\tau = B_r\omega$	$\tau = B_r\frac{d\theta}{dt}$	$\tau = B_r\int \alpha\,dt$		
		$\alpha = \frac{1}{B_r}\frac{d\tau}{dt}$	$\theta = \frac{1}{B_r}\int \tau\,dt$		
	$\tau = K_r\theta$	$\omega = \frac{1}{K_r}\frac{d\tau}{dt}$	$\tau = K_r\int \omega\,dt$	$\alpha = \frac{1}{K_r}\frac{d^2\tau}{dt^2}$	$\tau = K_r\int\left[\int \alpha\,dt\right]dt$

Acoustical[3]	$xS = C_a p$	$vS = C_a \frac{dp}{dt}$	$p = \frac{1}{C_a}\int (vS)\,dt$	$aS = C_a \frac{d^2p}{dt^2}$	$p = \frac{1}{C_a}\int\left[\int aS\,dt\right]dt$
	$p = R(vS)$	$aS = \frac{1}{R}\frac{dp}{dt}$	$p = R\int (aS)\,dt$		
		$p = R\frac{d(xS)}{dt}$	$xS = \frac{1}{R}\int p\,dt$		
	$p = M_a(aS)$	$p = M_a\frac{d(vS)}{dt}$	$vS = \frac{1}{M_a}\int p\,dt$	$p = M_a\frac{d^2(xS)}{dt^2}$	$xS = \frac{1}{Ma}\int\left[\int p\,dt\right]dt$
Thermal[4]	$t^\circ = R_t Q$	$Q = C_t\frac{dt^\circ}{dt}$	$t_0 = \frac{1}{C_t}\int Q\,dt$		

[1] a = acceleration, meters/sec^2
x = distance, meters
M = analogous to electrical capacitance and must be considered when velocity is varied
B_t = analogous to electrical conductance and is encountered with a dashpot
K_t = analogous to the reciprocal of electrical inductance and is associated with a spring Friction, which frequently is a variant with velocity, must be ignored or considered a constant of proportionality between force and velocity to make this analogy valid.

[2] α = angular acceleration, radians/sec^2
θ = angle of rotation, radians
J = analogous to electrical capacitance
B_r = analogous to electrical conductance and is encountered with a viscous damping medium opposing angular rotation
$1/K_r$ = analogous to electrical resistance inductance and is related to the torsional resistance of a shaft

[3] S = cross-sectional area of flow path, meters^2
x = length of flow path, meters
a = acceleration, meters/sec^2
M = inertance = x/S if the density of medium is in kg/meter^3
Inertance is encountered in accelerating a fluid mass, as in a long narrow tube
Capacitance is associated with a large volume chamber
Resistance is the opposition to pressure waves, such as encountered with a perforated membrane

[4] $1/R_t$ = overall heat transfer coefficient across the barrier and area concerned. In some cases, R_t cannot be assumed as a constant coefficient and in such cases this analogy is invalid.

that once an electrical circuit model is set up, an oscillograph would disclose the waveform. By following rules for model theory, practical component sizes and magnitude of the excitation can be selected.

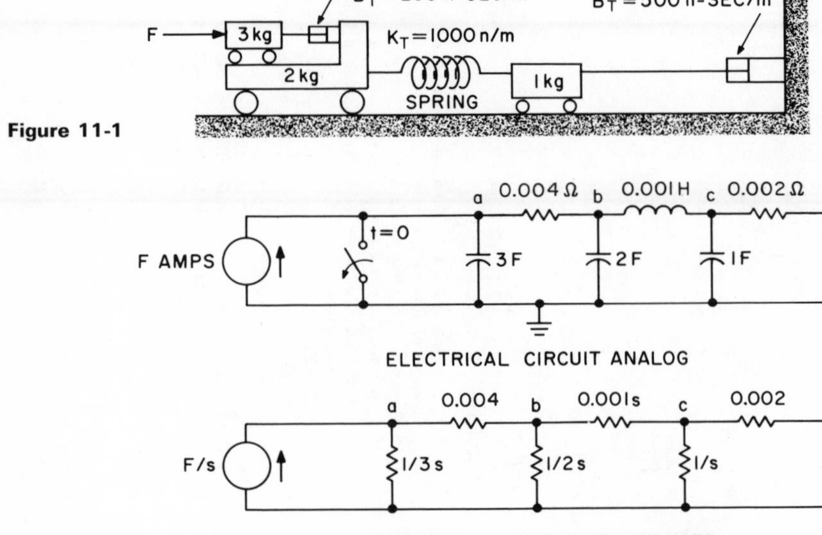

Figure 11-1

Figure 11-2

Problem 11-2 Electrical analog of weights on springs

A velocity of 3 sin ωt meters/sec is applied vertically at point N in Fig. 11-3. Express the necessary relationship between K_2 and M_2 to prevent M_1 from vibrating.

Solution:

If M_1 is to be motionless, then there is no potential across (or current through) the capacitor that represents M_1 in the electrical analog (since velocity is analogous to potential). Therefore, solve for current through C_1 and let it equal zero. I_{C1} is the difference between mesh currents. See Fig. 11-4.

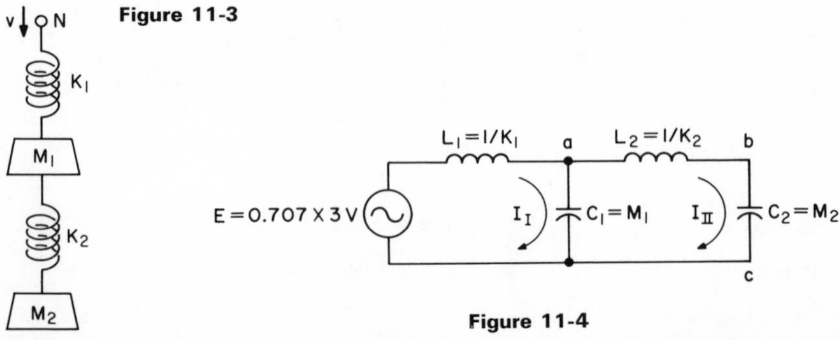

Figure 11-3

Figure 11-4

Another viewpoint is: for current through C_1 to be zero, C_1 must be short-circuited; $Z_{abc} = 0$.

$$Z_{abc} = j(\omega L_2 - 1/\omega C_2) = 0$$
$$L_2 = 1/\omega^2 C_2$$
$$K_2 = \omega^2 M_2 \qquad \textit{Answer}$$

Problem 11-3 Electrical analog of gas pressure flow through piping

Gases at constant inlet pressure flow through the piping arrangement shown in Fig. 11-5, exhausting to the atmosphere. Suddenly, the inlet pressure is reduced to atmospheric pressure. Draw the electrical circuit analog for this system and the transform admittance diagram. Give the values of the electrical parameters in terms of the piping system parameters.

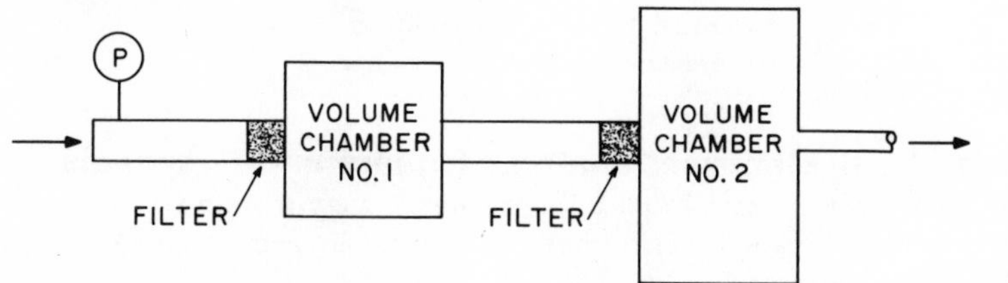

Figure 11-5

Solution:

This is essentially a switching circuit analogy for an acoustical system. Note that prior to $t = 0$, the volume flow rate (current in the electrical analog) is constant and equal to $P/(R_1 + R_2)$. Adiabatic flow is assumed.

See Figs. 11-6 and 11-7, for the electrical circuit analog and for the transfer admittance diagram, respectively.

From Figs. 11-6 and 11-7,

$E = P$ volts (P is the gauge pressure in MKS units equal to 0.145×10^{-3} psig)
$I_0 = E/(R_1 + R_2)$ amperes = cu meters/sec through the piping
$V'_0 = E - R_1 I_0$ volts
$V''_0 = E - (R_1 + R_2)I_0$ volts
$L = M$ henrys (M is the inertial constant of the gas in the piping and is equal to $\rho_0 l/S$, ρ_0 is the density of the gas in the piping, l is the length of the pipe, and S is the cross-sectional area of the pipe)
$C = C_a$ farads (C_a is the acoustical capacitance of the volume chamber and is equal to $P_0\gamma/V_0$, γ is c_p/c_v (=1.14 for air), P_0 and V_0 are the conditions of the

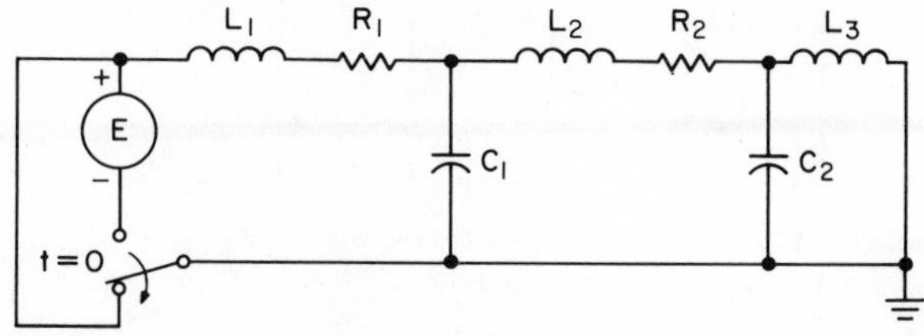

Figure 11-6. Electrical circuit analog.

gas entering the chamber. C_a is considered a constant of the chamber for a particular gas.)

$R = R_a$ ohms (R_a is the pressure drop per unit volume flow and is considered to be constant for a particular barrier or filter for a given gas)

All units should be in the same system for compatibility.

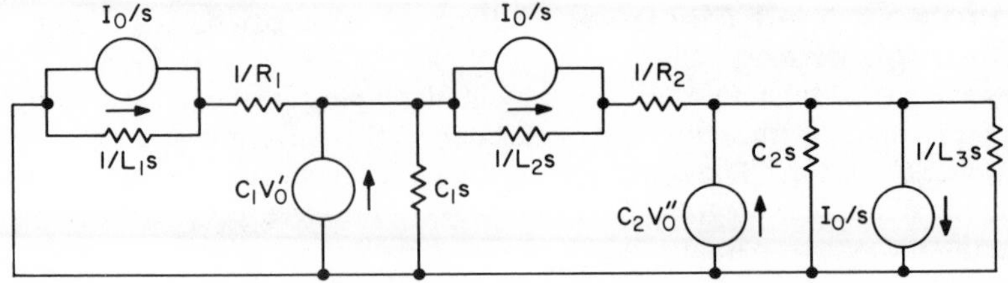

Figure 11-7. Transform admittance diagram.

Problem 11-4 Electrical analog of gears and flywheels

At 180 rpm, it has been observed that a second harmonic vibration occurs in the shaft of Fig. 11-8, presumably due to imperfections in the gear design. In which flywheel will this be more apparent?

For the shaft,

$K_1 = 500$ newton-meters/radian $\quad J_1 = 0.005$ newton-meter/radian/sec^2

$K_2 = 250$ newton-meters/radian $\quad J_2 = 0.010$ newton-meter/radian/sec^2

$K_3 = 200$ newton-meters/radian $\quad B_r = 0.5$ newton-meter/radian/sec

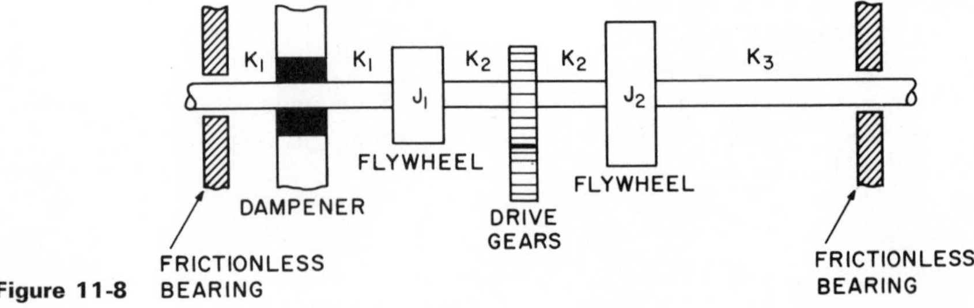

Figure 11-8

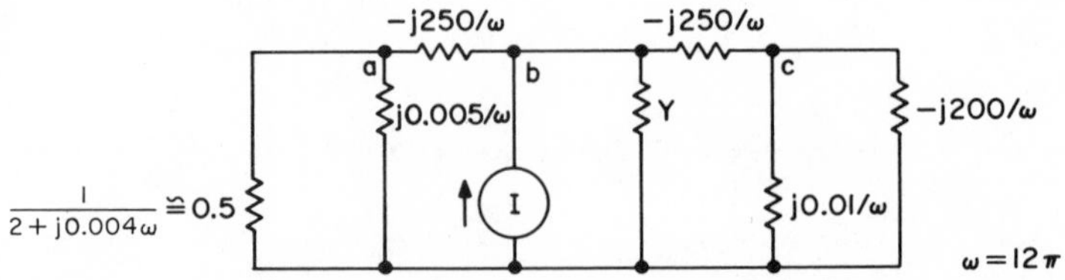

$-j250/\omega$ $\quad -j250/\omega$ $\quad$ a $\quad$ b $\quad$ c $\quad j0.005/\omega$ $\quad$ Y $\quad -j200/\omega$ $\quad \frac{1}{2+j0.004\omega} \cong 0.5$ $\quad$ I $\quad j0.01/\omega$ $\quad \omega = 12\pi$

Figure 11-9. Electrical analog circuit (admittance values shown in mhos)

Solution:

The problem, reduced to the electrical analog circuit, is to determine the voltage across the capacitors when a sinusoidal voltage (i.e., angular velocity) is inserted. See Fig. 11-9. The amplitudes of the nodal voltages are analogous to the swings in angular velocity (from normal) of the flywheels. Note that the magnitude of the vibrational excitation is unknown and is represented by a voltage source with a series impedance (or a current source with a shunt admittance).

$$E_a = \frac{\begin{vmatrix} 0 & -j6.46 & 0 \\ I & Y - j13.3 & j6.65 \\ 0 & j6.65 & -j11.57 \end{vmatrix}}{|\Delta|} = 74.7I \text{ volts}$$

$$E_b = \frac{\begin{vmatrix} 0.5 & -j6.46 & 0 \\ j6.65 & Y - j13.3 & I \\ 0 & j6.65 & 0 \end{vmatrix}}{|\Delta|} = j3.32I$$

Therefore, the vibration of flywheel J, will be appreciably greater. *Answer*. Note that the vibration waveforms are out of phase by 90°.

chapter 12
MISCELLANEOUS PROBLEMS

The following problems are those that are of a general engineering nature or are not representative of everyday professional electrical engineering problems.

Problem 12-1 Economics of hauling coal to electric generating station (electro-mechanical conversion)

Material is to be hauled 6 miles from a pit. The desirability of doing this with an electric locomotive hauling a train of cars is being studied. The locomotive should be capable of hauling 10 cars, each weighing 15 tons loaded, up a 2% grade at 15 miles/hr. The mechanical efficiency is about 50%. If the electricity will cost \$0.0098 per kWh, how much will it cost to convey a ton of material?

Solution:

Use 1 ton = 2000 lb
Time to travel 6 miles = 24 min
Vertical lift in 6 miles = 0.12 miles

$$\text{hp} = \frac{\text{ft-lb/min}}{33{,}000}$$

$$= \frac{2000 \times 0.12 \times 5280}{24 \times 33{,}000 \times 0.50} = 3.18$$

$$\text{Cost per ton} = \$0.0098 \times 0.746 \times 3.18 \times 24/60$$

$$= \$0.0093/\text{ton} \qquad \textit{Answer}$$

Problem 12-2 Calculation of kW necessary to operate a water still (electro-thermal conversion)

The rating of heating elements is to be specified for a continuously operating water still that will supply 10 gal/hr of distilled water. The intake water is first passed through the condenser where it is brought to boiling and then sent to the evaporating chambers. Approximately 10 percent of the power required for evaporation will be lost through the insulated walls of the still. Specify the rating of the heating elements required for the still.

Solution:
Since the electrical input is used solely for evaporating 10 gal/hr of water at saturation temperature and for supplying losses, all heat transfer external to the evaporator is irrelevant.

Latent heat of evaporation = 960 Btu/lb
One gallon = 8.31 lb
One Btu = 0.292×10^{-3} kWh

$$\text{Input} = 1.1 \times 10 \times 8.31 \times 960 \times 0.292 \times 10^{-3}$$
$$= 25.6 \text{ kW} \qquad \textit{Answer}$$

Problem 12-3 Chain rectifier circuit

In the circuit shown in Fig. 12-1, the voltage across the transformer secondary has an rms value E.

(a) Indicate the polarity of each capacitor.
(b) State the voltage across each capacitor.
(c) State the voltage from each capacitor to ground.
(d) State the peak-inverse voltage across each diode.
(e) State the voltage between each cathode and its grounded heater.

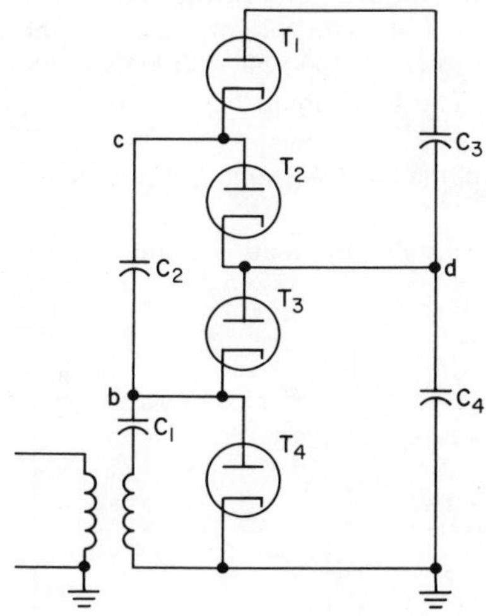

Figure 12-1

Solution:
This is known as a chain rectifier circuit. From the instant the circuit is energized, the charges on the capacitors progressively build up over several cycles. During the first half wave, capacitor C_1 *only* becomes charged! In Fig. 12-2, the dash line indicates no flow. C_1 becomes charged as shown.

During the second half wave, C_1 discharges 50 percent; C_4 charges as shown in Fig. 12-3.

This process continues until all capacitors are charged to 2E′ volts, except C_1. The potential of point d in Fig. 12-1 is −4E′ above ground. C_1 is charged to E′

and the potential from point b to ground alternates between −2E′ and zero. The final state will have negative polarity on the plates of the diodes. The peak inverse voltage across each diode varies from 2E′ to zero. See Fig. 12-4.

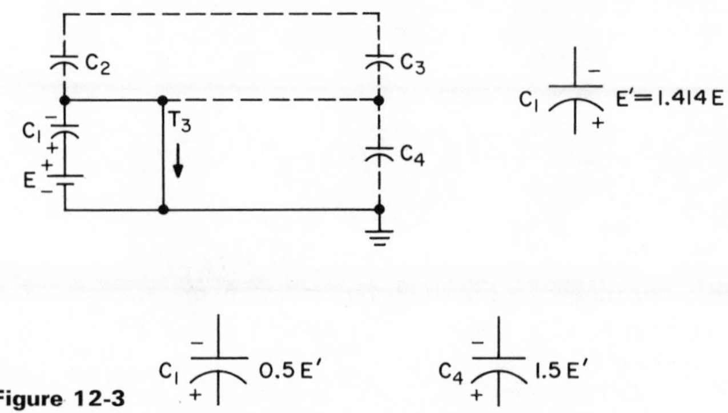

Figure 12-3

Problem 12-4 The magnetic amplifier

The magnetic amplifier shown in Fig. 12-5 controls the current in load R_L. Magnetic characteristics are also shown. The d-c control current is set and held constant at 50 milliamps in the direction shown. A 100-volt, 400-Hz source supplies the load circuit through an ideal diode. The load circuit has 200 turns. The load resistance is 5 ohms.

(a) Show the waveform of the load current. Indicate the conduction period and compute its angle.

(b) Compute the average value of the load current.

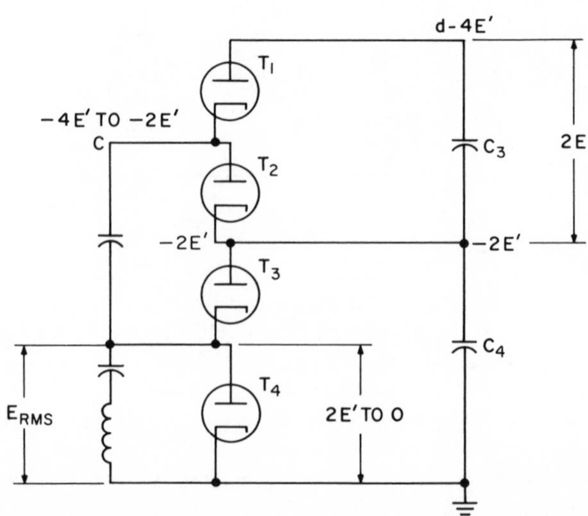

Figure 12-4

Solution:

In the unsaturated condition of the core, the load circuit has a considerable inductance (proportional to the permeability, which is constant). In the saturated condition (when flux reaches 30 kilolines), permeability is that of free space, and there is virtually no inductance; the diode "fires" (i.e., causes an appreciable current to flow).

(a) First, determine the firing angle. Firing occurs when

$$(NI)_{load} = 5$$
$$i_{load} = 0.025 \text{ amp}$$

With no saturation,

$$i_{max} = \sqrt{2}E/Z$$

where $Z = 5 + j\omega L$

$$\omega = 2\pi f = 2512$$

$$L\,\Delta i = N\,\Delta\phi \times 10^{-8}$$
$$L = 1.2 \text{ henry}$$
$$\omega L = 3015 \text{ ohms}$$
$$Z \cong 3015\ \underline{/90^\circ}$$
$$\therefore\ i_{max} = \frac{\sqrt{2} \times 100}{3015} = 0.0468 \text{ amp}$$
$$\begin{aligned} i_{load} &= 0.025 \text{ amp} \\ &= 0.0468 \sin(\omega t - 90^\circ) \\ &= 0.0468 \cos \omega t \\ \alpha = \omega t &= \cos^{-1} 0.535 \\ &= 57.6^\circ \\ &\cong 1 \text{ radian} \qquad \textit{Answer} \end{aligned}$$

A sine wave approximates the actual transient (see Fig. 12-6).
Second, find the reentrant angle.

$$\begin{aligned} i_{load} &= \frac{E_{max} \sin \omega t}{5 \text{ ohms}} = 0.025 \text{ amp} \\ &= \frac{2 \times 100 \sin \omega t}{5};\ \omega t \cong \pi \qquad \textit{Answer} \end{aligned}$$

(b) Finally, determine load current.

$$\begin{aligned} i_{avg} &= \frac{1}{\pi - 1} \int_1^\pi i_{max} \sin \omega t\, d\omega t \\ &= 6.15 \text{ amps} \qquad \textit{Answer} \end{aligned}$$

Problem 12-5 Pulse transmission

A rectangular voltage pulse of time duration T is shown in Fig. 12-7(A). Certain possible responses are shown in Fig. 12-7(B), (C), (D), and (E).

Indicate which illustration corresponds to transmission of the original signal through:

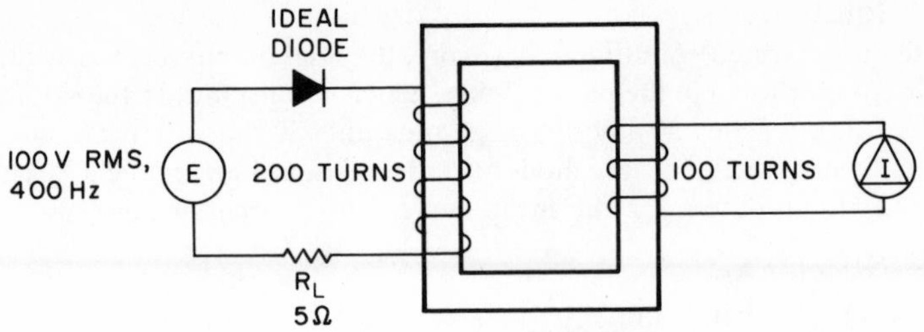

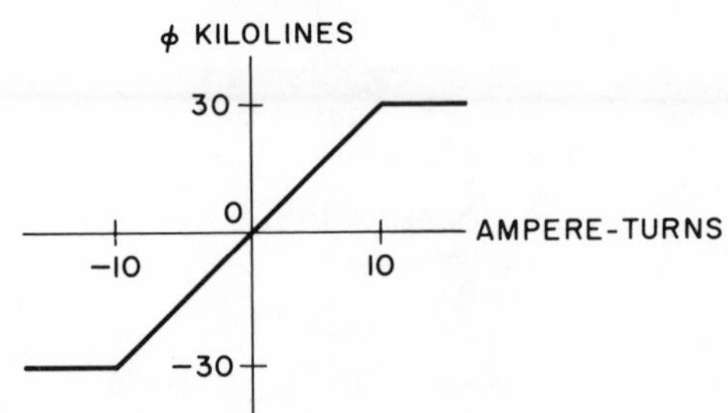

Figure 12-5

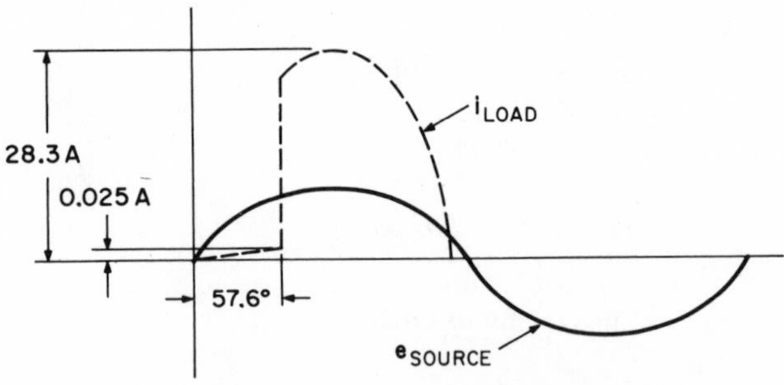

Figure 12-6

(a) A wideband channel with a linear phase-vs.-frequency characteristic.
(b) A physically unrealizable network.
(c) A narrowband channel.
(d) A wideband channel with a nonlinear phase-vs.-frequency characteristic.
(e) A purely resistive network.

Solution:

The Fourier analysis of this rectilinear waveform input signal shows the waveform to be the sum of a steady (d-c) component, a fundamental, and odd harmonics only. Using the t = 0 reference point in the problem, the waveform equation is

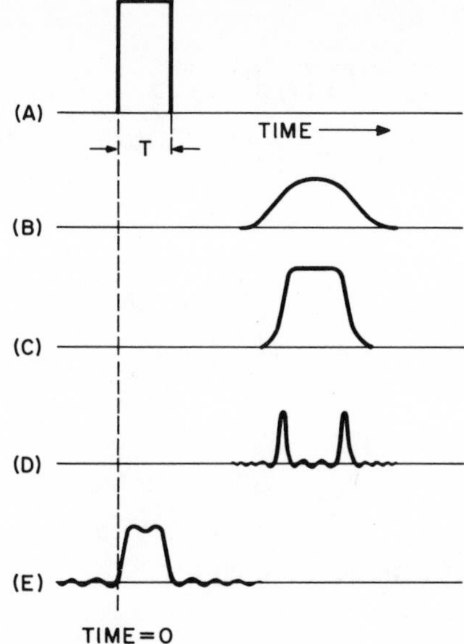

Figure 12-7

$$f(t) = A + \frac{4A}{\pi}\cos\left(\theta - \frac{T}{T_0}\pi\right) - \frac{4A}{3\pi}\cos\left(3\theta - \frac{T}{T_0}\pi\right) + \cdots$$

where T_0 = period = $2\pi t/T_0$ radians

$$A = \frac{T}{T_0} \times \text{(amplitude of the original pulse)}.$$

By observation, the following can be deduced:

Figure 12-7(A) is the response through a purely resistive network, since no components are filtered *Answer, part (e).*

Figure 12-7(B) is the response through a narrowband channel that permits only the fundamental to pass *Answer, part (c).*

Figure 12-7(D) is physically unrealizable *Answer, part (b).*

Figure 12-7(C) is the response through a network having a nonlinear phase-vs.-frequency characteristic *Answer, part (d).*

Figure 12-7(E) is the response through a network having a linear phase-vs.-frequency relationship *Answer, part (a).*

The complete mathematical explanation of the above solution can be made by the frequency response method of analysis, which is beyond the scope of this book. Recommended is *Principles of Electrical Engineering* by V. Del Toro (Prentice-Hall, Inc.).

appendix UNITS, CONVERSION CONSTANTS, AND FORMULAS

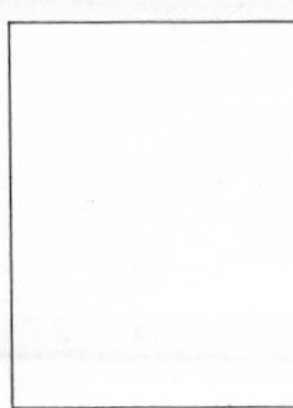

A-1 UNITS AND CONVERSION CONSTANTS

Force

1 newton = 0.225 lb = 0.102 kg = 10^5 dynes

Torque

1 newton-meter = 0.738 lb-ft

1 kilogram-meter = 7.23 lb-ft

1 pound-foot = 0.1383 kg-meter

Inertial Moment

1 kilogram-meter^2 = 23.7 lb-ft^2

Power

1 horsepower = 0.746 kilowatt

Energy

1 hp-hr = 2545 Btu

1 kWh = 3413 Btu

1 joule (watt-second) = 0.738 ft-lb

1 joule = 8.856 in.-lb

Length

1 meter = 3.28 ft

= 39.4 in.

Volume

1 gallon (USA) = 0.835 gal (Imperial)

Pressure

1 pound per square inch = 2.31 ft water

1 atmosphere = 14.7 lb/sq in.

1 kilogram per cm^2 = 14.2 lb/sq in.

Magnetic flux

1 weber = 10^8 maxwells (lines)

Magnetomotive Force

1 pragilbert = 0.1 gilbert

1 ampere-turn = 1.257 gilberts

	MKS System			
	"Practical"	*"Rationalized"*	*CGS System*	*English System*
Flux (Φ)	weber	weber	maxwell	maxwell
Mmf ($\mathfrak{F}$)	pragilbert	ampere-turn	gilbert	ampere-turn
Permeability (of air) (μ_0)	10^{-7}	4×10^{-7}	1.0	3.192
Force (f)	newton	newton	dyne	pound
Energy (W)	joule	joule	erg	inch-pound
Length (L)	meter	meter	centimeter	inch
Area (A)	$meter^2$	$meter^2$	$centimeter^2$	$inch^2$

A-2 FREQUENTLY USED FORMULAS

Energy in a magnetic field.

$W = \mathfrak{F}\,\phi/8\pi$ joules, using the practical MKS system

$= \frac{1}{2}\,\mathfrak{F}\,\phi$ joules, using the rationalized MKS system

$= 4.43 \times 10^{-8}\,\mathfrak{F}\,\phi$ in.-lb, using the English system.

Energy contained in a rotating mass.

$$W = \frac{0.231 \times J \times (\text{rpm})^2}{1000} \text{ joules}$$

where J = inertial moment in lb-ft^2

Torque.

$$\text{Torque (ft-lb)} = \frac{5250}{\text{rpm}} \times \text{horsepower}$$

Force exerted by a magnetic field in air.

$f = \beta^2 A/2\mu_0$ newtons, using the rationalized MKS system.

$= \beta^2 A/8\pi\mu_0$ newtons, using the practical MKS system.

$= \dfrac{0.0443 \times 10^{-6}\beta^2 A}{\mu_0}$ lb, using the English system, where β is the flux density

ECONOMICS AND ETHICS

chapter 1

ENGINEERING ECONOMY

1-1 TOPICS COVERED IN ENGINEERING ECONOMY

Engineering economics, as a discipline, includes those techniques that are useful in the comparison of engineering alternatives. More specifically, most of the chapters that follow are devoted to the use of compound interest and methods that derive from interest, such as annual cost determinatives, present valuation, rate of return and break-even analyses, incremental analysis, etc.

There is more to engineering economy than use of interest formulas, however. Decision-making requires careful assessment of the engineering information as well as correct use of economic analysis. Knowledge of depreciation theory and techniques, income tax regulations, and accounting is also essential. Each of these items is covered to the extent necessary for solution of problems found by professional engineers and candidates for the license.

1-2 RELATIONSHIP TO ENGINEERING

It is essential to point out that engineering decisions always involve costs. Also, cost decisions involve engineering. A first step in the solution of any problem is to determine the alternatives. Complete knowledge of the engineering involved is certainly essential in establishing alternatives.

All cost decisions presuppose a correct selection of alternatives. This can be accomplished only if the engineer thoroughly understands his field and has sufficient imagination to include all possibilities for consideration.

1-3 RELATIONSHIP TO ACCOUNTING

Engineering economy uses the same type of cost data as accounting, but the purposes and techniques are vastly different. Accounting basically is concerned with recording, grouping, and reporting financial occurrences in a form useful to management, credit officers, and other interested groups. The data used is usually historical and the reports, such as balance sheets and income statements, are barometers of financial health.

The primary purpose of engineering economy is to develop techniques that can be used in decision-making concerning future income and expenditures. A typical engineering economy analysis will use accounting data, market analysis, and other available information along with specialized techniques to forecast differences among alternatives.

Several topics normally considered to be within the province of accounting are covered because they have been included in various license examinations.

1-4 ROLE OF INTEREST IN ENGINEERING ECONOMY

Interest is a factor in engineering economy because all expenditures and income do not occur simultaneously. The usual case would involve a large expenditure at the start of a project, smaller expenditures throughout the life of the project, and income received at various times after the start.

The date that money is spent or received is of great consequence. An expenditure today is not the same as an expenditure of an identical amount at some time in the future. Money available at the present can earn interest and will therefore amount to a greater sum in the future. Money to be received in the future will not benefit from interest earned between now and then.

In the solution of any problem in which income and expenditure occur at different times, interest must be considered. Failure to do so will result in incorrect solutions.

1-5 SOME DEFINITIONS

In order to use interest correctly in the solution of problems, it will be necessary to define some terms and introduce several formulas.

Interest: payment for the use of money.

Interest rate: the ratio, usually expressed as a percentage, of the amount paid at the end of a period of time and the amount of money owed at the start of the period.

Interest period: the time period for which the interest rate is applied.

Principal: the amount of money outstanding at the start of an interest period.

Simple interest: Where money is borrowed for a number of periods, interest is paid only on the amount of the original principal. Interest is not paid on accumulated interest. This is rarely used.

Compound interest: interest paid on the principal and on any accumulated interest.

Nominal interest rate: an annual rate expressed as a simple product of the rate for a smaller period multiplied by the number of these periods in a year. Thus, with a 1% interest rate for three months, the nominal annual rate would be 4%.

Effective interest rate: the actual annual rate determined from the rate for a shorter period.

If we use i as the interest rate for the short period and n as the number of periods (in this case in each year), then

$$\text{Effective rate} = (1 + i)^n - 1$$

1-6 NONINTEREST RATE PROBLEMS

Most problems that appear on license examinations require the use of interest. Occasionally, however, a problem is offered that does not. This type of problem does not involve delays between expenditures and income.

Problem 1-1 Cost alternants in chemical plant as influenced by material, freight, handling, and dilution components

A plant requires 50 lb of anhydrous NaOH as a 40% aqueous solution per ton of product made.

Caustic soda may be purchased as 50% or 73% solution or 98% solid at \$0.039, \$0.042, and \$0.048 per pound, respectively, of pure 100% NaOH contained. Railroad freight costs are \$0.01 per pound net as shipped for all grades. Handling and diluting costs are \$0.004 times the fractional concentration of the grade purchased per pound of final diluted mixture.

What are the costs involved for each grade per ton of product made?

Solution:

The solution to this problem involves the calculation of three different costs for each grade.

1. Material costs: 50 lb × \$(0.039/lb, 0.042/lb, 0.048/lb), respectively, for the three grades
2. Freight costs: \$0.01 × (100 lb, 67.5 lb, 51 lb)
3. Handling and diluting costs: \$0.004 × (0.50, 0.73, 0.98) × 125, where final diluted mixture is 50 lb/0.40 = 125 lb

Summing the costs, we have

	50%	73%	98%
Material	\$1.95	\$2.10	\$2.40
Freight	1.00	0.67	0.51
Handling	0.30	0.44	0.59
	\$3.25	\$3.21	\$3.50

chapter 2
INTEREST PROBLEMS

2-1 FORMULAS AND EQUIVALENCE

Solution of engineering economy problems requires the establishment of relationships among (a) present value (P), (b) sum at the end of a number of periods (S), and (c) a uniform end of period amount (K). The symbol used for interest rate is i and for number of periods is n.

The three basic formulas are

$$S = P(1 + i)^n \tag{2-1}$$

$$S = K\left[\frac{(1 + i)^n - 1}{i}\right] \tag{2-2}$$

$$P = K\left[\frac{(1 + i)^n - 1}{i(1 + i)^n}\right] \tag{2-3}$$

Reciprocals of these factors can be used to obtain P or K, given S; and K, given P.

These formulas allow money to be expressed in terms of other amounts at other times. Thus, an amount today can be converted into an equivalent amount at some time in the future, at some interest rate. The two amounts are not equal, in terms of exactness, but they are *equivalent.* One can be exchanged for another, with no inequity, if the interest rate used is acceptable. Thus, \$10,000 today is equivalent to \$17,910 ten years from today, if the interest rate is 6%.

Similarly, sums can be converted into uniform series that are equivalent—\$10,000 today is equivalent to \$1359 a year for the next 10 years, if the interest rate is 6%.

Understanding the use of these formulas is of great importance in engineering economy.

2-2 USE OF TABLES

It is usually not necessary to substitute in the formulas in order to obtain solutions. Tables have been provided in the Appendix which give values for the factors directly, for most interest rates and periods used.

These tables will be used extensively in the problems solved in the remainder of this book.

2-3 SOLVING FOR AN ACCUMULATED SUM

In this type of problem, a present value or principal, interest rate, and number of periods are given and the sum is sought.

Problem 2-1 Final value of principal with fixed interest added for a given number of years

Calculate the following correct to the third place: the value, at the end of eight years, of $10,000 placed on deposit today at 7% interest.

Solution:

Using Eq. (2-1),

$$S = P(1 + i)^n = 10{,}000(1.07)^8$$

From Table A-1, we find $(1.07)^8 = 1.718$

$$\therefore S = 17{,}180$$

To the third place, S = $17,200 *Answer*

2-4 SOLVING FOR PRESENT VALUE

If present value is sought, given a sum after n periods, and an interest rate i, the reciprocal of Eq. (2–1) is used.

Problem 2-2 Present worth of single future sum based on fixed interest

Calculate correct to the third place, the present worth of a single payment of $5000 to be made 5 years from now, with interest at 6%.

Solution:

$$P = S\left[\frac{1}{(1 + i)^n}\right]$$

$$= 5000\left[\frac{1}{(1.06)^5}\right] = 5000\left(\frac{1}{1.338}\right)$$

$$= 5000(0.7473) = \$3736$$

To the third place, P = $3740 *Answer*

2-5 UNIFORM ANNUAL SERIES

In addition to converting a present value into its equivalent value at a future date, and finding the present value of some future sum, it is also necessary to work with uniform periodic (usually annual) series. Equations (2-2) and (2-3) and their reciprocals allow direct conversion to and from uniform series.

A word of caution must be expressed about the use of these formulas. Certain "ground rules" must be observed concerning the location in time of the starting and terminating payment in a series relative to the present value and sum. In deriving Eq. (2-2) and Eq. (2-3), the first payment was one period after the date of the present value. The final payment was on the date of the sum. Figure 2-1 illustrates this relationship graphically.

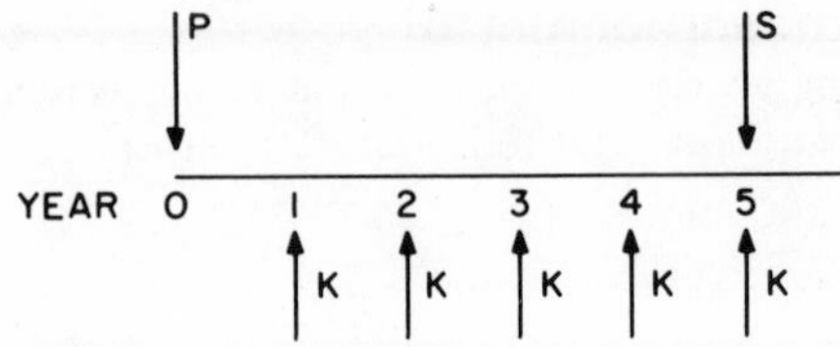

Figure 2–1.

Whenever the formulas, and the tables derived from the formulas, are used, it is necessary to keep this in mind. Present values and sums can be found at other dates, of course, but this requires use of a combination of formulas.

It should be noted that in series formulas n refers to the number of *payments,* since no two terms will earn interest for the same number of periods.

Problem 2-3 Uniform annual payment required to amortize a debt

Calculate the uniform annual payment required to amortize a debt of $20,000 in 10 years with interest at 4%.

Solution:

$$K = P\left[\frac{i(1+i)^n}{(1+i)^n - 1}\right] \qquad \text{[reciprocal of Eq. (2-3)]}$$

$$= \$20{,}000\left(\frac{1}{8.111}\right)$$

$$= \$2460 \qquad \textit{Answer}$$

Problem 2-4 Final sum of annual deposits with interest

Calculate the amount realized at the end of 13 years through annual deposits of $1000, with interest at 3%.

Solution:

$$S = K\left[\frac{(1+i)^n - 1}{i}\right] \tag{2-2}$$

$$= \$1000(15.62)$$

$$= \$15{,}620 \qquad \textit{Answer}$$

Introduction of the uniform series concept permits solution of problems more complex than those illustrated above.

Problem 2-5 Final sum of annual stock purchases accounting for fixed dividends, appreciation, and taxes

An engineer is considering investing \$2000 per year in common stocks. It is estimated that the stocks will pay dividends of 4% per year, 25% of which will have to be paid annually as federal income tax thereon. The balance of the annual dividends will be reinvested annually in the same stocks. Assume no state taxes. The engineer also estimates that the stocks will appreciate in value at the rate of 5% per year. How much would he have, before paying any capital gains taxes, if he sold all of the stocks at the end of 25 years?

Solution:

Of the 4% dividend received each year, ¼ or 1% will be immediately paid in federal taxes, leaving 3% for the engineer. The appreciation in value of the stock of 5% each year will have exactly the same effect as the dividend, resulting in total interest of 8% per year.

After 25 years, before capital gains taxes, he will have

$$S = K\left[\frac{(1+i)^n - 1}{i}\right] = 2000(73.11) = \$146{,}220 \qquad \textit{Answer}$$

This solution assumes that the first investment will be made at the end of the year.

Problem 2-6 Seventeen-year annual deposits to pay four-year college education starting in the eighteenth year

An engineer desires to establish a fund for his newborn son's college education. He estimates the needs will be \$2500 on the son's 18th, 19th, 20th, and 21st birthdays. The fund is to receive a lump sum of \$2000 on the day of the son's birth and a fixed amount on the son's first through 17th birthdays, inclusive.

If the fund earns 3½% per annum, what should the annual deposit be?

Solution:

\$2500 on the son's 18th, 19th, 20th, and 21st birthdays represents a uniform annual series. A present value can be found which is equivalent to this series at the son's 17th birthday from

$$P = K\left[\frac{(1+i)^n - 1}{i\,(1+i)^n}\right] = 2500(3.673) = \$9182$$

Part of the \$9182 will be covered by the initial deposit of \$2000 and the interest this amount has earned for 17 years.

$$\begin{aligned} S &= P(1+i)^n = 2000(1.035)^{17} \\ &= 2000(1.795) = \$3590 \end{aligned}$$

The balance needed at the 17th birthday is \$9182 − \$3590, or \$5592. \$5592 must be built up by annual deposits on the son's first through 17th birthdays.

$$K = S\left[\frac{i}{(1+i)^n - 1}\right]$$

$$= 5592\left(\frac{1}{22.71}\right)$$

$$= \$246 \quad \textit{Answer}$$

Problem 2-7 Twenty-year annual deposits to pay fixed costs beginning the tenth year

Chemical plant facilities, estimated to have a life of 20 years, are to be constructed. The facilities will require no maintenance for the first ten years, but will require \$2000 per year for the second ten years. How much must be invested annually at 3½% interest during the life of the facilities to pay maintenance costs?

Solution:

A 10-year series, starting at the end of year 11 (unless otherwise stated, payments are assumed at the end of the period), must be converted into an equivalent 20-year series.

First, find the sum of the 10-year series.

$$S = K_1\left[\frac{(1+i)^n - 1}{i}\right] = 2000(11.73) = \$23{,}460$$

The 20-year series must have the same sum, since the two series must be equivalent.

$$\therefore K_2 = S\left[\frac{i}{(1+i)^n - 1}\right] = 23{,}460\left(\frac{1}{28.28}\right)$$

$$= \$840 \quad \textit{Answer}$$

2-6 SOLVING FOR AN UNKNOWN INTEREST RATE

The interest rate earned in a series of transactions can be determined if n is known and all payments and receipts are also known.

Problem 2-8 Rate of return on investment computed from buying and selling price, and time

\$1800 was invested in a lot on December 31, 1965. It was sold on December 31, 1970 for \$3000. What rate of return was earned in this investment?

Solution:

Equation (2-1) establishes a relationship between S and P:

$$S = P(1+i)^n$$

Substituting known values in this formula,

$$3000 = 1800(1 + i)^5$$

$$(1 + i)^5 = 1.667$$

From Table A-1, i is between 10% and 11%. By interpolation, i = 10.76% *Answer.*

Problems of a more complex nature concerning determination of interest rate are presented in Sec. 5-8.

2-7 SOLVING FOR AN UNKNOWN LIFE

If sufficient information is given about other factors, an unknown life can be determined.

Problem 2-9 Annual scholarships awarded from fund consisting of principal, annual deposits, and interest

A technical society desires to award a $1200 scholarship annually to an engineering student for as long as its scholarship fund shall last. The fund was started July 1, 1969 by a gift of $6000. The society invested this sum at that time at 4% per annum and plans on adding $200 per year to the fund from its dues, starting July 1, 1970 for so long as awards are made.

(a) For how many years, starting July 1, 1970, can scholarships be awarded, and (b) what will be the balance in the fund after the last award is made?

Solution:

(a) $1200 is required every year starting in 1970. $200 will be provided from dues, therefore, $1000 must be withdrawn from the fund established by the gift. The number of years that $1000 can be withdrawn can be found from Eq. (2-3).

$$P = K\left[\frac{(1 + i)^n - 1}{i\,(1 + i)^n}\right]$$

$$6000 = 1000\left[\frac{(1.04)^n - 1}{0.04(1.04)^n}\right]$$

$$\frac{(1.04)^n - 1}{0.04\,(1.04)^n} = 6$$

From Table A-3, n lies between 6 and 7. (*Note:* Although 6 is very close to 6.002, the value of n = 7; a full 1000 will not be available in the seventh year.)

$\therefore n = 6$ *Answer*

(b) The balance in the fund after 6 years can be found by first finding the unused portion of the $6000 and then its value after 6 years.

$$P = K\left[\frac{(1 + i)^n - 1}{i\,(1 + i)^n}\right]$$

$$P = 1000\left[\frac{(1.04)^6 - 1}{0.04(1.04)^6}\right]$$
$$= \$5242$$

Therefore, \$758 was not used (\$6000 − \$5242). After 6 years, \$758 grew to

$$S = P(1 + i)^n = 758(1.04)^6$$
$$= \$960 \qquad \textit{Answer}$$

2-8 INTEREST COMPOUNDED ON OTHER THAN ANNUAL BASIS

The formulas presented in Sec. 2-1 are general and apply to any uniform interest periods. Most problems that appear on license examinations use annual interest periods. Problems do occasionally appear that have other period lengths. The same principles apply to these problems.

Problem 2-10 Uniform quarterly deposits in interest account to repay loan maturing in ten years

A man borrows \$10,000 from a private person under the following conditions. The principal is to be repaid in 10 years with interest compounded annually at 6%. To repay the loan systematically, the borrower intends to make a quarterly deposit in a savings bank where compound interest is computed quarterly at an annual rate of 2%. What should the quarterly deposit be?

Solution:

The amount that must be repaid in 10 years is

$$S = P(1 + i)^n = 10{,}000(1.06)^{10} = \$17{,}910$$

An annual interest rate of 2% compounded quarterly is 0.5% every three months. There are 40 such periods in 10 years. The amount which must be deposited at the end of each such period is

$$K = S\left[\frac{i}{(1 + i)^n - 1}\right] = 17{,}910\left(\frac{1}{44.16}\right)$$
$$= \$405 \qquad \textit{Answer}$$

chapter 3
DEPRECIATION

3-1 VARIETY OF MEANINGS

The word *depreciation* is used in several different technical fields, as well as in ordinary usage. It is therefore not surprising that a number of different meanings are associated with the word. It is, of course, important to know which usage is involved any time it is used.

An engineer, or other user of equipment, would probably define depreciation as the loss of value of equipment with use, or over a period of time. He might define depreciation as the difference in value between a new asset and the used asset currently in service.

An accountant, more concerned with record keeping, defines depreciation in terms of the charge to a particular year's operations for the use of the asset. He wants to "write off" the value of the asset over its expected life and charge each year with an appropriate share. It is not critical that at any time during the life of an asset its "real" or market value would differ from the accounting or "book" value.

The accountant's definition—the portion of asset cost attributable to a year or other production period—will be used in engineering economy. This is due to its wide acceptance and ease of use.

3-2 DETERMINING ASSET LIFE

In order to calculate depreciation, two factors are required: a depreciation technique and asset life. Several depreciation techniques are in common use and are described below.

Determination of asset life could involve many considerations. Historical data could be used. A forecast could be prepared based upon historical data, expected use, improvements, etc. Obsolescence is an important factor.

Federal tax regulations, however, are the most important considerations in determining asset life. Therefore the asset life used in determining depreciation is most often the life allowable under Federal Income Tax laws.

3-3 RELATIONSHIP TO INCOME TAXES

How does depreciation fit into the accounting methods used by industry? Why does a company bother with depreciation? Is this another form of governmental red tape or corporate tax avoidance?

Depreciation as an accounting concept far preceded the Federal Income Tax Law. Accounting techniques require that only income and expenses attributable to a year be used in determining profit for that year. Therefore, you cannot charge the entire cost of an asset to one year if the asset will last for 10 years. Its cost must be apportioned to each of the 10 years. This is the policy that was also adopted in the tax laws.

Federal tax laws have had a profound effect upon depreciation accounting. Rather than use separate accounts for tax purposes, most firms use allowable depreciation techniques for both tax and corporate purposes. Regulations regarding depreciation have been liberalized in recent years, both in regard to allowable asset life and depreciation technique. As depreciation is a legitimate expense, deductible from income, measures which increase allowable deductions decrease taxes.

3-4 STRAIGHT LINE METHOD

Federal tax regulations, in addition to specifying allowable accounting lives for many assets, also limit methods used in establishing depreciation charge in a given year to several acceptable techniques. The straight line method is the simplest and was, until 1954, the most widely used. Straight line depreciation, in any year, is the original cost (P) less the salvage value after n years (L), divided by the asset life (n):

$$\text{Depreciation} = \frac{P - L}{n} \tag{3-1}$$

Problem 3-1 Straight line depreciation of machine with given useful life and salvage value

Calculate the depreciated value after 6 years of a \$10,000 machine having a useful life of 10 years and a salvage value of 10% of its first cost at that time, using straight line depreciation.

Solution:

$P = \$10{,}000 \qquad L = \$1000 \text{ and } \qquad n = 10$

The depreciation charge each year is

$$\frac{10{,}000 - 1000}{10} = \$900$$

After 6 years, 6(\$900) = \$5400 has been depreciated. This leaves a value of \$4600 for the machine *Answer.*

Problem 3-2 Straight line depreciation of building and its equipment

An office building that cost, exclusive of its elevators and mechanical equipment, \$1,000,000.00 has an estimated useful life of 40 years and has no salvage value. Its elevators and mechanical equipment, which cost \$320,000.00, have an estimated useful life of 20 years and a salvage value of \$20,000.00. Using the straight line method of depreciation, determine the value of the building and its equipment at the end of 10 years' service.

Solution:

Building:

$$P = \$1{,}000{,}000 \qquad L = \$0 \qquad \text{and} \qquad n = 40$$

$$\text{Depreciation each year} = \frac{\$1{,}000{,}000}{40} = \$25{,}000$$

After 10 years: 10(\$25,000) = \$250,000 depreciation
Building value = \$1,000,000 − \$250,000 = \$750,000

Equipment:

$$P = \$320{,}000 \qquad L = \$20{,}000 \qquad \text{and} \qquad n = 20 \text{ years}$$

$$\text{Depreciation each year} = \frac{\$320{,}000 - \$20{,}000}{20} = \$15{,}000$$

After 10 years: 10(\$15,000) = \$150,000 depreciation
Equipment value = \$320,000 − \$150,000 = \$170,000

Total value = \$750,000 + \$170,000 = \$920,000 *Answer*

3-5 FIXED PERCENTAGE ON A DECLINING BALANCE METHOD

The 1954 revision to the Federal Income Tax law allowed two additional depreciation methods—Fixed Percentage on a Declining Balance and Sum of Years Digits—with a more rapid write-off available to firms using either technique. Both methods have been widely used since 1954.

The fixed percentage method uses, as does the straight line method, a fixed percentage charge each year. This method, however, uses the fixed percentage against the book value of the asset at the beginning of the period rather than against P.

If we take an asset with a cost of \$10,000 and a fixed percentage (i) of 10%, depreciation in year one will be \$1000, in year two the new balance would be \$9000 and depreciation \$900, and so on.

This formula can be used to determine book value, using the fixed percentage method:

$$\text{Book value} = P(1 - i)^{r} \tag{3-2}$$

where P is first cost, i is the fixed percentage, and r is the number of years elapsed since purchase date.

It should be noted that this method does not completely depreciate the asset after any finite number of years. Also, an independent salvage value cannot exist, since P and i will determine the value after any number of years. These do not deter use of the method.

Problem 3-3 Fixed percentage depreciation of asset having given life expectancy and salvage value

Calculate, correct to the third place, the depreciation charge for each year, using the fixed-percentage method, of an asset costing \$1000, having a life-expectancy of 5 years and an estimated salvage value of \$400.

Solution:

Referring to Eq. (3-2), the book value, P, and r are known. The unknown is i, the fixed percentage.

$$\begin{aligned}\text{Book value} &= P(1 - i)^r \\ \$400 &= \$1000(1 - i)^5 \\ (1 - i)^5 &= 0.4 \\ 1 - i &= 0.835 \\ i &= 0.165\end{aligned}$$

Depreciation charges:

$$\begin{aligned}\text{Year } 1 &= \$1000(0.165) = \$165 \\ 2 &= 835(0.165) = 138 \\ 3 &= 697(0.165) = 115 \\ 4 &= 582(0.165) = 96 \\ 5 &= 486(0.165) = 80\end{aligned}$$ *Answers*

3-6 SUM-OF-YEARS DIGITS METHOD

Depreciation in any year, in this method, is determined by multiplying (P − L) by a fraction. The denominator of the fraction is the sum of all digits from 1 through n (asset life). The numerator is (n − r + 1), where r is the year for which the depreciation charge is sought.

$$\text{Depreciation} = (P - L)\left[\frac{n - r + 1}{n + (n - 1) + \cdot \quad \cdot \quad \cdot + 1}\right]$$

Problem 3-4 Sum-of-integers depreciation of machine having given life expectancy and salvage value

Determine the book value at the end of 4 years of a machine costing \$20,000, having a serviceable life of 8 years and a salvage value of \$2000 at the end of that time, using the sum-of-integers, or sum-of-the-years, method.

Solution:

The book value will be the amount remaining after depreciation has been charged for 4 years. Depreciation in Year 1 will be

$$(\$20{,}000 - \$2000)\left(\frac{8}{8+7+6+5+4+3+2+1}\right)$$

In Year 2,

$$(\$20{,}000 - \$2000)\left(\frac{7}{8+7+6+5+4+3+2+1}\right) \quad \text{and so on}$$

For the first 4 years, therefore, the total depreciated will be

$$(\$20{,}000 - \$2000)\left(\frac{8+7+6+5}{8+7+6+5+4+3+2+1}\right) = \$13{,}000$$

Book value = \$20,000 − \$13,000 = \$7000 *Answer*

3-7 GROUP DEPRECIATION METHODS

Firms having many assets of the same type can avoid individual calculation of depreciation by use of a group method that depreciates all assets of the same type at one time. This method requires use of several conventions. An entire list, or schedule, of assets is depreciated at one time. Assets are added to the schedule as acquired and removed when retired from service. In the acquisition year and the retirement year, ½ of the normal charge is applied. This assumes an average acquisition date and retirement date of July 1 if calendar year accounting is used.

An important assumption, if this technique is used, is that the estimated asset life is correct on average and that there will be approximately a normal distribution of actual asset life around this average life.

3-8 ASSESSED VALUE, BOOK VALUE, AND MARKET VALUE

Asset valuation is required for a number of purposes and each purpose may evolve a different value. Commonly used valuations include:

Assessed value: the value used for property tax purposes. It is usually obtained by appraisal.

Book value: the value carried in the books of account of the firm. It is the acquisition cost less depreciation charged to date.

Market value: the amount that could be received for the asset from a willing buyer.

Other values that are used include scrap value, salvage value, and replacement value. Their definitions are apparent.

3-9 USE OF DEPRECIATION IN ENGINEERING ECONOMY

In engineering economy, all costs that are attributable to a proposed project must be included in the analysis. In many projects, where capital investment is large, a major cost is asset acquisition. These assets will wear down or depreciate during the life of the project. It is therefore essential in engineering economy studies to include as a cost that portion of the asset value that will be "consumed." Use of the annual cost method, covered in the next chapter, will require use of some form of depreciation in order to include in annual cost computations this asset consumption.

chapter 4
ANNUAL COST

4-1 CAPITAL RECOVERY

In Chapters 2 and 3, the basic tools of engineering economy—interest and depreciation—were covered. It is now possible to proceed to the solution of problems using these techniques.

A simplified engineering economy problem would typically contain first costs for the several alternatives, some costs that occur on an annual basis, and possibly others that occur on a nonrecurring basis. A comparison cannot be made by inspection, since payments occur at different times and therefore interest must be included. A solution is found by converting the given costs into a form that will permit comparison. The technique of capital recovery can be illustrated by a simple problem.

Problem 4-1 Equivalent annual cost of alternative plans for water storage

A refinery can provide for water storage with a steel tank on a steel tower adjacent to the plant or a concrete standpipe on a hill some distance away. The elevated tank is estimated to cost $82,000, while the standpipe and extra length of service line is estimated to cost $60,000. The standpipe installation will require an additional capital expenditure of $6000 for pumps and controls. Operating and maintenance costs for the pumps and standpipe is estimated at $500 per year. The maintenance cost of the elevated tank is estimated to be $150 per year.

Using an interest rate of 5%, a life of 30 years, and assuming no salvage value, compute the equivalent annual cost for each plan.

Solution:

Each plan above has a first cost and an annual maintenance cost. Due to the time value of money, they cannot be combined directly. The technique of annual cost involves the conversion of all costs that are not on an annual basis to annual costs. First, consider the elevated tank. It costs $82,000 and will last 30 years. It must be depreciated over its 30-year life. Also, the fact that $82,000 must be spent at the beginning, requires an interest charge over the 30-year period for the use of money.

The factor

$$\frac{i(1+i)^n}{(1+i)^n - 1}$$

the reciprocal of Eq. (2-3), permits conversion of a present value to a uniform annual series. This series includes an amount each year to recover original investment (depreciation) plus interest on the balance remaining. Use of this factor will therefore convert a present value into an equivalent series. This series can then be combined with any other series that represents a cost of the project. This is the basis for the capital recovery method of annual cost, used in solving engineering economy problems.

Referring back to the statement of Problem 4-1, costs involved in the elevated tank alternative are \$82,000 first cost and \$150 per year for maintenance.

Convert \$82,000 to an annual series:

$i = 5\%$ and $n = 30$

$$K = P\left[\frac{i(1+i)^n}{(1+i)^n - 1}\right]$$

$$= \$82{,}000(1/15.37) = \$5340$$

This 30-year series can be added to the 30-year maintenance series to give a total annual cost = \$150 + \$5340 = \$5490 *Answer*

For the standpipe: P = \$66,000.

$$K = 66{,}000(1/15.37) = \$4300$$

Total annual cost = \$500 + \$4300 = \$4800 *Answer*

Problem 4-2 Comparative annual cost of steel and aluminum window frames for building

For installation in a certain new building both steel and aluminum window frames are being considered. Comparative costs may be tabulated as follows:

	Steel	*Aluminum*
First cost installed and painted	32,000	36,000
Repainting average cost per year	700	not required
Taxes plus insurance	2%	2%

Set up a comparative annual cost study for the two types of window frames assuming a 40-year life with no salvage, and the interest rate at 4%, compounded annually.

Solution:

Steel:

$$K = P\left[\frac{i(1+i)^n}{(1+i)^n - 1}\right] = 32{,}000\left(\frac{1}{19.79}\right) = \$1620$$

Annual cost for repainting = $700
Annual taxes = 32,000(0.02) = $640
Total annual cost = $1620 + $640 + $700 = $2960 *Answer*

Aluminum:

$$K = P\left[\frac{i(1+i)^n}{(1+i)^n - 1}\right] = 36{,}000\left(\frac{1}{19.79}\right) = \$1820$$

Annual taxes = 36,000(0.02) = $720
Total annual cost = $1820 + $720 = $2540 *Answer*

4-2 DIFFERENCE IN LIVES

In many analyses, the various alternatives do not have the same predicted lives. The annual cost method handles this complication automatically. Renewals could be projected indefinitely resulting (as long as costs do not increase) in the same annual cost forever. The factor used will be higher for alternatives with shorter lives, thereby "penalizing" these alternatives in comparison with those of longer life.

Problem 4-3 Machine alternatives having differences in lives compared by the annual cost method

A company is planning on purchasing a new plastic molding press. Four different presses are available. The differences as to cost and operating expenses are as follows:

Press	*A*	*B*	*C*	*D*
Installed cost in $	3000	4500	5400	6800
Power in $/yr	340	340	800	800
Labor in $/yr	3300	3000	2400	2200
Maintenance in $/yr	200	250	350	300
Taxes and insurance in %	2	2	2	2
Economic life in yr	5	5	9	8

Each press will produce the same number of units. Other items of expense than those listed will not vary appreciably. Capital is worth 10% to this company.

Which press should be bought?

Solution:

The annual cost analysis for press A: First cost P is converted to a uniform annual series as follows:

$n = 5$

$$K = P\left[\frac{i(1+i)^n}{(1+i)^n - 1}\right] = 3000\left(\frac{1}{3.791}\right)$$

$$= \$791$$

Taxes and insurance = $3000(0.02) = $60
Total annual cost = $791 + $60 + $340 + $3300 + $200 = $4691 *Answer*

The annual cost analysis for press B:

$$K = P\left[\frac{i(1+i)^n}{(1+i)^n - 1}\right] = 4500\left(\frac{1}{3.791}\right)$$

$$= \$1190/\text{yr}$$

Taxes and insurance = $4500(0.02) = $90
Total annual cost = $1190 + $90 + $340 + $3000 + $250 = $4870 *Answer*

The annual cost analysis for press C:

$$K = P\left[\frac{i(1+i)^n}{(1+i)^n - 1}\right] = 5400\left(\frac{1}{5.759}\right)$$

$$= \$936$$

Taxes and insurance = $5400(0.02) = $108
Total annual cost = $936 + $108 + $800 + $2400 + $350 = $4594 *Answer*

The annual cost analysis for press D:

$$K = P\left[\frac{i(1+i)^n}{(1+i)^n - 1}\right] = 6800\left(\frac{1}{5.335}\right)$$

$$= \$1273$$

Taxes and insurance = $6800(0.02) = $136
Total annual cost = $1273 + $136 + $800 + $2200 + $300 = $4709 *Answer*
Press C is most economical *Answer.*

4-3 SALVAGE VALUE

If an asset will have recoverable value at the end of its useful life and if this salvage value can be forecast, it must be considered in the selection of alternatives. Salvage value will reduce the cost of an alternative. Its effect can be calculated in several ways; the method selected here was chosen because of its ease of calculation.

To calculate the annual cost of an asset with salvage value, subtract the salvage value from the first cost of the asset, multiply the difference by the factor

$$\frac{i(1+i)^n}{(1+i)^n - 1}$$

and add to this annual cost the salvage value multiplied by the interest rate. This technique recognizes that only the difference between investment and salvage must be recovered. The balance, or salvage value, need only be charged with interest for its use, since it will be recovered at the end of n years.

Problem 4-4 Annual cost and annual savings in purchase of alternative machines

Assume you are required to decide on which of two machines to purchase for a given manufacturing process. Both machines have been judged to be equally desirable in all matters except cost. The following data are available:

	Machine A	*Machine B*
Delivered cost in $	25,000	40,000
Installation expense in $	5000	10000
Estimated life in yr	6	8
Net salvage value in $	0	12,000
Annual operating costs in $/yr:		
Labor	3000	2000
Power	2000	1750
Repairs	2000	1000
Taxes	450	750
Interest rate in %	6	6

Which machine will have the lower annual cost and what annual savings will accrue from its purchase?

Machine A: First cost P is converted to a uniform annual series:

$$K = P\left[\frac{i(1+i)^n}{(1+i)^n - 1}\right] = [25{,}000 + 5000]\left[\frac{1}{4.917}\right]$$

$$= \$6100$$

Total cost = $6100 + $3000 + $2000 + $2000 + $450 = $13,550 *Answer*

Machine B: Salvage must be considered.
Total first cost, installed = $40,000 + $10,000 = $50,000
If L = salvage value, therefore

$$K = [P - L]\left[\frac{i(1+i)^n}{(1+i)^n - 1}\right] + Li$$

$$= 38{,}000\left[\frac{1}{6.210}\right] + 12{,}000(0.06)$$

$$= 6120 + 720 = \$6840$$

Total cost = $6840 + $2000 + $1750 + $1000 + $750 = $12,340 *Answer*
Machine B is cheaper *Answer.*

4-4 APPROXIMATE METHOD

An alternate method of converting a first cost to a uniform annual series is an approximate method based upon straight line depreciation and average interest.

In using this method, conversion of a first cost and salvage value to a uniform series is accomplished by use of the formula:

$$K = \frac{P - L}{n} + (P - L)\left(\frac{i}{2}\right)\left(\frac{n+1}{n}\right) + Li,$$

where K = uniform annual amount
P = present or first cost
L = salvage value
n = life, in years
i = interest rate, per year

This method does not involve use of tables, but this advantage is offset by a decrease in accuracy and an increase in computations. The method should ordinarily not be used if a difference in lives exists for the alternatives.

Problem 4-5 Annual cost of alternative plans using straight line depreciation and average interest

In the planning of a state police radio system, it is desired to maintain a specified minimum signal strength at all points in the state. Two plans for accomplishing this are proposed for comparison.

Plan 1 involves the establishment of six transmitting stations of low power. The investment at each of these in buildings, ground improvements, piping and tower—all assumed to have a life of 25 years—is estimated as $35,000. The investment in transmitting equipment for each station—assumed, because of the probability of obsolescence, to have a life of 8 years—is estimated as $25,000. The monthly disbursements for operation of each station are estimated as $1050.

Plan 2 involves the establishment of only two transmitting stations of much higher power. The investment in buildings, etc., at each of these stations is estimated as $45,000, and the useful life of these facilities is estimated at 25 years. The investment in transmitting equipment at each station is estimated as $220,000, and the life of this equipment is estimated as 8 years. The monthly operating cost is established as $1400 per station.

Compare the annual costs of these plans, using straight line depreciation plus average interest with an interest rate of 6% per annum.

Solution:

Plan 1: Annual cost due to investment in buildings, etc.

$$K = \frac{P}{n} + P\left(\frac{i}{2}\right)\left(\frac{n+1}{n}\right)$$

$$= \frac{35{,}000(6)}{25} + 35{,}000(6)\left(\frac{0.06}{2}\right)\left(\frac{26}{25}\right)$$

$$= \$14{,}952$$

Annual cost due to investment in transmitting equipment:

$$K = \frac{P}{n} + P\left(\frac{i}{2}\right)\left(\frac{n+1}{n}\right)$$

$$= \frac{25{,}000(6)}{8} + 25{,}000(6)\left(\frac{0.06}{2}\right)\left(\frac{9}{8}\right)$$

$$= \$23{,}812$$

Total annual costs (Plan 1) = \$14,952 + \$23,812 + \$6(12)(1050)
= \$114,364 *Answer*

Plan 2: Annual cost due to investment in buildings, etc.:

$$K = \frac{P}{n} + P\left(\frac{i}{2}\right)\left(\frac{n+1}{n}\right)$$

$$= \frac{45{,}000(2)}{25} + 45{,}000(2)\left(\frac{0.06}{2}\right)\left(\frac{26}{25}\right)$$

$$= 3600 + 2810 = \$6410$$

Annual cost due to investment in transmitting equipment:

$$K = \frac{P}{n} + P\left(\frac{i}{2}\right)\left(\frac{n+1}{n}\right)$$

$$= \frac{220{,}000(2)}{8} + 220{,}000(2)\left(\frac{0.06}{2}\right)\left(\frac{9}{8}\right)$$

$$= 55{,}000 + 14{,}850 = \$69{,}850$$

Total annual costs = \$6410 + \$69,850 + \$1400(2)(12) = \$109,860 *Answer*

4-5 EFFECT OF SOURCE OF FUNDS

The techniques described in this chapter deal with cost figures. Expenditures at the start of a program are converted to uniform annual series which are equivalent to the first costs. These approximate the depreciation and interest expense items which appear in the company's financial statements.

Where the funds come from does not enter into the calculations. For an economic analysis, interest is charged on investment funds whether company supplied or borrowed. Although the Internal Revenue Code does not permit deduction of interest for company supplied funds, this is a real cost of the alternative and must be included for analysis purposes.

Many people find it easier to conceptualize the annual cost techniques by assuming all funds to be borrowed. They assume that the annual costs, used as equivalent to first cost, are the amounts repaid each year under the loan. This is acceptable if the repayment amount is based upon the same interest rate and number of years as used for analysis purposes. If the asset has a life different from the repayment series, the life of the asset must be used in the calculations.

chapter 5
PRESENT VALUATION AND RETURN ON INVESTMENT

5-1 PRESENT WORTH

The annual cost method outlined in the previous chapter involved conversion of all costs to equivalent uniform annual series. The present worth method involves conversion of all costs to an equivalent present worth.

Although most comparisons could theoretically be made by either method, there is usually a practical reason for using one method in preference to the other. Also, there are special cases, covered below, which require a present worth analysis.

Problem 5-1 Present worth analysis of purchase vs. lease of manufacturing equipment

The Pracdifoil Corporation faces a decision whether to lease or purchase a piece of manufacturing equipment.

The purchase price is $250,000 and installation costs will be $25,000. The equipment can be expected to have a useful life of 5 years after which it can be sold as scrap with a net realization of $25,000. To maintain the equipment is expected to require $3000 per year; taxes and insurance $1200. Assume that the annual outlays occur at the beginning of each year.

The machine can be leased for 5 years at an annual rental fee of $58,500, payable in five equal annual installments at the beginning of each year. The lessor agrees to install the equipment ready to use, to remove it at the end of five years, and to see that it is kept in working order. The Pracdifoil Corporation will have to spend about $1000/yr for ordinary maintenance and $500/yr for insurance.

Alternative investment opportunities would produce a 5% return to the Pracdifoil Corporation at this time. What should the corporation management decide to do? Use present value comparison method.

Solution:

Purchase: All costs must be converted to present values.

Purchase price and installation cost are already in this form. Present value of salvage must be deducted.

Beginning-of-year payments can be handled with end-of-year formulas by noting that the first payment is already a present value and the remaining payments form a series of $(n - 1)$ terms.

$$P = 250{,}000 + 25{,}000 - 25{,}000 \left[\frac{1}{(1 + 0.05)^5}\right] + 3000$$

$$+\ 3000 \left[\frac{(1.05)^4 - 1}{0.05(1.05)^4}\right] + 1200 + 1200 \left[\frac{(1.05)^4 - 1}{0.05(1.05)^4}\right]$$

$$= 250{,}000 + 25{,}000 - 25{,}000(1/1.276) + 3000$$

$$+\ 3000(3.546) + 1200 + 1200(3.546)$$

$$= \$274{,}500 \qquad \textit{Answer}$$

Lease:

$$P = 58{,}500 + 58{,}500 \left[\frac{(1.05)^4 - 1}{0.05(1.05)^4}\right] + 1500$$

$$+\ 1500 \left[\frac{(1.05)^4 - 1}{0.05(1.05)^4}\right]$$

$$= 58{,}500 + 1500 + 60{,}000(3.546)$$

$$= \$272{,}700 \qquad \textit{Answer}$$

It is slightly advantageous to lease.

Problem 5-2 Present worth of asset that yields equal year-end payments to owner for given number of years

The owner of a quarry signs a contract to sell his stone on the following basis: The purchaser is to remove the stone from certain portions of the pit according to a fixed schedule of volume, price, and time. The contract is to run 18 years as follows:

Eight years excavating a total of 20,000 yards per year at 10 cents per yard.

The remaining 10 years excavating a total of 50,000 yards per year at 15 cents per yard.

On the basis of equal year end payments during each period by the purchaser, what is the present worth of the pit to the owner on the basis of 5% interest?

Solution:

The present worth of the pit to the owner is the sum of all payments he will receive brought back to the present time.

The present value of the first eight years' excavations:

$$P = 2000 \left[\frac{(1.05)^8 - 1}{0.05(1.05)^8}\right]$$

$$= 2000(6.463)$$

$$= \$12{,}926$$

The next 10 years will result in income of \$7500 per year. To find the present value will require two steps since the value derived from the formula would be at the end of the eighth year. This value must be brought back to the present.

$$P = 7500\left[\frac{(1.05)^{10} - 1}{0.05(1.05)^{10}}\right]$$

$$= 7500(7.722)$$

$$= \$57{,}900 \qquad \text{(at end of year 8)}$$

$$P = 57{,}900\left[\frac{1}{(1.05)^{8}}\right]$$

$$= 57{,}900(1/1.477)$$

$$= \$39{,}200 \qquad \text{(at present)}$$

Total value = \$12,926 + \$39,200 = \$52,126 *Answer*

5-2 DIFFERENCES IN LIVES

Comparison of alternatives with different expected lives requires use of some technique to equalize the lives if present worth analysis is used. A practical solution is to find a least common denominator, assume renewals as required, and calculate the present value of the entire series.

Problem 5-3 Two types of bridges compared on the basis of present worth

Compare two types of bridges on the basis of present worth at 5% interest. Bridge A has an estimated life of 25 years, initial cost \$50,000, renewal cost \$50,000, annual maintenance \$500, additional repairs every 5 years \$2000, and salvage value (in 25 years) \$5000. Bridge B has an estimated life of 50 years, initial cost \$75,000, annual maintenance cost \$100, additional repairs every 5 years \$1000, and salvage value \$10,000.

Solution:

Bridge A: Use 50 years as study period. At end of 25 years, \$50,000 will be required; however, \$5000 of this will be provided by salvage value.

P = \$50,000

Present worth of renewal − Salvage value $= 45{,}000\left[\frac{1}{(1+i)^{n}}\right]$

$= 45{,}000\left[\frac{1}{3.386}\right]$ = 13,300

−Salvage after 50 yr $= -5000\left[\frac{1}{(1+i)^{n}}\right]$

$= -5000\left[\frac{1}{11.47}\right]$ = −436

$$\text{Present worth of annual maintenance for 50 yr} = 500\left[\frac{(1+i)^n - 1}{i(1+i)^n}\right]$$

$$= 500(18.26) \qquad = 9130$$

Present worth of additional maintenance every 5 yr. First convert to a uniform annual series.

$$K = 2000\left[\frac{i}{(1+i)^n - 1}\right] = 2000\left[\frac{1}{5.526}\right]$$

$$= \$362$$

$$\text{Present worth for 50 years} = 362\left[\frac{(1+i)^n - 1}{i(1+i)^n}\right]$$

$$= 362(18.26) = \$6600$$

Total present cost of Bridge A = \$78,594 *Answer*

Bridge B:

$$P = \qquad \$75{,}000$$

$$-\text{Salvage after 50 years} = -10{,}000\left[\frac{1}{11.47}\right] \qquad = -872$$

$$\text{Present worth of annual maintenance} = 100\left[\frac{(1+i)^n - 1}{i(1+i)^n}\right]$$

$$= 100(18.26) \qquad = 1826$$

$$\text{Present worth of additional repairs} = 1000\left[\frac{1}{(1+i)^n - 1}\right]$$

$$= 1000\left[\frac{1}{5.526}\right] = 181$$

$$\text{Present worth for 50 years} = 181\left[\frac{(1+i)^n - 1}{i(1+i)^n}\right]$$

$$= 181(18.26) \qquad = 3300$$

Total present cost of Bridge B = \$79,254 *Answer*
Bridge A is slightly less *Answer.*

5-3 INVESTMENT JUSTIFIED BY SAVINGS

Certain special cases require present worth solutions. One case is the determination of a present investment justified by future savings or earnings.

Problem 5-4 Investment justified by present worth determination of future savings

The use of a sextuple-effect evaporator in lieu of a quintuple-effect unit results in increasing the steam economy from 4.1 to 5.1.

The steam cost is \$0.50 per M lb and the evaporator system must concentrate a feed of 500 gal/min having a specific gravity of 1.05 from 13% to 52% total solids. Operation will be 24 hours per day for 300 days per year.

If the interest rate is 6% and the expected life is 20 years, how much more investment is justified for the sextuple- over the quintuple-effect evaporator? Neglect any differences in water and power consumption and assume that the maintenance and miscellaneous operating costs are the same.

Solution:

It is first necessary to calculate the number of pounds of liquid to be evaporated each year.

In order to concentrate feed from 13% to 52% total solids, 75% of the solution must be evaporated. (From 13 pounds in each 100 pounds, the solution must be changed to 13 pounds in each 25 pounds.)

$$\begin{aligned}\text{Total number of pounds of feed/year} &= 500\text{ gal/min} \times 60\text{ min/hr} \times 24\text{ hr/day} \\ &\quad \times 300\text{ days/yr} \times 8.34\text{ lb/gal} \times 1.05 \\ &= 1.9\text{ billion pounds of feed} \\ \text{The amount of liquid to be evaporated} &= 1.9\text{ billion lb }(0.75) \\ &= 1.425\text{ billion pounds of liquid}\end{aligned}$$

The amount of steam required:

Quintuple

$$\frac{1.425\text{ billion}}{4.1} = 348\text{ million}$$

Sextuple

$$\frac{1.425\text{ billion}}{5.1} = 279\text{ million}$$

The difference is 69 million pounds of steam or \$34,500/yr.
The present investment justified to save \$34,500 per year for 20 years at 6% is

$$P = 34{,}500\left[\frac{(1+i)^n - 1}{i(1+i)^n}\right]$$

$$= 34{,}500(11.47) = 395{,}000 \qquad \textit{Answer}$$

Problem 5-5 Investment justified by present worth determination of future income

A market analysis estimates that sales of a new product will be as follows:

First Year: 1,000,000 pounds at 50 cents/lb
Next 4 years: 6,000,000 pounds at 50 cents/lb
Next 5 years: 5,000,000 pounds at 30 cents/lb

Investigation shows that the product can be produced for 20 cents per pound plus overhead and fixed charges on the investment required. Overhead is estimated at \$100,000 per year.

If the interest rate is 6% and the company wishes to make a profit before taxes of 10% on its sales income, how much can it afford to invest in a plant to produce this product?

Solution:

Net income can be determined for each period as follows:

First Year:

Sales income	$500,000
Less production cost (1,000,000 at 0.20)	200,000
	300,000
Less overhead	100,000
	$200,000

Next 4 Years: (Assume sales of 6,000,000 lb/yr)

Sales income	$3,000,000
Less production cost (6,000,000 at 0.20)	1,200,000
	1,800,000
Less overhead	100,000
	$1,700,000

Next 5 Years: (Assume sales of 5,000,000 lb/yr)

Sales income	$1,500,000
Less production cost (5,000,000 at 0.20)	1,000,000
	500,000
Less overhead	100,000
	$400,000

The present investment justified to produce this income is the present value of the income for the ten years.

$$P = 200,000\left[\frac{1}{(1+0.10)^1}\right] + 1,700,000\left[\frac{(1+0.10)^4-1}{0.10(1+0.10)^4}\right]\left[\frac{1}{(1+0.10)^1}\right]$$

$$+ 400,000\left[\frac{(1+0.10)^5-1}{0.10(1+0.10)^5}\right]\left[\frac{1}{(1+0.10)^5}\right]$$

$$= 181,500 + 4,900,000 + 940,000$$

$$= \$6,021,500 \quad \textit{Answer}$$

5-4 PROBLEMS INVOLVING TWO INTEREST RATES

It might be desirable to consider net income from investment as being divided into two or more uses, each earning a different return. The present worth of the amounts to be received would be calculated using the interest rates designated.

Problem 5-6 Annual income and sinking fund deposits provided by depleting mine asset

It is estimated that the Deep Gulch Mine, now operating, can be expected to make a net profit after all taxes are paid of \$150,000 per year for 35 years, at which time it will be exhausted and have no salvage value.

What can you afford to pay for the mine now, so that you will have an annual income of 12% on your investment after you have made an annual deposit into a fund that, at 3% interest, will accumulate to the amount of your investment in 35 years, when the mine will be exhausted?

Solution:

The \$150,000 per year will have to provide a 12% return on the original investment, plus enough for deposits in a sinking fund that will build to the amount of the original investment in 35 years. This can be expressed in the form of an equation:

$$150{,}000 = P(0.12) + P\left[\frac{i}{(1+i)^n - 1}\right]$$

$$= P(0.12) + P\left[\frac{0.03}{(1.03)^{35} - 1}\right]$$

$$= 0.13657P$$

$$P = \$1{,}100{,}000 \qquad \textit{Answer}$$

5-5 CAPITALIZED COST

In Sec. 5-2, it was noted that comparison of alternatives with different expected lives requires equalization of lives if present worth analysis is used. Problem 5-3 was solved by using a uniform study period. Another technique involves finding the present cost of perpetual service for all alternatives. This method is called capitalized cost.

Solution of problems by this technique usually involves finding the equivalent present value of uniform annual series of infinite life and of nonannual repetitive amounts. Problems 5-7 and 5-8 illustrate use of capitalized cost.

Problem 5-7 Capitalized cost method analysis of financing and maintaining an institution on a 50-year building cycle

What amount must be donated to build an institution having an initial cost of \$500,000, provide an annual upkeep of \$50,000 and have \$500,000 at the end of each 50-year period to rebuild the institution? Assume that invested funds return 4%.

Solution:

The amount required includes:

(a) Present cost of constructing institution = \$500,000.

(b) Present equivalent of \$50,000 per year in perpetuity. The present value of an infinite uniform annual series can be found by dividing the annual amount by the interest rate:

$$P = \$50{,}000/0.04 = \$1{,}250{,}000$$

(c) Amount required to provide \$500,000 after 50 years and every 50 years thereafter. A uniform annual series can be found that would develop \$500,000 in 50 years from the following:

$$K = 500{,}000 \left[\frac{i}{(1+i)^n - 1}\right]$$

$$= 500{,}000 \left[\frac{0.04}{(1.04)^{50} - 1}\right]$$

$$= 500{,}000 \left[\frac{1}{152.7}\right] = \$3280$$

This amount, \$3280, if deposited at the end of each year for 50 years, would build up to \$500,000 in 50 years. If the series were extended to infinity, it would provide \$500,000 every 50 years.

The present amount required to provide \$3280 every year can be found from:

$$P = \$3280/0.04 = \$82{,}000$$

$$\text{Total amount needed} = \$500{,}000 + \$1{,}250{,}000 + \$82{,}000$$
$$= \$1{,}832{,}000 \quad \textit{Answer}$$

Problem 5-8 Capitalized cost method analysis of two-stage development plan vs. full development plan

A two-stage program of development of a public project is offered as an alternate to immediate development. The two-stage program, Alternate A, will require an investment of \$500,000 now and \$600,000 additional in 10 years, both for properties assumed to be permanent. Annual operation and maintenance will be \$50,000 for the first 10 years, and \$75,000 thereafter. The full development plan, Alternate B, will involve an expenditure of \$1,000,000 for permanent properties requiring \$65,000 annually for operation and maintenance.

Calculate the capitalized cost of each plan and show the difference in costs, assuming interest at 6%.

Solution:

Alternate A

The capitalized cost for Alternate A will be the sum of the present investment, the present value of the addition after 10 years, and the present value of perpetual maintenance.

$$P = 500{,}000 + 600{,}000\left[\frac{1}{(1+0.06)^{10}}\right] + 50{,}000\left[\frac{(1+0.06)^{10}-1}{0.06(1+0.06)^{10}}\right]$$

$$+ \frac{75{,}000}{0.06}\left[\frac{1}{(1+0.06)^{10}}\right]$$

$$= 500{,}000 + 600{,}000(1/1.791) + 50{,}000(7.360) + 1{,}250{,}000(1/1.791)$$

$$= \$1{,}899{,}000 \qquad \textit{Answer}$$

Alternate B

Capitalized cost = \$1,000,000 + 65,000/0.06
= \$2,083,333 *Answer*

Difference in costs = \$2,083,333 − 1,899,000
= \$184,333 *Answer*

5-6 VALUATION OF BONDS

The present worth method can be used to value a bond, given the interest to be received and the amount to be received at maturation.

Problem 5-9 Present worth analysis of value of a bond

What should a prospective investor pay for a bond, if he desires a 6% return on his investment and the bond will return \$50 per year for 20 years and \$1000 after 20 years?

Solution:

$$P = 50\left[\frac{(1+0.06)^{20}-1}{0.06(1+0.06)^{20}}\right] + 1000\left[\frac{1}{(1+0.06)^{20}}\right]$$

$$= 573.50 + 312$$

$$= \$885.50 \qquad \textit{Answer}$$

5-7 BOND YIELDS

Bond valuation problems suggest a more common problem—determination of the yield (interest) earned by an investment if the interest and maturity payments are known. Solution for yield is a special case of the rate of return problem discussed in the next section.

The method of solution involves recognition that the amount invested is equivalent to the return at the unknown interest rate. This unknown interest rate can be determined by setting the investment equal to the amounts received at some convenient point in time.

Problem 5-10 Determination of the yield (interest) earned on a bond

Interest on a 4%, \$1000 bond due in 20 years is payable semiannually with the first payment 6 months hence. The bond is for sale for \$950. Determine the approximate rate of return to be received by an investor who buys the bond at this price.

Solution:

For the \$950 investment, the investor will receive \$20 every 6 months and \$1000 after 20 years (40 periods). The rate of return, or bond yield, would be the interest rate earned on the investment. This can be determined by finding the present value of the payments to be received and equating the total to the \$950 investment.

$$\$950 = \$20\left[\frac{(1+i)^{40}-1}{i(1+i)^{40}}\right] + 1000\left[\frac{1}{(1+i)^{40}}\right]$$

The return can be approximated by trial and error. Using 2% interest:

$$\$950 \stackrel{?}{=} 20(27.36) + 1000(0.453) = \$1000$$

Using 2½% interest:

$$\$950 \stackrel{?}{=} 20(25.10) + 1000(0.373) = 502 + 373 = \$875$$

Interpolating, i (for 6 months) is approximately 2.2%.
The nominal annual rate is 4.4% *Answer.*

5-8 RATE OF RETURN

The previous section covered a technique that is a special case of the general rate of return solution. The same technique is used for other problems in which the interest rate is unknown.

Problem 5-11 Equivalent rate of interest of capital gain realized from sale of property

A man bought a piece of property for \$1000. Five years later he bought a second piece for \$2000. After five years more, he sold the two pieces for \$4467.30. The income had meanwhile first paid for taxes and repairs. To what rate of interest, compounded annually, would his profit be equivalent?

Solution:

A suitable reference point for this problem is the date at which the properties were sold. The equation at this point is

$$1000(1+i)^{10} + 2000(1+i)^{5} = \$4467.30$$

Using 5.5% interest:

$$1000(1.708) + 2000(1.307) = \$4322$$

Using 6.0% interest:

$1000(1.791) + 2000(1.338) = \$4467$

Therefore, $i = 6\%$ *Answer.* In this problem, interpolation was not necessary.

chapter 6
BREAK-EVEN ANALYSIS

6-1 BREAK-EVEN CONCEPT

This concept is often used in business in determining the scale of production that would be necessary to develop sufficient revenue to just cover expenses. A level of production under this break-even point would result in a loss; a higher level of production would result in a gain. Although the degree of accuracy required to develop correct models of income and expense is not always present, the concept is quite useful as a rough gage.

The break-even concept is used in economy studies to choose between two alternatives as well as to find minimum production levels. The technique is useful where an unknown parameter, such as capacity or production level, is involved. The decision to be made by management will be based upon its estimate of this unknown parameter.

6-2 BREAK-EVEN WITHOUT INTEREST

Problem 6-1 Alternative production methods for break-even costs

A telephone switchboard containing 150 pair cable can be made up with either enameled wire or tinned wire. There will be 550 soldered connections. The cost of soldering a connection on the enameled wire will be 1.85 cents; on the tinned wire, it will be 1.25 cents. A 150-pair cable made up with enameled wire costs 65 cents per linear foot; and made up with tinned wire, 83 cents per linear foot. Calculate the length of cable run in feet so that the cost of each installation will be the same.

Solution:

Let x = the unknown parameter, length of cable run in feet.
Cost of enameled wire = $550(0.0185) + 0.65x$
Cost of tinned wire = $550(0.0125) + 0.83x$

At the break-even point the two costs would be equal:

$$550(0.0185) + 0.65x = 550(0.0125) + 0.83x$$

$$x = 18.3 \text{ ft} \qquad \textit{Answer}$$

6-3 CAPACITY AS A BREAK-EVEN FACTOR

Problem 6-2 Hotel capacity determination for break-even costs

The complete cost of constructing a new all-season hotel is $980,000. The cost of the land is $300,000, and it is considered not to depreciate in value. Fixtures will cost $150,000, and a working capital of 30 days gross income at 100% capacity will be required. The investment in the fixtures should be recovered in 7 years and the investment in the structure should be recovered in 25 years.

When operating at 100% capacity, the gross income will be $1200 per day. Operating expenses, exclusive of capital recovery and interest, will amount to a fixed cost of $115,000 per year, and a variable cost, varying in direct proportion to the level of operation, of $78,000 per year for 100% capacity.

If interest is taken at 6% compounded annually, at what percent of capacity must the hotel operate to break even?

Solution:

Let x = capacity at which hotel operates (expressed as a decimal fraction). Break-even will occur at capacity for which income and expenses are equal.

$$\text{Income} = \$1200(365)(x)$$

$$\text{Expenses} = 980{,}000\left[\frac{0.06(1.06)^{25}}{(1.06)^{25} - 1}\right] + 300{,}000(0.06) + 150{,}000\left[\frac{0.06(1.06)^{7}}{(1.06)^{7} - 1}\right]$$

$$+ 30(1200)(0.06) + 115{,}000 + 78{,}000(x)$$

Setting expenses equal to income and solving for x, the capacity required for break-even is 66% *Answer.*

6-4 PRODUCTION AS A BREAK-EVEN FACTOR

Problem 6-3 Production rate determination for break-even costs

Companies A and B manufacture the same article. Company A, relying mostly on machines, has fixed expenses of $12,000 per month and a direct cost of $8 per unit. Company B, using more hand work, has fixed expenses of $4000 and a direct cost of $20 per unit. At what monthly production rate will the total cost per unit be the same for the two companies?

Solution:

Let x = monthly production rate. The two companies will have equal costs when:

$$12{,}000 + 8x = 4000 + 20x$$

$$x = 667 \text{ units} \qquad \textit{Answer}$$

6-5 OTHER PROBLEMS USING THE BREAK-EVEN CONCEPT

Problem 6-4 Break-even costs of motor operation determine choice of alternants

Two 100-hp motors are under consideration for an intermittant service. Motor A costs \$1600 and has an efficiency of 90%. Motor B costs \$1300 and has an efficiency of 87%. If all charges for depreciation, maintenance, insurance, etc., are a total of 15% of the initial cost, and if power costs 1.1 cents per kW-hr, how many hours of full-load operation per year are necessary to justify purchase of motor A? (Assume each motor has a life of 25 years with no salvage value and that money can be borrowed at 6%.)

Solution:

Let x = number of hours of full-load operation per year. The two types of cost involved for each motor are the annual cost due to initial cost and cost of power.

If we assume that "depreciation, maintenance, insurance, etc." includes interest, then (0.15P) will include all costs other than power.

Motor A:

$$\text{Total cost} = 1600(0.15) + \frac{(100\text{ hp})(0.746\text{ kW/hp})(x\text{ hr})(0.011\text{ \$/kW-hr})}{0.90}$$

$$= 240 + 0.911x$$

Motor B:

$$\text{Total cost} = 1300(0.15) + \frac{100(0.746)(x)(0.011)}{0.87}$$

$$= 195 + 0.941x$$

Setting the two costs equal:

$$0.03x = 45$$

$$x = 1500\text{ hr}$$ *Answer*

Problem 6-5 Minimum service life for break-even costs of pump alternants

An engineer must select a pump for a service requiring 14,000 gal/min at 11 ft total dynamic head. The specific gravity of the liquid is 1.45.

Supplier A offers a pump of all-iron construction with an efficiency of 70% at a price of \$5600; Supplier B offers a pump of all-monel construction with an efficiency of 75% at a price of \$14,700. Iron contamination of the product can be tolerated.

Installation costs and/or replacement costs for either pump are \$1000. Routine maintenance costs are assumed the same in either case, and power is available at \$0.01/kW-hr. Operation will be 24 hours per day for 300 days per year.

It is expected that the monel pump will last for 20 years, at which time the plant will be obsolete, and the monel pump will have a salvage value of 25% of its original cost.

If money is available at 6%, what minimum service life must be expected from the all-iron pump in order to justify its selection?

Solution:

In this problem, the minimum service life will be found by setting equal the annual costs of the two pumps. The only unknown will be the life of the iron pump.

Iron pump:

$$\text{Annual cost} = (5600 + 1000)\left[\frac{0.06(1.06)^n}{(1.06)^n - 1}\right]$$

$$+ \left[\frac{11(14{,}000)(0.746)(1.45)(300)(24)(0.01)}{(3960)(0.70)}\right]^*$$

$$= 6600\left[\frac{0.06(1.06)^n}{(1.06)^n - 1}\right] + 4360$$

Monel Pump:

$$\text{Annual cost} = [(14{,}700 + 1000) - 3675]\left[\frac{0.06(1.06)^{20}}{(1.06)^{20} - 1}\right]$$

$$+ 3675(0.06) + \left[\frac{11(14{,}000)(0.746)(1.45)(300)(24)(0.01)}{3960(0.75)}\right]^*$$

$$= 1050 + 221 + 4070$$
$$= \$5341$$

Setting the two equal:

$$\left[\frac{0.06(1.06)^n}{(1.06)^n - 1}\right] = 0.1489$$

n (from table) = 9 + yr *Answer*

Practically, this would require a life of 10 years, since less would necessitate two renewals.

---

*This cumbersome fraction gives the cost each year for power consumption. Dynamic head times gal/min times specific gravity divided by 3960 results in horsepower output required. This is divided by efficiency to give input required. Multiplication by 0.746 results in kilowatt input required. The product is then multiplied by number of hours of operation per year and cost per kW-hr to arrive at a cost figure.

chapter 7

INCREMENTAL ANALYSIS AND REPLACEMENT ECONOMY

7-1 UNIT COSTS

The costs of operating an enterprise or a center are often expressed in terms of cost per piece, cost per pound, cost per foot, etc., depending upon the product of the operation. This concept is widely used and has certain advantages. For cost control purposes, it may provide a warning signal if costs increase relative to production. It can also be valuable in determining the selling price required in order to earn a profit.

Unit costs, however, can be very easily misinterpreted and misused. A thorough understanding of the components of cost should be prerequisite to use of unit cost figures for decision-making purposes.

As an illustration, assume that a plant produces 1,000,000 parts per year and the total cost of running the plant is $2,000,000. We would therefore have an average cost per unit of $2.00. Since the unit cost was based on a production rate of 1,000,000 parts, this average unit cost only applies if production is maintained at that level and costs do not change. It can therefore be used as a basis for pricing only if production will stay at about 1,000,000 units.

7-2 FIXED AND VARIABLE COSTS

In the illustration above, a decrease in production to 500,000 units would probably not result in a decrease in cost to $1,000,000. This is because certain costs, such as rent, taxes, heat, light and power, administrative and supervisory salaries, and many others, do not change in direct proportion to production level. These costs, which remain relatively stable over a large segment of the production curve, are called fixed costs. Other expenses—direct labor and direct materials—do vary almost directly with production and are called variable costs.

Referring again to the illustration in Sec. 7-1, if we determine that the $2,000,000 required to run the plant is made up of $1,000,000 in fixed costs and $1,000,000 in variable costs, we can develop the total operating cost for other levels of production. The $1,000,000 fixed cost will remain constant for a substantial portion of the production curve. The variable cost will be $1,000,000/1,000,000 units, or $1 per piece. For a production level of 500,000 units, the total cost would be $1,000,000 (fixed) + $500,000 (variable), or $1,500,000.

Use of variable and fixed costs in the manner described above is, of course, a simplification of reality. Costs that we classify as fixed are usually not completely invariable and variable costs may not vary on a one to one basis with production. However, an analysis of this type can result in a usable approximation and is therefore a valuable technique.

7-3 USE OF INCREMENTAL ANALYSIS

Consideration of the effect of change on cost or income is incremental analysis. Fixed and variable costs were segregated above, and it was noted that a change in production would affect only the variable cost. Any decision that assumed that *total* costs would vary directly with production would be based upon incorrect analysis.

Problem 7-1 Incremental cost analysis of manufactured product

The ABC Corporation seeks to enlarge the market for its product, sold under the brand name ExxDRA. Examine the following information and then state which action the corporation should take. Show computations.

At present, 400,000 units of ExxDRA are produced and sold each year. The current selling price is 30¢ each. On the basis of a thorough investigation and analysis, the management believes that it can increase sales by 50,000 units/year if it should lower the price from 30¢ to 29¢; by 150,000 if the price should be reduced to 28¢; and by 300,000 if the price should be lowered to 26¢.

The present capacity of the plant on a one-shift 40-hr week is 600,000 units. Operating at capacity, its cost structure would be as follows:

Fixed costs	$40,000 per year
Present advertising budget	$20,000 per year
Variable costs	0.16 per unit of output

To produce in excess of 600,000 on a one-shift basis would require overtime premium pay. The variable costs for the units over 600,000 would be 0.20 per unit.

If the company should raise its annual advertising budget to $30,000, it could expect to sell 500,000 units without lowering the price from 30¢; to $45,000, it could expect to sell 600,000 at 30¢.

Solution:

The company should take the action which will maximize its net income.

Present net income	=	$120,000
	−	64,000 variable costs
	−	40,000 fixed costs
	−	20,000 advertising
or a net loss of		$ 4000/yr

If sales are increased to 450,000/units/yr at $0.29,

Net income	= $130,500
	− 72,000 variable costs
	− 40,000 fixed costs
	− 20,000 advertising
or a net loss of	$ 1500/yr

If sales are increased to 550,000/units/at $0.28,

Net income	= $154,000
	− 88,000 variable costs
	− 40,000 fixed costs
	− 20,000 advertising
or a net income of	$ 6000/yr

If sales are increased to 700,000/units/yr at $0.26,

Net income	= $182,000
	− 116,000 variable costs
	− 40,000 fixed costs
	− 20,000 advertising
or a net income of	$ 6000/yr

If advertising budget is increased to 30,000 − sales at 500,000,

Net income	= $150,000
	− 80,000 variable costs
	− 40,000 fixed costs
	− 30,000 advertising
or a net income of	0

If budget is increased to $45,000,

Net income	= $180,000
	− 96,000 variable costs
	− 40,000 fixed costs
	− 45,000 advertising
or a net loss of	$ 1000/yr

The correct decision would be to increase sales to 700,000 at $0.26/unit or 550,000 at $0.28/unit *Answer.*

Problem 7-2 Incremental cost analysis involving temporary surplus plant capacity

The energy from a hydroelectric plant will go to waste if not used in the production of metal. A metal reduction plant with a capacity of 10,000,000 lb of metal per year is constructed to make use of the energy from the hydroelectric plant. Two million dollars worth of 6% bonds are sold to pay for the plant. Taxes and company overhead are $130,000 per year and ordinary charges to the reserve fund are $50,000 per year. Production cost and raw materials cost are 4 cents per pound of metal produced. The metal has sold for 10 cents per lb. During a depression, the demand for the product drops to 50% of plant capacity and the price falls to 9 cents per lb. Should the company continue to manufacture at full capacity, or shut down, or run at half capacity? The company estimates that the depression will last two years and that it will be 5 years after the depression ends before any surplus can be marketed. Give reasons and figures to support your opinion.

Solution:

The fixed costs for this company are:

$$2{,}000{,}000(0.06) + 130{,}000 + 50{,}000 = \$300{,}000$$

These costs for interest, taxes and overhead, and reserve fund will be constant regardless of the level of operation.

(a) If the company shuts down, the only costs will be the fixed costs and the net loss per year will = $300,000.

(b) If the company operates at 50% capacity, total cost will include fixed cost plus production and material costs and is equal to

$$300{,}000 + 5{,}000{,}000(0.04) = \$500{,}000$$

At 50% capacity, sales income will be

$$5{,}000{,}000(0.09) = \$450{,}000$$

Therefore net loss = $450,000 − $500,000 = $50,000.

(c) At 100% capacity, the total cost is

$$300{,}000 + 10{,}000{,}000(0.04) = \$700{,}000$$

Immediate sales income = $450,000. However, an additional 5,000,000 pounds of metal will be produced that can be sold in seven years. The present value of this future income is

$$500{,}000[1/(1.06)^7] = \$332{,}550$$

Total value of income = $450,000 + 332,500 = $782,550
Total cost = $700,000
Net profit = $782,550 − $700,000 = $82,550
The company should therefore operate at full capacity *Answer.*

7-4 REPLACEMENT ECONOMY

A special case of comparison of alternatives exists if one of the alternatives is to keep in service a presently used asset. This situation is treated exactly as any other comparison of alternatives with one important exception—the present value of the presently used asset is the current market value of this asset. (Market value can be given as trade-in value, salvage value, scrap value, etc.) This treatment assigns as a cost the amount *not* received if the old asset is kept in service. The original purchase price of the asset is not pertinent for this purpose, since this amount was spent in the past and should not affect current considerations. Such a cost is called a *sunk cost.*

Problem 7-3 Difference in equivalent annual cost for two machines

To undertake production of a new product, an inventor purchased a simple machine that required much hand labor. The machine cost \$4400 and was estimated to have a useful life of 5 years, at the end of which there would be no salvage value. Annual operating and maintenance costs, exclusive of depreciation and interest, were \$2600. At the end of the first year, he was urged to purchase a semiautomatic machine for \$6200 that could match production of the first machine and that would have an annual operating and maintenance cost, exclusive of depreciation and interest, of \$800. Trade-in value of the first machine on the new machine would be \$1600. The new machine is estimated to have a life of 4 years and no salvage value.

Using an interest rate of 8%, calculate the difference in equivalent annual cost for the two machines, and state which machine should be used for the next 4 years.

Solution:

Correct solution of this problem requires use of \$1600 as the present value of the simple machine. Its annual cost will be

$$1600\left[\frac{0.08(1.08)^4}{(1.08)^4 - 1}\right] + 2600 = \$3080$$

For the new machine, the annual cost will be

$$6200\left[\frac{0.08(1.08)^4}{(1.08)^4 - 1}\right] + 800 = \$2665$$

The difference in equivalent annual costs is \$415, in favor of the new machine *Answer.*

Problem 7-4 Replacement economy of steam electric plant

Fourteen years ago a 1200-kW steam electric plant was constructed at a cost of \$220/kW. Annual operating expenses have been \$31,000 to produce the annual demand of 5,400,000 kW-hr. It is estimated that the annual operating expenses and demand for current will continue. The original estimate of a 20-year life with a 5% salvage value at that time is still expected to be correct.

The company is contemplating the replacement of the old steam plant with a new diesel plant. The old plant can be sold now for \$75,000, while the new diesel plant will cost \$245/kW to construct. The diesel plant will have a life of 25 years with a salvage value of 10% at the end of that time and will cost \$23,000 annually to operate. Annual taxes and insurance will be 2.3% of the first cost of either plant.

Using an interest rate of 5%, determine whether the company is financially justified in replacing the old steam plant now.

Solution:

Use $75,000 as the present value of the old plant.

Annual cost for the *steam electric plant* (original cost was $264,000):

$$(75{,}000 - 13{,}200)\left[\frac{(0.05)(1.05)^6}{(1.05)^6 - 1}\right] + 13{,}200(0.05) + 31{,}000$$

$$+ (264{,}000)(0.023) = \$49{,}902$$

Annual cost for the *diesel plant:*

$$[294{,}000 - 29{,}400]\left[\frac{(0.05)(1.05)^{25}}{(1.05)^{25} - 1}\right] + 29{,}400(0.05) + 23{,}000$$

$$+ 294{,}000(0.023) = \$49{,}937$$

It would not be financially justifiable to replace the steam electric plant at this time *Answer.*

Note that an incorrect solution would have been found had the value of the old plant been deducted from the first cost of the diesel plant. This is a common error that would have depreciated the steam electric plant over 25 years, rather than the actual remaining life of 6 years.

Problem 7-5 Economy of replacement vs. expansion of existing system

A flood has demonstrated that the drainage structure of a certain area is not adequate. In planning the improvement, three possible courses are considered:

(1) Leave an existing undamaged 24-in. corrugated steel culvert in place and install another of the same size alongside. (Assume the existing culvert has a remaining life of 20 years.)

(2) Remove the above-mentioned 24-in. culvert and replace it with a single culvert of 36-in. diameter.

(3) Remove the above-mentioned culvert and replace it with a reinforced concrete culvert of adequate cross section.

The present 24-in. pipe has a salvage value of $300.00. Estimates of the new installation have been made as shown below:

	24-inch	*36-inch*	*Concrete*
Cost of pipes, delivered	$750.00	$1,500.00	-----
Installation cost	375.00	525.00	$2,100.00
Life, estimated	20 yr	20 yr	40 yr

Interest is charged at 5% annually. Which of the possible courses of action is the most economical, and by how much? (Assume replacement costs of the 24- and 36-in. steel culverts 20 years hence to be the same as today's costs.)

Solution:

The first cost of the 24-in. pipes will be \$750 + \$375 + \$300, for the first 20 years. This amount (\$1425) will provide 20 years of service and is by inspection cheaper than the 36-in. installation. After 20 years, however, the 36-in. pipe is cheaper than two new 24-in. pipes.

Assuming indefinite service requirements, first compare the first 20 years.

24-in. culvert:

$$1425\left[\frac{0.05(1.05)^{20}}{(1.05)^{20}-1}\right] = \$114$$

Concrete culvert:

$$2100\left[\frac{0.05(1.05)^{40}}{(1.05)^{40}-1}\right] = \$122$$

It is therefore advantageous, for 20 years, to install an additional 24-in. pipe. The savings would be \$8/yr.

After 20 years, the cost of metal pipes would be

$$2250\left[\frac{0.05(1.05)^{20}}{(1.05)^{20}-1}\right] = \$181$$

For continuous service, after 20 years, it would be advantageous to install concrete *Answer.* (Savings would be \$59 per year.)

chapter 8
MINIMUM COST AND RISK

8-1 KELVIN'S LAW

A decision among alternatives is often based upon a choice of size or amount of certain factor. The appropriate method of handling these problems is to determine the minimum cost point of the total cost equation.

Many years ago Lord Kelvin demonstrated that the most economical wire size was the one in which costs that vary directly with wire size were exactly equal to the energy loss, which varies inversely with the size of the wire. This law only applies if the costs are actually directly and inversely proportional to changes in wire size.

Despite this severe limitation, a class of problems exist that can be solved by this technique.

Problem 8-1 Economic lot size in production run

A manufacturer has to produce 50,000 parts a year and wishes to select the most economical lot size to be equally spaced during the year. The annual cost of storage and interest on investment varies directly with the lot size and is $1000 when the entire annual requirement is manufactured in one lot. The cost of setting up and dismantling the machine for each run is $30. What is the most economical lot size?

Solution:

Although this problem has nothing to do with copper wire, the storage and investment cost varies directly with lot size and setup cost varies inversely. The situation is analogous to Lord Kelvin's and can be solved by his technique.

Let x = size of lot produced in one run.

Storage and interest = $1000(x/50{,}000)$
Setup = 30(number of runs) = $30(50{,}000/x)$

Setting one equal to the other and solving for x:

$$1000(x/50{,}000) = 30(50{,}000/x)$$
$$x^2 = 75{,}000{,}000$$
$$x = 8700 \text{ parts in each run} \qquad \textit{Answer}$$

8-2 ECONOMIC LOT SIZE

The above was a special case of the economic lot size problem. A more generalized approach, which would result in a correct solution even if costs do not vary directly and inversely, involves setting up an equation in total cost. This equation is differentiated and set equal to zero. A solution for the unknown will result in a minimum cost. (If second derivative is negative, a maximum cost would be the result.)

Problem 8-2 Economic lot size in purchasing raw material

A certain chemical compound is purchased for use as a raw material in a manufacturing plant. The clerical and accounting costs involved in making a purchase are $21 per purchase order regardless of the size of the lot purchased. Throughout the year, 3000 gallons of this compound are consumed at a fairly uniform rate. It is purchased and stored in 50-gallon drums. Its purchase price per gallon, including freight, is $3.30. Annual storage costs are estimated as 50 cents per drum of maximum inventory. Annual carrying charges are estimated as 12% on average inventory. To assure continuous operations at least 200 gallons should be maintained on hand at all times as an emergency stock. What is the most economical size of lot to purchase?

Solution:

Let x = size of lot in drums.
Order cost = $21(60/x)
Cost of material = 3000($3.30)
Maximum inventory = 4 + x
Storage cost = 0.50(4 + x)
Average inventory = 4 + x/2
Inventory cost = (0.12)(165)(4 + x/2)
Total cost = 21(60/x) + 3000(3.30) + 0.50(4 + x) + (0.12)(165)(4 + x/2)

Differentiate and set equal to zero:

$$0 = -1260/x^2 + 0.50 + 9.90$$

$$10.4x^2 = 1260$$

$$x = 11$$ *Answer*

8-3 OTHER USES OF ECONOMIC LOT SIZE

The technique employed above can be used in other applications where costs are to be minimized.

Problem 8-3 Economic speed for machining operation

The operating cost, in dollars per hour, of a certain machining operation is proportional to the cube of the cutting speed, and equals $12.00/hr when the cutting speed is 2000 in./hr. Fixed charges on the machine are $5.00/hr. Determine the most economical speed for an operation that required the equivalent of machining 40,000 inches.

Solution:

Let x = cutting speed.

Number of hours of operation = 40,000/x
Operating cost = $12(x/2000)^3(40,000/x)$
Fixed charges = 5(40,000/x)
Total cost = $12(x/2000)^3(40,000/x) + 5(40,000/x)$

Differentiate and set equal to zero:

$$0 = 12x/100{,}000 - 200{,}000/x^2$$

$$x^3 = 1.66 \times 10^9$$

$$x = 1190 \text{ in./hr}$$

8-4 INSURANCE

Insurance charges have been treated, up to this point, as ordinary annual costs and have been included as such in total annual costs computed for an alternative. This actually involves an assumption that insurance coverage will be complete, that is, any losses sustained will be fully paid for by the insurance company. This is, of course, not always the case. In many policies, the insured company must share the loss.

A closer look at insurance is warranted. An insurance company will contract to relieve the policy-holder of a certain risk in exchange for a payment (premium). This premium represents the amount the insurance company needs to cover losses, expenses, and profit. The insurance company will write many such policies and can anticipate its losses based upon probabilities and charge appropriate premiums.

The portion of the risk that is covered by insurance can be included in an economy study simply by adding the insurance premium to the annual cost. If this represents only a portion of the risk, the balance is borne by the insured. This amount should also be included as a part of annual cost. An acceptable estimate of this cost can be obtained from the insurance company payment. For example, if the insurance company premium payment is $3000 and this would cover 75% of any loss, an appropriate charge for the company share of this risk is

$$25/75 \times 3000 = \$1000$$

This assumes that all of the $3000 premium was for risk (ignoring other costs and profit). Although this is a simplifying assumption, it is on the conservative side and results in an acceptable approximation.

8-5 INCORPORATION OF RISK IN ECONOMY STUDIES

In Sec. 8-4, the risk was covered (in part, at least) by an insurance company. Where this is not the case, the risk must still be accounted for in determining annual cost. If the probability of a loss and the amount of the loss are known, the annual cost due to risk is calculated as the product of the two.

Problem 8-4 Annual cost of new bridge vs. old bridge considering probability of loss

A small stream subject to heavy spring floods runs through a town. One of the bridges crossing the stream has been found unsafe and must be rebuilt.

The cost of constructing a new bridge and approaches capable of withstanding stream flows of varying crest, and the cost of rebuilding the bridge if damaged by flood, are estimated as follows:

Plan	*A*	*B*	*C*
Crest (above normal)	5 ft	8 ft	12 ft
Probable frequency of occurrence years	1 in 10	1 in 40	1 in 160
Initial cost of structure	\$320,000	\$400,000	\$490,000
Annual maintenance	\$9500	\$11,700	\$13,600
Estimated cost of rebuilding	\$285,000	\$320,000	\$400,000

Assume the life of the structure at 40 years, no salvage value and 4% interest rate. Calculate the annual costs for each of the three alternatives, including the cost of probable rebuilding, and determine which will result in the lowest annual cost.

Solution:

Plan A:

$$\text{Total annual cost} = 320{,}000\left[\frac{0.04(1.04)^{40}}{(1.04)^{40}-1}\right] + 9500 + \frac{1}{10}(285{,}000)$$

$$= \$54{,}200 \quad \textit{Answer}$$

Plan B:

$$\text{Total annual cost} = 400{,}000\left[\frac{0.04(1.04)^{40}}{(1.04)^{40}-1}\right] + 11{,}700 + \frac{1}{40}(320{,}000)$$

$$= \$39{,}900 \quad \textit{Answer}$$

Plan C:

$$\text{Total annual cost} = 490{,}000\left[\frac{0.04(1.04)^{40}}{(1.04)^{40}-1}\right] + 13{,}600 + \frac{1}{160}(400{,}000)$$

$$= \$40{,}900 \quad \textit{Answer}$$

chapter 9
INCOME TAXES

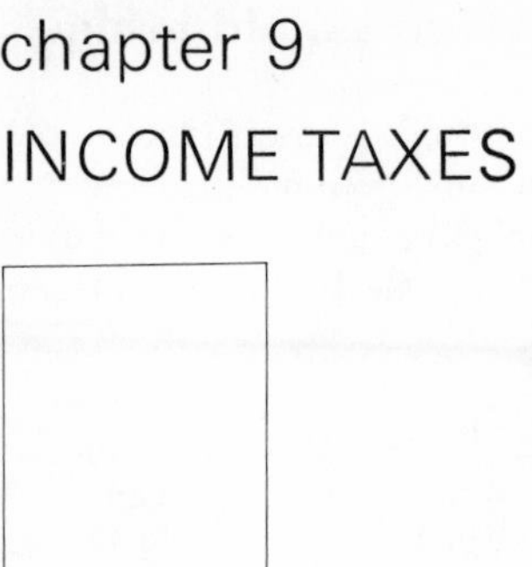

9-1 RELATIONSHIP TO ENGINEERING ECONOMY

Most taxes, such as property taxes, are treated in engineering economy as annual costs in the same manner as insurance, maintenance, and supplies. Income taxes, however, are based upon earnings and cannot be determined until all income and other expenses are known. A further problem arises because the tax is *graduated,* that is, the rate increases as earnings increase.

Federal Income Tax is a complicated subject. A large number of professionals dedicate all of their time to taxes and schools of law and business administration offer many courses in this subject. The engineer is not expected to be a tax expert, but it is critical that he understand the effect of taxes before undertaking an economy study.

In the ordinary case, if Alternative A is superior to Alternative B prior to income tax considerations, it will also be superior after taxes. There are special cases, however, that can change this relationship and make one type of income superior to another of the same amount. These cases are considered in Secs. 9-2, 9-3, and 9-4.

The Federal Income Tax is a graduated tax based upon earnings. Individuals, partnerships, and corporations must file, and each of these groups is treated differently.

For the individual, the tax computation starts with determination of total income. From this can be deducted nontaxable income (Sec. 9-4). There are also certain other allowable deductions and exemptions. After all deductions have been made, the balance, called taxable income, is the amount upon which the tax is computed. The tax is graduated with succeeding amounts of income being taxed at progressively higher rates. The total tax is the sum of these incremental amounts.

Partnerships do not pay taxes directly, but the income from partnership earnings is prorated to the partners who must include it in their individual returns. Corporations are discussed in Sec. 9-5.

Change is the rule in Federal Income Taxes. Rates go up and down and allowable deductions change, as do amounts for certain items. Current rates and regulations are available from offices of the Internal Revenue Service.

9-2 CAPITAL GAINS

Capital assets can roughly be defined, for tax purposes, as securities (stocks and bonds), real estate, and depreciable assets used in a business. If a capital asset is owned for six months or less and a gain resulted from the sale, this gain is called a "short-term gain," treated as ordinary income, and taxed at regular rates. If the capital asset is owned for more than six months, the gain is called a "long-term gain," and the taxpayer can select one of two alternatives, each of which would result in a smaller tax payment than ordinary income.

Alternate one allows the taxpayer to take 50% of the gain and add it to ordinary income. This reduces the amount of tax paid by at least one-half paid on ordinary income.

The second alternate is to pay a tax of 50% on one-half of the long-term gain. This limits the tax on income from long-term gains to 25%. The effect of these two alternates is a minimum savings of 50% on the tax that would be paid on ordinary income. For high income taxpayers, the savings are considerably higher. The taxpayer can use the alternative that results in the lower tax.

9-3 DEPLETION ALLOWANCE

Natural resources, such as oil, coal and ores, are depleted as they are removed from the ground. Depletion of these resources is analogous to depreciation of buildings and machinery.

Federal Income Tax Laws provide a method of computing depletion charges, however, that allows total depletion charges to exceed costs. This is not the case in computing depreciation charges. The method allows a flat percentage of gross income from the property to be taken as a depletion deduction from income. The deduction may not exceed 50% of the taxable net income from the property computed without a depletion charge.

9-4 NONTAXABLE INCOME

All income is not treated equally under Federal tax law. As indicated above, capital gains income and income from depletable resources can be of greater value than ordinary income.

Some income is completely tax exempt. Examples of this category are:

Interest earned on state and municipal bonds
Life insurance benefits
Portion of annuities
Social security benefits
Disability insurance benefits
Unemployment insurance payments

9-5 CORPORATION TAX

The tax on corporations is graduated, but, unlike individual taxes, only in two steps. The tax rates have varied from year to year, but have had one rate for income below $25,000 and a higher rate for income over $25,000.

The tax rates are applied to net income. Net income used in computation of Federal Income Tax is approximately the same income calculated for corporate purposes.

Problem 9-1 Rate of sales for given annual net profit after taxes

A private corporation desires to build a water system to serve a newly developed community. This community will use 150,000,000 gallons of water per year. The facilities to be installed will cost \$700,000, and it is estimated that operation and maintenance of the system will cost \$39,300 annually. Operating taxes will be \$14,000 per year and income taxes will be 30% of the first \$25,000 net revenue and 52% of net revenue over \$25,000. The life of the water system properties is 70 years, and a 4% sinking fund is to be established for depreciation. At what rate per 1000 gallons must the water be sold to return an annual net profit of 6% after income taxes on the original investment?

Solution:

The solution of this problem requires preparation of a profit and loss statement in reverse. We know the profit desired and we must calculate the income necessary to produce this profit.

(a) Profit after taxes = \$700,000(0.06) = \$42,000

(b) The income before taxes, x, required to produce \$42,000 after taxes can be considered to be in two parts: \$25,000 and x − \$25,000. The tax on \$25,000 is \$25,000(0.30) = \$7500. Thus, \$17,500 remains from the first \$25,000 in income after taxes have been applied. This leaves \$24,500 in income after taxes to be obtained from income over \$25,000. Therefore,

$$(x - 25{,}000)0.48 = 24{,}500 \qquad (0.48 \text{ is } 100\% - 52\%)$$
$$x = 51{,}000 + 25{,}000 = \$76{,}000$$

(c) To obtain gross income from the net income calculated above, expenses must be added to \$76,000.

Expenses:

Operation and maintenance	= \$39,300
Operating taxes	= 14,000
Depreciation $700{,}000\left(\dfrac{0.04}{(1.04)^{70} - 1}\right)$	= 1,925
	\$55,225

Gross income = \$76,000 + \$55,225 = \$131,225

Rate required per 1000 gallons = 131,225/150,000 = \$0.875 *Answer*

9-6 CARRY-BACK AND CARRY-OVER

Some businesses are of the "feast-or-famine" type and have very good years and very bad ones. In order to minimize unfair taxation relative to companies with a more stabilized income, the Federal Income Tax Law provides that net operating losses can be carried back to offset profits earned in three previous years, and if a portion of the loss remained, forward for five years.

For example, a company with a net operating loss of $10,000 in 1966, could reduce the taxable income, if any, in 1963, 1964, or 1965. If income in these years was $2000, $4000, and $1000, respectively, they could eliminate the tax payable for those years. Since only $7000 of the $10,000 has been used, $3000 can be applied against income for 1967 or four years thereafter.

chapter 10
CORPORATE FINANCE

10-1 FINANCIAL STATEMENTS

Corporate finance is a complex study and has been the subject of much study. The presentation here will be brief, limited to a look at some of the items in the corporate financial statements, why they are there, and how they affect financial position.

The two basic financial statements prepared by all corporations are the statement of financial position (balance sheet) and the statement of income and expenditures (profit and loss). Other statements are often prepared, but they are subsidiary or supplementary to the financial position and income statements.

The statement of financial position balances assets against liabilities and capital. The income statement lists revenues, costs and other deductions, and net income. Net income, less dividends paid, is added to capital each year and therefore the two statements are interrelated, with the income statement really a subsidiary. A statement of financial position contains:

Assets

Cash
Marketable securities
Notes and accounts receivable
Inventories
Property, plant, and equipment

Liabilities

Notes and loans payable
Accounts payable
Long-term debt

Capital

Preferred stock
Common stock
Reinvested earnings

10-2 CORPORATE BONDS

Corporate bonds are included in the liabilities section, under long-term debt. They are obligations of the corporation. Corporations borrow large sums of money, usually to meet a long-term need, by selling bonds. The bonds are sold through investment bankers or brokers to individuals, companies, or others who want to earn the interest paid for the use of their money. The bond holder receives a specific amount of interest each year and the original principal is returned after the term of the bond has expired. The bond holder, as a creditor of the corporation, must be paid the interest due to him. Failure of the corporation to meet this obligation can lead to bankruptcy.

Bonds can be classified as mortgage bonds or debenture bonds. A mortgage bond has a specific asset, such as a building, serving as security for the indebtedness. A debenture bond has no specific asset pledged in security. The difference is of importance only in the event of failure of the corporation. If this occurs, the mortgage bond holder will have first claim to the pledged assets; the debenture bond holders will have to wait in line with all other creditors for a share of the proceeds from other assets. This difference results in debenture bonds offering a higher interest rate than mortgage bonds of the same corporation. Debenture bonds issued by a sound corporation, however, are to be preferred to the mortgage bonds of a shaky company.

In order to make a bond issue more attractive to the public, a "convertible" feature is sometimes included. This permits the bond holder to convert his bonds into common stock at a predesignated ratio. This enables the bond holder to share in major increases in value that may accrue to the common stock.

A "serial" bond issue is one in which some of the bonds are made to mature each year, or half year, instead of all on a single date.

10-3 COMMON STOCK

Common stock represents the ownership interest of the corporation. This interest is divided into shares or units. Common stock ordinarily carries voting rights in the corporation, by which the owners can control the corporation. Common stockholders can receive dividends, if the earnings of the corporation are sufficient. There is no legal requirement that the corporation pay dividends and they can be skipped in lean years.

Par value: the sum stated in the charter as the nominal value of a share of stock.

No-par value stock: In order to eliminate the misleading par-value listing on the stock certificate, many corporations issue common stock with no par listed.

Book value: The book value of a share of common stock can be determined by subtracting total liabilities and preferred stock from total asset value and dividing the difference by the total number of shares of common stock outstanding.

Market value: the price at which a share of stock can be bought or sold on an exchange or over-the-counter.

Non-voting common stock: Some corporations have issued common stock with the same dividend rights as ordinary common, but without voting privileges. This technique can be used to maintain company control.

10-4 PREFERRED STOCK

Preferred stock has prior right to dividends. It usually does not bring voting rights to the owners and the dividend is fixed and cannot be higher than the specified amount.

Many preferred stocks are cumulative in dividend payments. If a dividend payment is skipped for a cumulative preferred stock, it is necessary that the corporation pay all such skipped dividends prior to payment of any common dividends.

Preferred stock, in some cases, is convertible. This provision allows preferred stock holders to convert their stock to common, at a prearranged rate.

10-5 INVENTORY

Inventory valuation affects indicated profit, equity of stock holders, and income tax payments. The problem arises because inventory items are purchased at varying prices and can be put into production at different prices.

Three methods on inventory valuation are first-in, first-out (FIFO), last-in, first-out (LIFO), and average cost. To illustrate these three methods, assume the XYZ Corporation starts the year with no inventory of raw material A. On January 2, they purchase 100 units at $10 per unit; on January 5, 100 units at $12 per unit; and on January 8, issue from stock into production 60 units.

Using FIFO, the inventory picture would be:

Date	
1/2	100 @ 10 = $1000
1/5	100 @ 12 = 1200
W.D. 1/8	60 @ 10 = 600
Balance 1/8	40 @ 10 = 400
	100 @ 12 = 1200
Inv. 1/8	$1600

Using LIFO,

Date	
1/2	100 @ 10 = $1000
1/5	100 @ 12 = 1200
W.D. 1/8	60 @ 12 = 720
Balance 1/8	100 @ 10 = 1000
	40 @ 12 = 480
Inv. 1/8	$1480

Using average cost,

Date	
1/2	100 @ 10 = $1000
1/5	100 @ 12 = 1200
W.D. 1/8	60 @ 11 = 660
Balance 1/8	140 @ 11 = $1540

It is obvious that different results are achieved with each of the three methods. Comparing LIFO and FIFO, for example, there is a difference of $120 in cost charged to production and therefore profit. Balance sheet inventory varied by the same amount in the opposite direction. This affects the tax paid by the corporation, the equity of the shareholders and the apparent cost of production.

It should be noted that the corporation has actually produced the same product and done as well financially in each case; it is the financial reporting of the results that varies.

10-6 CASH FLOW

Financial management of a corporation involves more than close attention to income and expenses. Although it is critical that a company earn a profit, financial management must also be concerned with availability of funds to meet corporate obligations. It is largely a question of timing purchases, and involvements in securities, to have cash available. The study of the receipt and disbursement of cash is known as cash flow.

Capital expenditures cannot be fully charged to the operations of the year in which they are made. Therefore, a corporation's expenditures can exceed its cash receipts even in profitable years by expending large sums on machinery, equipment or buildings. Means must be found to provide the cash needed. Sources of cash are bank loans, bonds, sale of securities held, and, depreciation.

Depreciation, although a legitimate expense, does not entail disbursement of cash. The cash was disbursed when the depreciable asset was purchased. Therefore, depreciation charges represent a source of funds and can be added to profits, when available funds are considered.

chapter 11

LEGAL AND ETHICAL CONSIDERATIONS

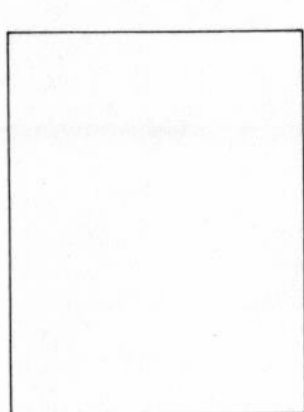

11-1 THE ENGINEERS' CODE

Each professional society has a code of principles to which they expect members to adhere. The canons listed below are those approved by the Engineers' Council for Professional Development.

Fundamental Principles of Professional Engineering Ethics

The Engineer, to uphold and advance the honor and dignity of the engineering profession and in keeping with high standards of ethical conduct:

I. Will be honest and impartial, and will serve with devotion his employer, his clients, and the public;

II. Will strive to increase the competence and prestige of the engineering profession;

III. Will use his knowledge and skill for the advancement of human welfare.

Relations with the Public

1.1 The Engineer will have proper regard for the safety, health and welfare of the public in the performance of his professional duties.

1.2 He will endeavor to extend public knowledge and appreciation of engineering and its achievements, and will oppose any untrue, unsupported, or exaggerated statements regarding engineering.

1.3 He will be dignified and modest in explaining his work and merit, will ever uphold the honor and dignity of his profession, and will refrain from self-laudatory advertising.

1.4 He will express an opinion on an engineering subject only when it is founded on adequate knowledge and honest conviction.

1.5 He will preface any *ex parte* statements, criticisms, or arguments that he may issue by clearly indicating on whose behalf they are made.

Relations with Employers and Clients

2.1 The Engineer will act in professional matters as a faithful agent or trustee for each employer or client.

2.2 He will act fairly and justly toward vendors and contractors, and will not accept from vendors or contractors, any commissions or allowances, directly or indirectly.

2.3 He will inform his employer or client if he is financially interested in any vendor or contractor, or in any invention, machine, or apparatus, which is involved in a project or work of his employer or client. He will not allow such interest to affect his decisions regarding engineering services which he may be called upon to perform.

2.4 He will indicate to his employer or client the adverse consequences to be expected if his engineering judgment is over-ruled.

2.5 He will undertake only those engineering assignments for which he is qualified. He will engage or advise his employer or client to engage specialists and will cooperate with them whenever his employer's or client's interests are served best by such an arrangement.

2.6 He will not disclose information concerning the business affairs or technical processes of any present or former employer or client without his consent.

2.7 He will not accept compensation—financial or otherwise—from more than one party for the same service, or for other services pertaining to the same work, without the consent of all interested parties.

2.8 The employed engineer will engage in supplementary employment or consulting practice only with the consent of his employer.

Relations with Engineers

3.1 The Engineer will take care that credit for engineering work is given to those to whom credit is properly due.

3.2 He will provide a prospective engineering employee with complete information on working conditions and his proposed status of employment, and after employment will keep him informed of any changes in them.

3.3 He will uphold the principle of appropriate and adequate compensation for those engaged in engineering work, including those in subordinate capacities.

3.4 He will endeavor to provide opportunity for the professional development and advancement of engineers in his employ or under his supervision.

3.5 He will not injure maliciously the professional reputation, prospects, or practice of another engineer. However, if he has proof that another engineer has been unethical, illegal, or unfair in his practice, he should so advise the proper authority.

3.6 He will not compete unfairly with another engineer.

3.7 He will not invite or submit price proposals for professional services, which require creative intellectual effort, on a basis that constitutes competition on price alone. Due regard should be given to all professional aspects of the engagement.

3.8 He will cooperate in advancing the engineering profession by interchanging information and experience with other engineers and students, and by contributing to public communication media, to the efforts of engineering and scientific societies and schools.

11-2 SELECTION OF AN ENGINEER

The American Society of Civil Engineers recommends the following procedure in obtaining the services of an engineer:

1. From a list of engineers recommended by qualified sources, such as other employers or engineering societies, select one or more engineers to be interviewed.
2. Determine which one of the engineers interviewed is best qualified for the particular engagement under consideration.
3. Negotiate with the engineer so selected for services of the nature and extent required.
4. The reasonableness of fees to be charged may be checked with the sources contacted during step 1 above.
5. Engagements involving preliminary investigation and reports should commit the engineer to limiting fees in case additional engineering services are required at a later date on the same project.

11-3 CONTRACTS FOR ENGINEERS' SERVICES

Contracts for engineering services are usually designated by the method of compensation. Several typical types are:

(a) *Cost plus Fixed Fee:* Covers all costs of the engineer plus a predetermined amount for profit. This type of contract has an advantage where the scope of services required cannot be accurately determined. Detailed records must be kept, however, in order to segregate costs.

(b) *Per Diem:* Based upon time the engineer and his staff devote to the work.

(c) *Retainer:* A minimum amount paid to the engineer to retain his services for the year. He can be paid for additional work beyond the minimum.

(d) *Percentage of Construction Cost:* Widely used, this method has the advantage of basing payment on the size of the project. Cost of financing the project and legal fees are generally not included as part of construction cost.

(e) *Lump-Sum Fee:* Predetermined fee based upon a percentage of expected construction cost.

11-4 OWNER, CONTRACTOR, ENGINEER

In construction contracts, the engineer is ordinarily the agent of the owner. The law specifically defines the legal implication of an agency relationship. An agent is limited in action to the scope of the agency; but within that scope he acts on behalf of the owner (principal). The principal is liable for the acts of his agent and is bound by contracts made in his name by the agent within the authority of the agency.

As an agent, the engineer is required to exercise care, skill, and diligence in carrying out his specified duties. He is liable for damages if errors occur due to lack of diligence. If the agency was obtained by misrepresentation of skills, he is liable for breach of contract or possibly for fraud.

The independent contractor specifies results to be obtained, but not methods and the owner has no control or direction over these methods. The owner is not liable for the actions of an independent contractor. It is therefore greatly to the advantage of the owner to have the contractor an independent contractor rather than an agent.

11-5 SOME OTHER CONSIDERATIONS

Subcontracts. The prime contractor is responsible for the acts of the subcontractors and is liable for any damages suffered by the owner at the hands of a subcontractor.

Combined contracts. If the owner does not choose to deal with both an engineer and a contractor, he may enter into one agreement to cover both aspects. In this case, the engineer is placed in partnership with the contractor. This type of agreement can impede the independent action of the engineer.

chapter 12
MISCELLANEOUS TOPICS

12-1 PATENTS

A patent may be obtained by the inventor or discoverer of any new and useful process, machine, manufacture, or composition of matter, or new and useful improvement thereof, unless:

(a) The invention was known or used by others, or patented, or described in a printed publication, prior to the invention by the applicant.
(b) The invention was patented or described more than one year prior to the date of application.
(c) The invention has been abandoned.
(d) The invention was first patented by the inventor or his representatives in a foreign country prior to the date of the application for patent in this country on an application filed more than twelve months before the filing in the United States.
(e) The invention was previously described in a patent granted in the United States.
(f) The applicant did not invent the subject matter sought to be patented.
(g) The invention was made in this country by another who had not abandoned, suppressed, or concealed it prior to the applicant's invention.

Application for a patent must be made in writing to the Commissioner of Patents. The application should include:

Specification. A written description of the invention, and of the manner and process of making and using it, in such full, clear, concise and exact terms as to enable any person skilled in the art to which it pertains to make and use the same, and shall set forth the best mode contemplated by the inventor of carrying out his invention.

Drawings. When appropriate, the applicant shall furnish a drawing.

Models, specimens. The Commissioner may require the applicant to furnish a model of convenient size to exhibit his invention. If a composition of matter, the applicant may be required to furnish specimens.

Oath of Applicant. The applicant shall make oath, before any person within the United States authorized by law to administer oaths, that he believes himself to be the original and first inventor of the process, machine, manufacture, or composition of matter, and shall state of what country he is a citizen.

If a patent is granted, the patentee has remedy by civil action for infringement of his patent. A patent is presumed valid. The burden of establishing invalidity of a patent rests on the party asserting invalidity. The courts may grant injunctions to prevent the violation of any right secured by a patent. Damages may be awarded by the court to compensate the patentee for infringement of his patent.

12-2 COPYRIGHTS

Copyright, limiting unauthorized use, can be obtained for books, periodicals, dramatic compositions, musical compositions, works of art, etc. Application is made to the Register of Copyrights, Library of Congress. The holder of a copyright has exclusive right to print, reprint, publish, copy, and sell the copyrighted work. He also has the right to perform or present the work if it is drama or a musical composition and to translate it to foreign languages.

Infringement of a copyright can lead to injunction restraining such infringement and award of damages to copyright owner that include profits made by the infringer.

12-3 TRADEMARKS

A trademark, as defined by the Trademark Act of 1946, "includes any word, name, symbol, or device, or any combination thereof adopted and used by a manufacturer or merchant to identify his goods and distinguish them from those manufactured or sold by others." Rights in a trademark are acquired only by use and the use must ordinarily continue if the rights so acquired are to be preserved.

The application for registration must be filed in the name of the owner of the mark. A complete application comprises:

(a) A written application, in the English language, on legal size paper. The application should contain the name, citizenship, domicile, and address of the applicant. It should state that the applicant has adopted the mark, the goods on which it is being used, and the date of first use.
(b) A drawing of the mark, upon pure white durable paper, in india ink.
(c) Five specimens or facsimiles of the mark.
(d) The required filing fee ($25 for registration).

A trademark may not be registered if it consists of immoral, deceptive, or scandalous matter or falsely suggests a connection with persons living or dead. A trademark will not be registered if it uses a national or state flag or resembles another mark sufficiently to cause mistake.

If it appears that applicant is entitled to have his mark registered, it is published in the Official Gazette and is subject to opposition. Opposition may be filed within 30 days after publication.

A trademark registration is issued for a 20-year period and may be renewed.

Any use of the trademark, without the consent of the registrant, shall make the infringer liable in a civil action by the registrant. The registrant shall not be entitled to recover profits or damages if acts are committed without intention.

Remedies under the trademark law are similar to remedies available to patent holders.

12-4 INDEX NUMBERS

An index number is a ratio between an aggregation of items at one time and a similar group at an earlier time.

Index numbers are used to indicate changes in a wide variety of conditions. They are popular because they can express in one number a combination of factors that can be easily used and understood. Comparison of changes over a period of time is facilitated through use of index numbers.

Some commonly used numbers are:

Wholesale Price Index. Published by Bureau of Labor Statistics and available monthly. It is widely used in government and industry. The Wholesale Price Index combines some 4000 items at the wholesale level.

Bureau of Labor Statistics Consumer's Price Index. Defines a "market basket" of goods and services bought by typical families and compares the cost in one week with the cost in 1947–1949.

U.S. Construction Cost Index. Prepared by *Engineering News Record,* it is a synthetic index based upon a combination of labor and material costs.

Table A-1. Compound Amount Factor

Compound amount factor $(1 + i)^n$ to determine future worth of a single amount. For present worth, use reciprocal factor.

n	.5%	1.0%	1.5%	2.0%	2.5%	3.0%	3.5%	4.0%	4.5%	5.0%	5.5%	6.0%
1	1.005	1.010	1.015	1.020	1.025	1.030	1.035	1.040	1.045	1.050	1.055	1.060
2	1.010	1.020	1.030	1.040	1.051	1.061	1.071	1.082	1.092	1.102	1.113	1.124
3	1.015	1.030	1.046	1.061	1.077	1.093	1.109	1.125	1.141	1.158	1.174	1.191
4	1.020	1.041	1.061	1.082	1.104	1.126	1.148	1.170	1.193	1.216	1.239	1.262
5	1.025	1.051	1.077	1.104	1.131	1.159	1.188	1.217	1.246	1.276	1.307	1.338
6	1.030	1.062	1.093	1.126	1.160	1.194	1.229	1.265	1.302	1.340	1.379	1.419
7	1.036	1.072	1.110	1.149	1.189	1.230	1.272	1.316	1.361	1.407	1.455	1.504
8	1.041	1.083	1.126	1.172	1.218	1.267	1.317	1.369	1.422	1.477	1.535	1.594
9	1.046	1.094	1.143	1.195	1.249	1.305	1.363	1.423	1.486	1.551	1.619	1.689
10	1.051	1.105	1.161	1.219	1.280	1.344	1.411	1.480	1.553	1.629	1.708	1.791
11	1.056	1.116	1.178	1.243	1.312	1.384	1.460	1.539	1.623	1.710	1.802	1.898
12	1.062	1.127	1.196	1.268	1.345	1.426	1.511	1.601	1.696	1.796	1.901	2.012
13	1.067	1.138	1.214	1.294	1.379	1.469	1.564	1.665	1.772	1.886	2.006	2.133
14	1.072	1.149	1.232	1.319	1.413	1.513	1.619	1.732	1.852	1.980	2.116	2.261
15	1.078	1.161	1.250	1.346	1.448	1.558	1.675	1.801	1.935	2.079	2.232	2.397
16	1.083	1.173	1.269	1.373	1.485	1.605	1.734	1.873	2.022	2.183	2.355	2.540
17	1.088	1.184	1.288	1.400	1.522	1.653	1.795	1.948	2.113	2.292	2.485	2.693
18	1.094	1.196	1.307	1.428	1.560	1.702	1.857	2.026	2.208	2.407	2.621	2.854
19	1.099	1.208	1.327	1.457	1.599	1.754	1.923	2.107	2.308	2.527	2.766	3.026
20	1.105	1.220	1.347	1.486	1.639	1.806	1.990	2.191	2.412	2.653	2.918	3.207
21	1.110	1.232	1.367	1.516	1.680	1.860	2.059	2.279	2.520	2.786	3.078	3.400
22	1.116	1.245	1.388	1.546	1.722	1.916	2.132	2.370	2.634	2.925	3.248	3.604
23	1.122	1.257	1.408	1.577	1.765	1.974	2.206	2.465	2.752	3.072	3.426	3.820
24	1.127	1.270	1.430	1.608	1.809	2.033	2.283	2.563	2.876	3.225	3.615	4.049
25	1.133	1.282	1.451	1.641	1.854	2.094	2.363	2.666	3.005	3.386	3.813	4.292
26	1.138	1.295	1.473	1.673	1.900	2.157	2.446	2.772	3.141	3.556	4.023	4.549
27	1.144	1.308	1.495	1.707	1.948	2.221	2.532	2.883	3.282	3.733	4.244	4.822
28	1.150	1.321	1.517	1.741	1.996	2.288	2.620	2.999	3.430	3.920	4.478	5.112
29	1.156	1.335	1.540	1.776	2.046	2.357	2.712	3.119	3.584	4.116	4.724	5.418
30	1.161	1.348	1.563	1.811	2.098	2.427	2.807	3.243	3.745	4.322	4.984	5.743
31	1.167	1.361	1.587	1.848	2.150	2.500	2.905	3.373	3.914	4.538	5.258	6.088
32	1.173	1.375	1.610	1.885	2.204	2.575	3.007	3.508	4.090	4.765	5.547	6.453
33	1.179	1.389	1.634	1.922	2.259	2.652	3.112	3.648	4.274	5.003	5.852	6.841
34	1.185	1.403	1.659	1.961	2.315	2.732	3.221	3.794	4.466	5.253	6.174	7.251
35	1.191	1.417	1.684	2.000	2.373	2.814	3.334	3.946	4.667	5.516	6.514	7.686
36	1.197	1.431	1.709	2.040	2.433	2.898	3.450	4.104	4.877	5.792	6.872	8.147
37	1.203	1.445	1.735	2.081	2.493	2.985	3.571	4.268	5.097	6.081	7.250	8.636
38	1.209	1.460	1.761	2.122	2.556	3.075	3.696	4.439	5.326	6.385	7.649	9.154
39	1.215	1.474	1.787	2.165	2.620	3.167	3.825	4.616	5.566	6.705	8.069	9.704
40	1.221	1.489	1.814	2.208	2.685	3.262	3.959	4.801	5.816	7.040	8.513	10.29
42	1.233	1.519	1.869	2.297	2.821	3.461	4.241	5.193	6.352	7.762	9.476	11.56
44	1.245	1.549	1.925	2.390	2.964	3.671	4.543	5.617	6.936	8.557	10.55	12.99
46	1.258	1.580	1.984	2.487	3.114	3.895	4.867	6.075	7.574	9.434	11.74	14.59
48	1.270	1.612	2.043	2.587	3.271	4.132	5.214	6.571	8.271	10.40	13.07	16.39
50	1.283	1.645	2.105	2.692	3.437	4.384	5.585	7.107	9.033	11.47	14.54	18.42
52	1.296	1.678	2.169	2.800	3.611	4.651	5.983	7.687	9.864	12.64	16.19	20.70
54	1.309	1.711	2.234	2.913	3.794	4.934	6.409	8.314	10.77	13.94	18.01	23.26
56	1.322	1.746	2.302	3.031	3.986	5.235	6.865	8.992	11.76	15.37	20.05	26.13
58	1.335	1.781	2.372	3.154	4.188	5.553	7.354	9.726	12.85	16.94	22.32	29.36
60	1.349	1.817	2.443	3.281	4.400	5.892	7.878	10.52	14.03	18.68	24.84	32.99
65	1.383	1.909	2.632	3.623	4.978	6.830	9.357	12.80	17.48	23.84	32.46	44.14
70	1.418	2.007	2.835	4.000	5.632	7.918	11.11	15.57	21.78	30.43	42.43	59.08
75	1.454	2.109	3.055	4.416	6.372	9.179	13.20	18.95	27.15	38.83	55.45	79.06
80	1.490	2.217	3.291	4.875	7.210	10.64	15.68	23.05	33.83	49.56	72.48	105.8
85	1.528	2.330	3.545	5.383	8.157	12.34	18.62	28.04	42.16	63.25	94.72	141.6
90	1.567	2.449	3.819	5.943	9.229	14.30	22.11	34.12	52.54	80.73	123.8	189.5
95	1.606	2.574	4.114	6.562	10.44	16.58	26.26	41.51	65.47	103.0	161.8	253.5
100	1.647	2.705	4.432	7.245	11.81	19.22	31.19	50.50	81.59	131.5	211.5	339.3

Note: Tables A-1, A-2, and A-3 are from *Project Economy* by Edwin S. Roscoe. Homewood, Illinois: Richard D. Irwin, Inc., 1961. Reprinted with permission.

Table A-1. Compound Amount Factor (Cont.)

n	7%	8%	9%	10%	11%	12%	13%	14%	15%	16%	17%	18%
1	1.070	1.080	1.090	1.100	1.110	1.120	1.130	1.140	1.150	1.160	1.170	1.180
2	1.145	1.166	1.188	1.210	1.232	1.254	1.277	1.300	1.322	1.346	1.369	1.392
3	1.225	1.260	1.295	1.331	1.368	1.405	1.443	1.482	1.521	1.561	1.602	1.643
4	1.311	1.360	1.412	1.464	1.518	1.574	1.630	1.689	1.749	1.811	1.874	1.939
5	1.403	1.469	1.539	1.611	1.685	1.762	1.842	1.925	2.011	2.100	2.192	2.288
6	1.501	1.587	1.677	1.772	1.870	1.974	2.082	2.195	2.313	2.436	2.565	2.700
7	1.606	1.714	1.828	1.949	2.076	2.211	2.353	2.502	2.660	2.826	3.001	3.185
8	1.718	1.851	1.993	2.144	2.305	2.476	2.658	2.853	3.059	3.278	3.511	3.759
9	1.838	1.999	2.172	2.358	2.558	2.773	3.004	3.252	3.518	3.803	4.108	4.435
10	1.967	2.159	2.367	2.594	2.839	3.106	3.395	3.707	4.046	4.411	4.807	5.234
11	2.105	2.332	2.580	2.853	3.152	3.479	3.836	4.226	4.652	5.117	5.624	6.176
12	2.252	2.518	2.813	3.138	3.498	3.896	4.335	4.818	5.350	5.936	6.580	7.288
13	2.410	2.720	3.066	3.452	3.883	4.363	4.898	5.492	6.153	6.886	7.699	8.599
14	2.579	2.937	3.342	3.797	4.310	4.887	5.535	6.261	7.076	7.988	9.007	10.15
15	2.759	3.172	3.642	4.177	4.785	5.474	6.254	7.138	8.137	9.266	10.54	11.97
16	2.952	3.426	3.970	4.595	5.311	6.130	7.067	8.137	9.358	10.75	12.33	14.13
17	3.159	3.700	4.328	5.054	5.895	6.866	7.986	9.276	10.76	12.47	14.43	16.67
18	3.380	3.996	4.717	5.560	6.544	7.690	9.024	10.58	12.38	14.46	16.88	19.67
19	3.617	4.316	5.142	6.116	7.263	8.613	10.20	12.06	14.23	16.78	19.75	23.21
20	3.870	4.661	5.604	6.727	8.062	9.646	11.52	13.74	16.37	19.46	23.11	27.39
22	4.430	5.437	6.659	8.140	9.934	12.10	14.71	17.86	21.64	26.19	31.63	38.14
24	5.072	6.341	7.911	9.850	12.24	15.18	18.79	23.21	28.63	35.24	43.30	53.11
26	5.807	7.396	9.399	11.92	15.08	19.04	23.99	30.17	37.86	47.41	59.27	73.95
28	6.649	8.627	11.17	14.42	18.58	23.88	30.63	39.20	50.07	63.80	81.13	103.0
30	7.612	10.06	13.27	17.45	22.89	29.96	39.12	50.95	66.21	85.85	111.1	143.4
32	8.715	11.74	15.76	21.11	28.21	37.58	49.95	66.21	87.57	115.5	152.0	199.6
34	9.978	13.69	18.73	25.55	34.75	47.14	63.78	86.05	115.8	155.4	208.1	278.0
36	11.42	15.97	22.25	30.91	42.82	59.14	81.44	111.8	153.2	209.2	284.9	387.0
38	13.08	18.63	26.44	37.40	52.76	74.18	104.0	145.3	202.5	281.5	390.0	538.9
40	14.97	21.72	31.41	45.26	65.00	93.05	132.8	188.9	267.9	378.7	533.9	750.4
45	21.00	31.92	48.33	72.89	109.5	164.0	244.6	363.7	538.8	795.4	1170.	1717.
50	29.46	46.90	74.36	117.4	184.6	289.0	450.7	700.2	1084.	1671.	2566.	3927
55	41.31	68.91	114.4	189.1	311.0	509.3	830.5	1348.	2180.	3509.	5626.	8985.
60	57.95	101.3	176.0	304.5	524.1	897.6	1530.	2596.	4384.	7370.		

n	20%	22%	24%	26%	28%	30%	32%	34%	36%	38%	40%	42%
1	1.200	1.220	1.240	1.260	1.280	1.300	1.320	1.340	1.360	1.380	1.400	1.420
2	1.440	1.488	1.538	1.588	1.638	1.690	1.742	1.796	1.850	1.904	1.960	2.016
3	1.728	1.816	1.907	2.000	2.097	2.197	2.300	2.406	2.515	2.628	2.744	2.863
4	2.074	2.215	2.364	2.520	2.684	2.856	3.036	3.224	3.421	3.627	3.842	4.066
5	2.488	2.703	2.932	3.176	3.436	3.713	4.007	4.320	4.653	5.005	5.378	5.774
6	2.986	3.297	3.635	4.002	4.398	4.827	5.290	5.789	6.328	6.907	7.530	8.198
7	3.583	4.023	4.508	5.042	5.629	6.275	6.983	7.758	8.605	9.531	10.54	11.64
8	4.300	4.908	5.590	6.353	7.206	8.157	9.217	10.40	11.70	13.15	14.76	16.53
9	5.160	5.987	6.931	8.005	9.223	10.60	12.17	13.93	15.92	18.15	20.66	23.47
10	6.192	7.305	8.594	10.09	11.81	13.79	16.06	18.67	21.65	25.05	28.93	33.33
11	7.430	8.912	10.66	12.71	15.11	17.92	21.20	25.01	29.44	34.57	40.50	47.33
12	8.916	10.87	13.21	16.01	19.34	23.30	27.98	33.52	40.04	47.70	56.69	67.21
13	10.70	13.26	16.39	20.18	24.76	30.29	36.94	44.91	54.45	65.83	79.37	95.44
14	12.84	16.18	20.32	25.42	31.69	39.37	48.76	60.18	74.05	90.85	111.1	135.5
15	15.41	19.74	25.20	32.03	40.56	51.19	64.36	80.64	100.7	125.4	155.6	192.5
16	18.49	24.09	31.24	40.36	51.92	66.54	84.95	108.1	137.0	173.0	217.8	273.3
18	26.62	35.85	48.04	64.07	85.07	112.5	148.0	194.0	253.3	329.5	426.9	551.0
20	38.34	53.36	73.86	101.7	139.4	190.0	257.9	348.4	468.6	627.5	836.7	1111
22	55.21	79.42	113.6	161.5	228.4	321.2	449.4	625.6	866.7	1195.	1640.	2240.
24	79.50	118.2	174.6	256.4	374.1	542.8	783.0	1123.	1603.	2276.	3214.	4518.
26	114.5	175.9	268.5	407.0	613.0	917.3	1364.	2017.	2965.	4334.	6300.	9110.
28	164.8	261.9	412.9	646.2	1004.	1550.	2377.	3622.	5484.	8253.		
30	237.4	389.8	634.8	1026.	1646.	2620.	4142.	6503.				

Table A-2. Sinking Fund Amount Factor

Sinking fund amount factor $[(1+i)^n - 1]/i$ to determine future worth of a uniform series of periodic amounts. To determine periodic amount equivalent to a future sum, use reciprocal factor.

n	.5%	1.0%	1.5%	2.0%	2.5%	3.0%	3.5%	4.0%	4.5%	5.0%	5.5%	6.0%
1	1.000	1.000	1.000	1.000	1.000	1.000	1.000	1.000	1.000	1.000	1.000	1.000
2	2.005	2.010	2.015	2.020	2.025	2.030	2.035	2.040	2.045	2.050	2.055	2.060
3	3.015	3.030	3.045	3.060	3.076	3.091	3.106	3.122	3.137	3.152	3.168	3.184
4	4.030	4.060	4.091	4.122	4.153	4.184	4.215	4.246	4.278	4.310	4.342	4.375
5	5.050	5.101	5.152	5.204	5.256	5.309	5.362	5.416	5.471	5.526	5.581	5.637
6	6.075	6.152	6.230	6.308	6.388	6.468	6.550	6.633	6.717	6.802	6.888	6.975
7	7.106	7.214	7.323	7.434	7.547	7.662	7.779	7.898	8.019	8.142	8.267	8.394
8	8.141	8.286	8.433	8.583	8.736	8.892	9.052	9.214	9.380	9.549	9.722	9.897
9	9.182	9.369	9.559	9.755	9.955	10.16	10.37	10.58	10.80	11.03	11.26	11.49
10	10.23	10.46	10.70	10.95	11.20	11.46	11.73	12.01	12.29	12.58	12.88	13.18
11	11.28	11.57	11.86	12.17	12.48	12.81	13.14	13.49	13.84	14.21	14.58	14.97
12	12.34	12.68	13.04	13.41	13.80	14.19	14.60	15.03	15.46	15.92	16.39	16.87
13	13.40	13.81	14.24	14.68	15.14	15.62	16.11	16.63	17.16	17.71	18.29	18.88
14	14.46	14.95	15.45	15.97	16.52	17.09	17.68	18.29	18.93	19.60	20.29	21.02
15	15.54	16.10	16.68	17.29	17.93	18.60	19.30	20.02	20.78	21.58	22.41	23.28
16	16.61	17.26	17.93	18.64	19.38	20.16	20.97	21.82	22.72	23.66	24.64	25.67
17	17.70	18.43	19.20	20.01	20.86	21.76	22.71	23.70	24.74	25.84	27.00	28.21
18	18.79	19.61	20.49	21.41	22.39	23.41	24.50	25.65	26.86	28.13	29.48	30.91
19	19.88	20.81	21.80	22.84	23.95	25.12	26.36	27.67	29.06	30.54	32.10	33.76
20	20.98	22.02	23.12	24.30	25.54	26.87	28.28	29.78	31.37	33.07	34.87	36.79
21	22.08	23.24	24.47	25.78	27.18	28.68	30.27	31.97	33.78	35.72	37.79	39.99
22	23.19	24.47	25.84	27.30	28.86	30.54	32.33	34.25	36.30	38.51	40.86	43.39
23	24.31	25.72	27.23	28.84	30.58	32.45	34.46	36.62	38.94	41.43	44.11	47.00
24	25.43	26.97	28.63	30.42	32.35	34.43	36.67	39.08	41.69	44.50	47.54	50.82
25	26.56	28.24	30.06	32.03	34.16	36.46	38.95	41.65	44.57	47 73	51.15	54.86
26	27.69	29.53	31.51	33.67	36.01	38.55	41.31	44.31	47.57	51.11	54.97	59.16
27	28.83	30.82	32.99	35.34	37.91	40.71	43.76	47.08	50.71	54.67	58.99	63.71
28	29.97	32.13	34.48	37.05	39.86	42.93	46.29	49.97	53.99	58.40	63.23	68.53
29	31.12	33.45	36.00	38.79	41.86	45.22	48.91	52.97	57.42	62.32	67.71	73.64
30	32.28	34.78	37.54	40.57	43.90	47.58	51.62	56.08	61.01	66.44	72.44	79.06
31	33.44	36.13	39.10	42.38	46.00	50.00	54.43	59.33	64.75	70.76	77.42	84.80
32	34.61	37.49	40.69	44.23	48.15	52.50	57.33	62.70	68.67	75.30	82.68	90.89
33	35.78	38.87	42.30	46.11	50.35	55.08	60.34	66.21	72.76	80.06	88.22	97.34
34	36.96	40.26	43.93	48.03	52.61	57.73	63.45	69.86	77.03	85.07	94.08	104.2
35	38.15	41.66	45.59	49.99	54.93	60.46	66.67	73.65	81.50	90.32	100.3	111.4
36	39.34	43.08	47.28	51.99	57.30	63.28	70.01	77.60	86.16	95.84	106.8	119.1
37	40.53	44.51	48.99	54.03	59.73	66.17	73.46	81.70	91.04	101.6	113.6	127.3
38	41.74	45.95	50.72	56.11	62.23	69.16	77.03	85.97	96.14	107.7	120.9	135.9
39	42.94	47.41	52.48	58.24	64.78	72.23	80.72	90.41	101.5	114.1	128.5	145.1
40	44.16	48.89	54.27	60.40	67.40	75.40	84.55	95.03	107.0	120.8	136.6	154.8
42	46.61	51.88	57.92	64.86	72.84	82.02	92.61	104.8	118.9	135.2	154.1	176.0
44	49.08	54.93	61.69	69.50	78.55	89.05	101.2	115.4	131.9	151.1	173.6	199.8
46	51.58	58.05	65.57	74.33	84.55	96.50	110.5	126.9	146.1	168.7	195.2	226.5
48	54.10	61.22	69.57	79.35	90.86	104.4	120.4	139.3	161.6	188.0	219.4	256.6
50	56.65	64.46	73.68	84.58	97.48	112.8	131.0	152.7	178.5	209.3	246.2	290.3
52	59.22	67.77	77.92	90.02	104.4	121.7	142.4	167.2	197.0	232.9	276.1	328.3
54	61.82	71.14	82.30	95.67	111.8	131.1	154.5	182.8	217.1	258.8	309.4	370.9
56	64.44	74.58	86.80	101.6	119.4	141.2	167.6	199.8	239.2	287.3	346.4	418.8
58	67 09	78.09	91.44	107.7	127.5	151.8	181.6	218.1	263.2	318.9	387.6	472.6
60	69.77	81.67	96.21	114.1	136.0	163.1	196.5	238.0	289.5	353.6	433.4	533.1
65	76.58	90.94	108.8	131.1	159.1	194.3	238.8	295.0	366.2	456.8	572.1	719.1
70	83.57	100.7	122.4	150.0	185.3	230.6	288.9	364.3	461.9	588.5	753.3	967.9
75	90.73	110.9	137.0	170.8	214.9	272.6	348.5	448.6	581.0	756.7	990.1	1301.
80	98.07	121.7	152.7	193.8	248.4	321.4	419.3	551.2	729.6	971.2	1300.	1747.
85	105.6	133.0	169.7	219.1	286.3	377.9	503.4	676.1	914.6	1245.	1704.	2343.
90	113.3	144.9	187.9	247.2	329.2	443.3	603.2	828.0	1145.	1595.	2233.	3141.
95	121.2	157.4	207.6	278.1	377.7	519.3	721.8	1013.	1433.	2041.	2924.	4209.
100	129.3	170.5	228.8	312.2	432.5	607.3	862.6	1238.	1791.	2610.	3827.	5638.

Table A-2. Sinking Fund Amount Factor (Cont.)

n	7%	8%	9%	10%	11%	12%	13%	14%	15%	16%	17%	18%
1	1.000	1.000	1.000	1.000	1.000	1.000	1.000	1.000	1.000	1.000	1.000	1.000
2	2.070	2.080	2.090	2.100	2.110	2.120	2.130	2.140	2.150	2.160	2.170	2.180
3	3.215	3.246	3.278	3.310	3.342	3.374	3.407	3.440	3.472	3.506	3.539	3.572
4	4.440	4.506	4.573	4.641	4.710	4.779	4.850	4.921	4.993	5.066	5.141	5.215
5	5.751	5.867	5.985	6.105	6.228	6.353	6.480	6.610	6.742	6.877	7.014	7.154
6	7.153	7.336	7.523	7.716	7.913	8.115	8.323	8.536	8.754	8.977	9.207	9.442
7	8.654	8.923	9.200	9.487	9.783	10.09	10.40	10.73	11.07	11.41	11.77	12.14
8	10.26	10.64	11.03	11.44	11.86	12.30	12.76	13.23	13.73	14.24	14.77	15.33
9	11.98	12.49	13.02	13.58	14.16	14.78	15.42	16.09	16.79	17.52	18.28	19.09
10	13.82	14.49	15.19	15.94	16.72	17.55	18.42	19.34	20.30	21.32	22.39	23.52
11	15.78	16.65	17.56	18.53	19.56	20.65	21.81	23.04	24.35	25.73	27.20	28.76
12	17.89	18.98	20.14	21.38	22.71	24.13	25.65	27.27	29.00	30.85	32.82	34.93
13	20.14	21.50	22.95	24.52	26.21	28.03	29.98	32.09	34.35	36.79	39.40	42.22
14	22.55	24.21	26.02	27.97	30.09	32.39	34.88	37.58	40.50	43.67	47.10	50.82
15	25.13	27.15	29.36	31.77	34.41	37.28	40.42	43.84	47.58	51.66	56.11	60.97
16	27.89	30.32	33.00	35.95	39.19	42.75	46.67	50.98	55.72	60.93	66.65	72.94
17	30.84	33.75	36.97	40.54	44.50	48.88	53.74	59.12	65.08	71.67	78.98	87.07
18	34.00	37.45	41.30	45.60	50.40	55.75	61.73	68.39	75.84	84.14	93.41	103.7
19	37.38	41.45	46.02	51.16	56.94	63.44	70.75	78.97	88.21	98.60	110.3	123.4
20	41.00	45.76	51.16	57.27	64.20	72.05	80.95	91.02	102.4	115.4	130.0	146.6
22	49.01	55.46	62.87	71.40	81.21	92.50	105.5	120.4	137.6	157.4	180.2	206.3
24	58.18	66.76	76.79	88.50	102.2	118.2	136.8	158.7	184.2	214.0	248.8	289.5
26	68.68	79.95	93.32	109.2	128.0	150.3	176.9	208.3	245.7	290.1	342.8	405.3
28	80.70	95.34	113.0	134.2	159.8	190.7	227.9	272.9	327.1	392.5	471.4	566.5
30	94.46	113.3	136.3	164.5	199.0	241.3	293.2	356.8	434.7	530.3	647.4	790.9
32	110.2	134.2	164.0	201.1	247.3	304.8	376.5	465.8	577.1	715.7	888.4	1103.
34	128.3	158.6	197.0	245.5	306.8	384.5	482.9	607.5	765.4	965.3	1218.	1539.
36	148.9	187.1	236.1	299.1	380.2	484.5	618.7	791.7	1014.	1301.	1670.	2145.
38	172.6	220.3	282.6	364.0	470.5	609.8	792.2	1031.	1344.	1753.	2288.	2988.
40	199.6	259.1	337.9	442.6	581.8	767.1	1014.	1342.	1779.	2361.	3135.	4163.
45	285.7	386.5	525.9	718.9	986.6	1358.	1874.	2591.	3585.	4965.	6879.	9532.
50	406.5	573.8	815.1	1164.	1669.	2400.	3460.	4995.	7218.			
55	575.9	848.9	1260.	1881.	2818.	4236.	6380.	9623.				
60	813.5	1253.	1945.	3035.	4755.	7472.						

n	20%	22%	24%	26%	28%	30%	32%	34%	36%	38%	40%	42%
1	1.000	1.000	1.000	1.000	1.000	1.000	1.000	1.000	1.000	1.000	1.000	1.000
2	2.200	2.220	2.240	2.260	2.280	2.300	2.320	2.340	2.360	2.380	2.400	2.420
3	3.640	3.708	3.778	3.848	3.918	3.990	4.062	4.136	4.210	4.284	4.360	4.436
4	5.368	5.524	5.684	5.848	6.016	6.187	6.362	6.542	6.725	6.912	7.104	7.300
5	7.442	7 740	8.048	8.368	8.700	9.043	9.398	9.766	10.15	10.54	10.95	11.37
6	9.930	10.44	10.98	11.54	12.14	12.76	13.41	14.09	14.80	15.54	16.32	17.14
7	12.92	13.74	14.62	15.55	16.53	17.58	18.70	19.88	21.13	22.45	23.85	25.34
8	16.50	17.76	19.12	20.59	22.16	23.86	25.68	27.63	29.73	31.98	34.39	36.98
9	20.80	22.67	24.71	26.94	29.37	32.01	34.90	38.03	41.43	45.14	49.15	53.51
10	25.96	28.66	31.64	34.94	38.59	42.62	47.06	51.96	57.35	63.29	69.81	76.98
11	32.15	35.96	40.24	45.03	50.40	56.41	63.12	70.62	79.00	88.34	98.74	110.3
12	39.58	44.87	50.89	57.74	65.51	74.33	84.32	95.64	108.4	122.9	139.2	157.7
13	48.50	55.75	64.11	73.75	84.85	97.63	112.3	129.2	148.5	170.6	195.9	224.9
14	59.20	69 01	80.50	93.93	109.6	127.9	149.2	174.1	202.9	236.4	275.3	320.3
15	72.04	85.19	100.8	119.3	141.3	167.3	198.0	234.2	277.0	327.3	386.4	455.8
16	87.44	104.9	126.0	151.4	181.9	218.5	262.4	314.9	377.7	452.7	542.0	648.3
18	128.1	158.4	196.0	242.6	300.3	371.5	459.4	567.8	700.9	864.4	1065.	1310.
20	186.7	238.0	303.6	387.4	494 2	630.2	802.9	1022.	1299.	1649.	2089.	2643.
22	271.0	356.4	469.1	617.3	812.0	1067.	1401.	1837.	2405.	3142.	4097.	5332.
24	392.5	532.7	723.5	982.3	1333.	1806.	2444.	3301.	4450.	5986.	8033.	
26	567.4	795.2	1115.	1562.	2186.	3054.	4260.	5930.	8233.			
28	819.2	1186.	1716.	2482.	3583.	5164.	7426.					
30	1182.	1767.	2641.	3942.	5873.	8730.						

Table A-3. Annuity Fund Factor

Annuity fund factor $[(1+i)^n - 1]/i(1+i)^n$ to determine present worth of a uniform series of periodic amounts. To determine periodic amount equivalent to an initial sum, use reciprocal factor (capital recovery factor).

n	.5%	1.0%	1.5%	2.0%	2.5%	3.0%	3.5%	4.0%	4.5%	5.0%	5.5%	6.0%
1	.9950	.9901	.9852	.9804	.9756	.9709	.9662	.9615	.9569	.9524	.9479	.9434
2	1.985	1.970	1.956	1.942	1.927	1.913	1.900	1.886	1.873	1.859	1.846	1.833
3	2.970	2.941	2.912	2 884	2.856	2.829	2.802	2.775	2.749	2.723	2.698	2.673
4	3.950	3.902	3.854	3.808	3.762	3.717	3.673	3.630	3.588	3.546	3.505	3.465
5	4.926	4.853	4 783	4.713	4.646	4.580	4.515	4.452	4.390	4.329	4.270	4.212
6	5.896	5.795	5.697	5.601	5.508	5.417	5.329	5.242	5.158	5.076	4.996	4.917
7	6.862	6.728	6.598	6.472	6.349	6.230	6.115	6.002	5.893	5.786	5.683	5.582
8	7.823	7.652	7.486	7.325	7.170	7.020	6.874	6.733	6.596	6.463	6.335	6.210
9	8.779	8.566	8.361	8.162	7.971	7.786	7.608	7.435	7.269	7.108	6.952	6.802
10	9.730	9.471	9.222	8.983	8.752	8.530	8.317	8.111	7.913	7.722	7.538	7.360
11	10.68	10.37	10.07	9.787	9.514	9.253	9.002	8.760	8.529	8.306	8.093	7.887
12	11.62	11.26	10.91	10.58	10.26	9.954	9.663	9.385	9.119	8.863	8.619	8.384
13	12.56	12.13	11.73	11.35	10.98	10.63	10.30	9.986	9.683	9.394	9.117	8.853
14	13.49	13.00	12.54	12.11	11.69	11.30	10.92	10.56	10.22	9.899	9.590	9.295
15	14.42	13.87	13.34	12.85	12.38	11.94	11.52	11.12	10.74	10.38	10.04	9.712
16	15.34	14.72	14.13	13.58	13.05	12.56	12.09	11.65	11.23	10.84	10.46	10.11
17	16.26	15.56	14.91	14.29	13.71	13.17	12.65	12.17	11.71	11.27	10.86	10.48
18	17.17	16.40	15.67	14.99	14.35	13.75	13.19	12.66	12.16	11.69	11.25	10.83
19	18.08	17.23	16.43	15.68	14.98	14.32	13.71	13.13	12.59	12.09	11.61	11.16
20	18.99	18.05	17.17	16.35	15.59	14.88	14.21	13.59	13.01	12.46	11.95	11.47
21	19.89	18.86	17.90	17.01	16.18	15.42	14.70	14.03	13.40	12.82	12.28	11.76
22	20.78	19.66	18.62	17.66	16.77	15.94	15.17	14.45	13.78	13.16	12.58	12.04
23	21.68	20.46	19.33	18.29	17.33	16.44	15.62	14.86	14.15	13.49	12.88	12.30
24	22.56	21.24	20.03	18.91	17.88	16.94	16.06	15.25	14.50	13.80	13.15	12.55
25	23.45	22.02	20.72	19.52	18.42	17.41	16.48	15.62	14.83	14.09	13.41	12.78
26	24.32	22.80	21.40	20.12	18.95	17.88	16.89	15.98	15.15	14.38	13.66	13.00
27	25.20	23.56	22.07	20.71	19.46	18.33	17.29	16.33	15.45	14.64	13.90	13.21
28	26.07	24.32	22.73	21.28	19.96	18.76	17.67	16.66	15.74	14.90	14.12	13.41
29	26.93	25.07	23.38	21.84	20.45	19.19	18.04	16.98	16.02	15.14	14.33	13.59
30	27.79	25.81	24.02	22.40	20.93	19.60	18.39	17.29	16.29	15.37	14.53	13.76
31	28.65	26.54	24.65	22.94	21.40	20.00	18.74	17.59	16.54	15.59	14.72	13.93
32	29.50	27.27	25.27	23.47	21.85	20.39	19.07	17.87	16.79	15.80	14.90	14.08
33	30.35	27.99	25.88	23.99	22.29	20.77	19.39	18.15	17.02	16.00	15.08	14.23
34	31.20	28.70	26.48	24.50	22.72	21.13	19.70	18.41	17.25	16.19	15.24	14.37
35	32.04	29.41	27.08	25.00	23.15	21.49	20.00	18.66	17.46	16.37	15.39	14.50
36	32.87	30.11	27.66	25.49	23.56	21.83	20.29	18.91	17.67	16.55	15.54	14.62
37	33 70	30.80	28.24	25.97	23.96	22.17	20.57	19.14	17.86	16.71	15.67	14.74
38	34.53	31.48	28.81	26.44	24.35	22.49	20.84	19.37	18.05	16.87	15.80	14.85
39	35.35	32.16	29.36	26.90	24.73	22.81	21.10	19.58	18.23	17.02	15.93	14.95
40	36.17	32.83	29.92	27.36	25.10	23.11	21.36	19.79	18.40	17.16	16.05	15.05
42	37.80	34.16	30.99	28.23	25.82	23.70	21.83	20.19	18.72	17.42	16.26	15.22
44	39.41	35.46	32.04	29.08	26.50	24.25	22.28	20.55	19.02	17.66	16.46	15.38
46	41.00	36.73	33.06	29.89	27.15	24.78	22.70	20.88	19.29	17.88	16.63	15.52
48	42.58	37.97	34.04	30.67	27.77	25.27	23.09	21.20	19.54	18.08	16.79	15.65
50	44.14	39.20	35.00	31.42	28.36	25.73	23.46	21.48	19.76	18.26	16.93	15.76
52	45.69	40.39	35.93	32.14	28.92	26.17	23.80	21.75	19.97	18.42	17.06	15.86
54	47.22	41.57	36.83	32.84	29.46	26.58	24.11	21.99	20.16	18.57	17.17	15.95
56	48.74	42.72	37.71	33.50	29.96	26.97	24.41	22.22	20.33	18.70	17.28	16.03
58	50.24	43.85	38.56	34.15	30.45	27.33	24.69	22.43	20.49	18.82	17.37	16.10
60	51.73	44.96	39.38	34.76	30.91	27.68	24.94	22.62	20.64	18.93	17.45	16.16
65	55.38	47.63	41.34	36.20	31.96	28.45	25.52	23.05	20.95	19.16	17.62	16.29
70	58.94	50.17	43.15	37.50	32.90	29.12	26.00	23.39	21.20	19.34	17.75	16.38
75	62.41	52.59	44.84	38.68	33.72	29.70	26.41	23.68	21.40	19.48	17.85	16.46
80	65.80	54.89	46.41	39.74	34.45	30.20	26.75	23.92	21.57	19.60	17.93	16.51
85	69.11	57.08	47.86	40.71	35.10	30.63	27.04	24.11	21.70	19.68	17.99	16.55
90	72.33	59.16	49.21	41.59	35.67	31.00	27.28	24.27	21.80	19.75	18.03	16.58
95	75.48	61.14	50.46	42.38	36.17	31.32	27.48	24.40	21.88	19.81	18.07	16.60
100	78.54	63.03	51.62	43.10	36.61	31.60	27.66	24.50	21.95	19.85	18.10	16.62

Table A-3. Annuity Fund Factor (Cont.)

n	7%	8%	9%	10%	11%	12%	13%	14%	15%	16%	17%	18%
1	.9346	.9259	.9174	.9091	.9009	.8929	.8850	.8772	.8696	.8621	.8547	.8475
2	1.808	1.783	1.759	1.736	1.713	1.690	1.668	1.647	1.626	1.605	1.585	1.566
3	2.624	2.577	2.531	2.487	2.444	2.402	2.361	2.322	2.283	2.246	2.210	2.174
4	3.387	3.312	3.240	3.170	3.102	3.037	2.974	2.914	2.855	2.798	2.743	2.690
5	4.100	3.993	3.890	3.791	3.696	3.605	3.517	3.433	3.352	3.274	3.199	3.127
6	4.767	4.623	4.486	4.355	4.231	4.111	3.998	3.889	3.784	3.685	3.589	3.498
7	5.389	5.206	5.033	4.868	4.712	4.564	4.423	4.288	4.160	4.039	3.922	3.812
8	5.971	5.747	5.535	5.335	5.146	4.968	4.799	4.639	4.487	4.344	4.207	4.078
9	6.515	6.247	5.995	5.759	5.537	5.328	5.132	4.946	4.772	4.607	4.451	4.303
10	7 024	6.710	6.418	6.145	5.889	5.650	5.426	5.216	5.019	4.833	4.659	4.494
11	7.499	7.139	6.805	6.495	6.207	5.938	5.687	5.453	5.234	5.029	4.836	4.656
12	7.943	7.536	7.161	6.814	6.492	6.194	5.918	5.660	5.421	5.197	4.988	4.793
13	8.358	7.904	7.487	7.103	6.750	6.424	6.122	5.842	5.583	5.342	5.118	4.910
14	8.745	8.244	7.786	7.367	6.982	6.628	6.302	6.002	5.724	5.468	5.229	5.008
15	9.108	8.559	8.061	7.606	7.191	6.811	6.462	6.142	5.847	5.575	5.324	5.092
16	9.447	8.851	8.313	7.824	7.379	6.974	6.604	6.265	5.954	5.668	5.405	5.162
17	9.763	9.122	8.544	8.022	7.549	7.120	6.729	6.373	6.047	5.749	5.475	5.222
18	10.06	9.372	8.756	8.201	7.702	7.250	6.840	6.467	6.128	5.818	5.534	5.273
19	10.34	9.604	8.950	8.365	7.839	7.366	6.938	6.550	6.198	5.877	5.584	5.316
20	10.59	9.818	9.129	8.514	7.963	7.469	7.025	6.623	6.259	5.929	5.628	5.353
22	11.06	10.20	9.442	8.772	8.176	7.645	7.170	6.743	6.359	6.011	5.696	5.410
24	11.47	10.53	9.707	8.985	8.348	7.784	7.283	6.835	6.434	6.073	5.746	5.451
26	11.83	10.81	9.929	9.161	8.488	7.896	7.372	6.906	6.491	6.118	5.783	5.480
28	12.14	11.05	10.12	9.307	8.602	7.984	7.441	6.961	6.534	6.152	5.810	5.502
30	12.41	11.26	10.27	9.427	8.694	8.055	7.496	7.003	6.566	6.177	5.829	5.517
32	12.65	11.43	10.41	9.526	8.769	8.112	7.538	7.035	6.591	6.196	5.844	5.528
34	12.85	11.59	10.52	9.609	8.829	8.157	7.572	7.060	6.609	6.210	5.854	5.536
36	13.04	11.72	10.61	9.677	8.879	8.192	7.598	7.079	6.623	6.220	5.862	5.541
38	13.19	11.83	10.69	9.733	8.919	8.221	7.618	7.094	6.634	6.228	5.867	5.545
40	13.33	11.92	10.76	9.779	8.951	8.244	7.634	7.105	6.642	6.233	5.871	5.548
45	13.61	12.11	10.88	9.863	9.008	8.283	7.661	7.123	6.654	6.242	5.877	5.552
50	13.80	12.23	10.96	9.915	9.042	8.304	7.675	7.133	6.661	6.246	5.880	5.554
55	13.94	12.32	11.01	9.947	9.062	8.317	7.683	7.138	6.664	6.248	5.881	5.555
60	14.04	12.38	11.05	9.967	9.074	8.324	7.687	7.140	6.665	6.249	5.882	5.555

n	20%	22%	24%	26%	28%	30%	32%	34%	36%	38%	40%	42%
1	.8333	.8197	.8065	.7937	.7812	.7692	.7576	.7463	.7353	.7246	.7143	.7042
2	1.528	1.492	1.457	1.424	1.392	1.361	1.331	1.303	1.276	1.250	1.224	1.200
3	2.106	2.042	1.981	1.923	1.868	1.816	1.766	1.719	1.673	1.630	1.589	1.549
4	2.589	2.494	2.404	2.320	2.241	2.166	2.096	2.029	1.966	1.906	1.849	1.795
5	2.991	2.864	2.745	2.635	2.532	2.436	2.345	2.260	2.181	2.106	2.035	1.969
6	3.326	3.167	3.020	2.885	2.759	2.643	2.534	2.433	2.339	2.251	2.168	2.091
7	3.605	3.416	3.242	3.083	2.937	2.802	2.677	2.562	2.455	2.355	2.263	2.176
8	3.837	3.619	3.421	3.241	3.076	2.925	2.786	2.658	2.540	2.432	2.331	2.237
9	4.031	3.786	3.566	3.366	3.184	3.019	2.868	2.730	2.603	2.487	2.379	2.280
10	4.192	3.923	3.682	3.465	3.269	3.092	2.930	2.784	2.649	2.527	2.414	2.310
11	4.327	4.035	3.776	3.543	3.335	3.147	2.978	2.824	2.683	2.555	2.438	2.331
12	4.439	4.127	3.851	3.606	3.387	3.190	3.013	2.853	2.708	2.576	2.456	2.346
13	4.533	4.203	3.912	3.656	3.427	3.223	3.040	2.876	2.727	2.592	2.469	2.356
14	4.611	4.265	3.962	3.695	3.459	3.249	3.061	2.892	2.740	2.603	2.478	2.363
15	4.675	4.315	4.001	3.726	3.483	3.268	3.076	2.905	2.750	2.611	2.484	2.369
16	4.730	4.357	4.033	3.751	3.503	3.283	3.088	2.914	2.757	2.616	2.489	2.372
18	4.812	4.419	4.080	3.786	3.529	3.304	3.104	2.926	2.767	2.624	2.494	2.377
20	4.870	4.460	4.110	3.808	3.546	3.316	3.113	2.933	2.772	2.627	2.497	2.379
22	4.909	4.488	4.130	3.822	3.556	3.323	3.118	2.936	2.775	2.629	2.498	2.380
24	4.937	4.507	4.143	3.831	3.562	3.327	3.121	2.939	2.776	2.630	2.499	2.380
26	4.956	4.520	4.151	3.837	3.566	3.330	3.123	2.940	2.777	2.631	2.500	2.381
28	4.970	4.528	4.157	3.840	3.568	3.331	3.124	2.940	2.777	2.631	2.500	2.381
30	4.979	4.534	4.160	3.842	3.569	3.332	3.124	2.941	2.778	2.631	2.500	2.381

BIBLIOGRAPHY

ELECTRICAL ENGINEERING

Angus, R. B. *Electrical Engineering Fundamentals*, 2nd ed. Reading, Mass.: Addison-Wesley, 1968.

Annett, F. A. *Elevators: Electric and Electrohydraulic Elevators, Escalators, Moving Sidewalks and Ramps*, 3rd ed. New York: McGraw-Hill, 1960.

Baumeister, T. and Marks, L. *Standard Handbook for Mechanical Engineers*, 7th ed. New York: McGraw-Hill, 1967.

Calabrese, G. O. *Symmetrical Components Applied to Electric Power Networks.* New York: Ronald Press, 1959.

Dudley, A. M. and Henderson, S. F. *Connecting Induction Motors*, 4th ed. New York: McGraw-Hill, 1960.

Everitt, W. L. and Anner, G. E. *Communication Engineering*, 3rd ed. New York: McGraw-Hill, 1956.

Fink, Donald G. et al. *Standard Handbook for Electrical Engineers*, 10th ed. New York: McGraw-Hill, 1968.

Fitzgerald, A. E. and Higginbotham, D. E. *Basic Electrical Engineering*, 3rd ed. New York: McGraw-Hill, 1967.

Fitzgerald, A. E. and Kingsley, Charles Jr. *Electric Machinery*, 2nd ed. New York: McGraw-Hill, 1961.

Greiner, Richard A. *Semiconductor Devices and Applications.* New York: McGraw-Hill, 1961.

Henney, K. *Radio Engineering Handbook,* 5th ed. New York: McGraw-Hill, 1959.

Illuminating Engineering Society. *IES Lighting Handbook*, 3rd ed. New York: Illuminating Engineering Society, 1959.

Kerchner, R. M. and Corcoran, G. F. *Alternating-Current Circuits*, 3rd ed. New York: John Wiley, 1955.

Kosow, Irving L. *Electric Machinery and Control.* Englewood Cliffs, New Jersey: Prentice-Hall, 1964.

Lo, Arthur W. et al. *Transistor Electronics.* Englewood Cliffs, New Jersey: Prentice-Hall, 1955.

Majmudar, H. *Electromechanical Energy Converters.* Boston: Allyn and Bacon, 1965.

Mandl, Matthew. *Fundamentals of Electric and Electronic Circuits.* Englewood Cliffs, New Jersey: Prentice-Hall, 1964.

Murphy, Gordon J. *Basic Automatic Control Theory.* Princeton, New Jersey: Van Nostrand, 1957.

Pender, H. and Del Mar, W. A. *Engineer's Relay Handbook*, 4th ed. vol. 1. New York: John Wiley, 1949.

Pender, H. and McIlwain, K. *Engineer's Relay Handbook*, 4th ed. vol. 2. New York: John Wiley, 1950.

Reference Data for Radio Engineers, 5th ed. New York: Howard W. Sams, 1968.

Siskind, C. S. *Electrical Machines: Direct and Alternating Currents*, 2nd ed. New York: McGraw-Hill, 1959.

Loew, E. A. and Bergseth, F. R. *Electricity: Direct and Alternating Currents*, 2nd ed. New York: McGraw-Hill, 1955.

Skilling, Hugh H. *Electromechanics.* New York: John Wiley, 1962.

Stetka, F. *N. F. P. A. Handbook of the National Electrical Code*, 2nd ed. New York: McGraw-Hill, 1969.

Stevenson, William D., Jr. *Elements of Power System Analysis*, 2nd ed. New York: McGraw-Hill, 1962.

ECONOMICS AND ETHICS

Abbett, R. W. *Engineering Contracts and Specifications*, 3rd ed. New York: Wiley, 1954.

Bach, G. L. *Economics.* New Jersey: Prentice-Hall, 1960.

Barish, N. N. *Economic Analysis.* New York: McGraw-Hill, 1962.

Grant, E. L. and Ireson, W. G. *Principles of Engineering Economy,* 4th ed. New York: Ronald Press, 1960.

Harding, C. F. and Canfield, D. T. *Legal and Ethical Phases of Engineering.* New York: McGraw-Hill, 1936.

Library of Congress, Copyright Office. *Copyright Enactments*, Bulletin no. 3 (revised).

Roscoe, E. S. *Project Economy*. Illinois: Irwin, 1960.

U.S. Department of Commerce. *Patent Laws*, 1961.

U.S. Department of Commerce. *Trademark Rules of Practice of the Patent Office,* 1963.

INDEX